A Comprehensive Geography of West Africa

REUBEN K. UDO

Professor of Geography, University of Ibadan

HEINEMANN EDUCATIONAL BOOKS (NIGERIA) LTD

IBADAN

Heinemann Educational Books (Nig.) Ltd.
Head Office: PMB 5205, Ighodaro Road, Ibadan
Phone: 62060, 62061   Telex: 31113   Cable: HEBOOKS, Ibadan

Area Offices & Branches:
Ibadan Ikeja Akure Benin Ilorin Owerri Enugu Uyo
Port Harcourt Jos Maiduguri Makurdi Zaria Kano Minna

Heinemann Educational Books Ltd 22 Bedford Square, London WC1B 3HH

NAIROBI   EDINBURGH   MELBOURNE   AUCKLAND
SINGAPORE   HONG KONG   KUALA LUMPUR   NEW DELHI   KINGSTON   PORT OF SPAIN

ISBN 0 435 95915 8 (Paper, UK)

ISBN 978-129-505-8   (Cased, Nigerian)
ISBN 978-129-506-6 (Paper, Nigerian)

Photoset in Malta by Interprint (Malta) Ltd
Printed by Butler & Tanner, Frome

PHOTOGRAPHS

Top left: Lagos city, Nigeria
Centre left: Market in Freetown, Sierra Leone
Bottom left: Suburb of Abidjan, Ivory Coast
Top right: Rock-cutting in Ghana
Bottom right: Yam mounds in Eastern Nigeria

Contents

List of Figures

List of Plates

List of Tables

Glossary

Banket—Dutch word meaning confectionery. Used to describe the thin bands of quartz-pebble conglomerates or 'reefs' in which gold occurs in South Africa. The weathered conglomerate resembles an almond confection.

Bantos faros—seasonally inundated swamps along the Gambia River.

Barchan dune—a crescent-shaped sand dune with the horns projecting in the direction of the wind. It has a gentle windward slope and a rather steep leeward slope.

Bolilands—fossil river channels which become flooded stagnant swamps during the rainy season (in the central plains of Sierra Leone).

Bowe (singular = *bowal*)—means no trees. The term is used to describe extensive areas of bare surface, hard impervious lateritic crust in the Guinea and Futa Jallon Highlands.

Dallol—see *wadi*.

Fadama—Hausa word for seasonally inundated river flood-plains.

Firki—dark clay soils (in the Lake Chad Basin) usually swampy during the rainy season but with a hard and brittle surface during the dry season.

Gallery forest—belt of forest trees along the course of a river or stream in the grass-woodland savanna zone. Often the height and density of the constituent trees, the narrowness of the stream and the nature of the banks allow the canopies to meet overhead enclosing the stream in a kind of wooded tunnel.

Harratine—serfs or descendants of freed slaves.

Huza—a system of land tenure amongst the Krobo migrant farmers of Southern Ghana, in which some migrants form themselves into a company to purchase land which is then laid out in strips and allocated to each member in proportion to the amount of money he contributed.

Inselberg—literally 'island mountain'—an isolated steep sided hill.

Kurmi—an island of woodland in an open savanna landscape.

Laterite—a red, ferruginous soil which hardens on exposure. It is found in tropical regions and may be rich enough in iron to be used as iron ore.

Levee—a naturally raised bank of a river formed during flooding by the deposition of sediment. Both levee and river bed may lie above the level of the floodplain and often the height and length of the levee is sufficient to divert the course of a tributary.

Marabouts—learned religious men amongst the Moors.

Mesas—flat-topped hills with steep sides in a desert or semi-desert environment. The word *mesa* in Spanish means 'table'.

Naiyes—marshy freshwater depressions (oases) trapped by sand dunes in the Cayor district of Senegal.

Seyane—lagoons and marshes formed behind coastal sand dunes in the St Louis area of Senegal.

Seif dune—a type of sand dune with a long sharp ridge lying parallel to the direction of the prevailing wind.

Tannes—salt flats along river channels draining into the Saloum estuary (Senegal).

Terre de Barre—clay plains extending from the coastlands of eastern Ghana through Togo to Benin.

Tro-tro—a multi-purpose mammy-wagon (lorry) for carrying passengers and goods, so called because the cost in the greater Accra area used to be three pence or 'tro' in pidgin English.

Wadi—a wide, shallow, sandy desert watercourse with steep sides which is usually dry, and contains water occasionally after a heavy rainstorm (same as dallol).

Zenaga—artisans amongst the Moors.

Preface

This volume is intended for students preparing for the West African School Certificate and the General Certificate of Education (O Level). It is divided into two parts, the first of which is a systematic study of the West Africa region. Special features of Part I include such neglected topics as land rights and land use, traders and organization of local trade, and an up-to-date study of aspects of the population and economy of West Africa. Sections B and D of Part I in particular are suitable for students in Advanced Teachers' Colleges, Colleges of Education and first year undergraduates. Specifically, I wish to draw the attention of more advanced students to the review of regional contrasts and the discussion of the West African Economic Community in Section D.

Part II presents a detailed study of each country of West Africa and is particularly suited for O level candidates. The French-speaking countries and Liberia have been treated in much greater detail than is to be found in any other similar textbook on West Africa. Candidates from member countries of the West African Examinations Council will find that the book also provides adequate detail to enable them to answer the compulsory questions on their country of origin.

You may find this book to be a geography of West Africa with a difference. I hope you will make the best use of it.

Reuben K. Udo
University of Ibadan

Introduction

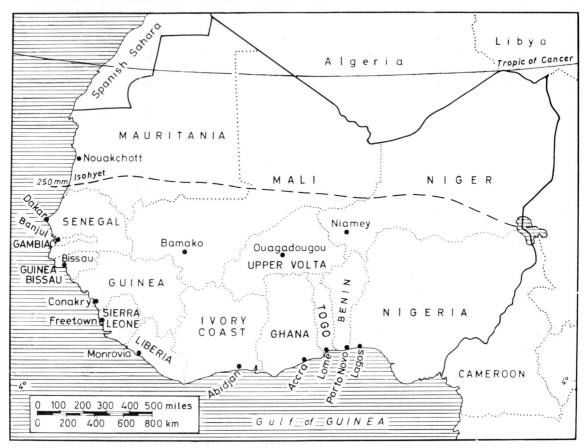

FIG. (i)—Boundaries and countries of West Africa

West Africa is one of the major geographical regions of Africa. It is bounded in the south and west by the Atlantic Ocean and in the east by the Cameroon-Adamawa Highlands which separate West Africa from Equatorial Africa. The northern boundary is less clearly defined and is generally considered to follow the southern limit of the Sahara Desert. Since desert conditions prevail where the annual rainfall is not more than 250mm (10in.), many people regard the 250mm isohyet as the northern boundary of West Africa. This isohyet, however, runs approximately along latitude 15°N. and therefore cuts the countries of Mauritania, Mali and Niger into two parts—see Fig. (i). It is therefore not a suitable boundary since statistical data on population, crop production and trade are usually given for political units rather than for climatically delimited regions. For this reason, it is convenient to consider the northern boundaries of Mauritania, Mali and Niger as the nothern boundary of West Africa.

The total area of West Africa is about 6.2 million sq.km (2½ million sq. miles) or about two-thirds the size of the United States of America. This land area is shared by fifteen countries (Fig. i), some of which are rather small in size and too poor to afford the administrative cost of an independent state. The total population of about 121 million may be compared with 203 million for the United States of America (1974). More than half the people live in Nigeria, which had an estimated population of about 71 million in 1973. The various countries, their areas and population are given in Table 1 (p. xii).

Table 1—Areas, population and currency of West African countries

Country	Capital city	Area sq.km.	sq. miles	Population (mn.) in 1974	Currency
1. Benin	Porto Novo	113,050	43,500	2.9	Franc CFA
2. Gambia	Banjul	11,300	4,360	0.5	Dalasi
3. Ghana	Accra	238,500	92,100	9.1	Cedi
4. Guinea Bissau	Bissau	36,130	14,000	0.56	Escudo
5. Guinea	Conakry	245,900	94,930	5.1	Guinea Franc
6. Ivory Coast	Abidjan	322,500	125,500	4.6	Franc CFA
7. Liberia	Monrovia	111,400	43,000	1.5	Dollar
8. Mali	Bamako	1,240,000	478,800	5.4	Mali Franc
9. Mauritania	Nouakchott	1,100,000	420,000	1.2	Franc CFA
10. Niger	Niamey	1,267,000	489,000	4.3	Franc CFA
11. Nigeria	Lagos	923,800	356,700	71.0	Naira
12. Senegal	Dakar	196,200	75,800	4.2	Franc CFA
13. Sierra Leone	Freetown	72,000	27,900	2.9	Leone
14. Togo	Lomé	56,600	21,620	2.2	Franc CFA
15. Upper Volta	Ouagadougou	274,200	106,600	5.7	Franc CFA

Source: *Africa South of the Sahara*, Europa Publications, 1975.

Along the coast, where the land comes under the full influence of the sea, heavy rainfall exceeding 2,000mm (80in.) per annum, spread over nine months, and featuring a two-maxima regime* is characteristic. Away from the coast, the total amount as well as the duration and reliability of the rain decreases considerably. This results in a northward dwindling of the dense forest vegetation along the coast, which gives way first to open forest, and then to varying grades of savanna woodland, through thorn scrub to desert vegetation in the far north. There is thus a marked west-east zonation of rainfall belts, vegetation belts and, as we shall see later, of soil, crops and cultural belts.

Several fundamental differences therefore exist between north and south in respect of the physical environment and agricultural practices and crops. These differences have also influenced the course of human history in West Africa. In pre-colonial days for example, the far north was relatively more developed than the south. This situation was made possible by the long trade and cultural contacts which the Sudan had with the Mediterranean world and the fact that the far north, unlike the south, had a relatively well developed transport system featuring the use of the horse, the camel and the donkey. Today the situation has been largely reversed. The Sudan now trades with the outside world through the seaports of the coast of Guinea instead

of across the saharan caravan routes. Developments in industry, trade and transportation are now concentrated along coastal areas.

The two-sector division of West Africa into interior and exterior sectors—see Fig. (ii)—is based on environmental and historical contrasts between north and south, as well as on differences associated with modern economic development. The exterior or developed sector is defined as the area lying approximately 240km (150 miles) from the coast. The ports, commercial plantations, most industrial establishments and the bulk of the population live in this sector. Generally, the exterior sector has a more suitable climate for agriculture and is relatively well provided with water for man and beast. The remaining parts of West Africa constitute the landlocked and sparsely settled interior sector.

Climatic data and farming practices, however, confirm the transitional character of the differences between north and south, a fact which is clearly exhibited by the vegetation of West Africa. Rainfall data for southern stations such as Lagos and Accra show a two-maxima regime while Sudanese stations like Kano and Dakar show a single-maximum regime. Figures for Kontagora and Bida, on the other hand, show a double maxima for some years, a single peak for other years, while there may be no peak at all in other years. With regard to agricultural production, the south is a zone of root crops and tree crops, while the far north produces grains (millet, guinea corn) and other annual crops. There is, however, a wide transitional zone in which both

---

*i.e. Two periods of maximum rainfall, usually June/July and September/October, with a break in August.

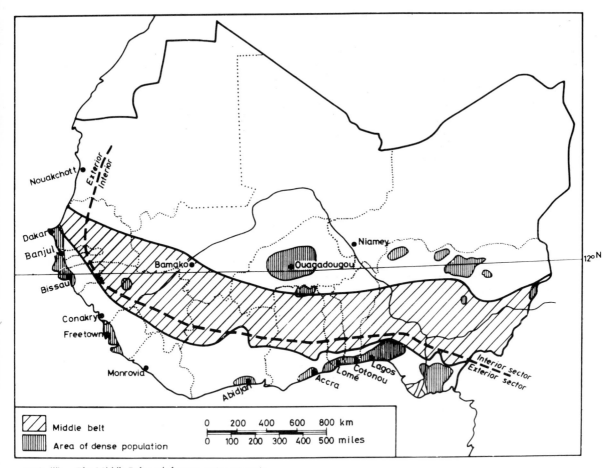

FIG. (ii)—The Middle Belt and the two-sector concepts

the crops of the south and those of the north are produced. The traveller through this zone will observe with interest that farmers cultivate their crops on both mounds and ridges whereas southern farmers plant on mounds, while northern farmers plant on ridges. This zone of transition is called the Middle Belt.

The Middle Belt extends approximately from $7\frac{1}{2}°$N. to 11°N. and is characterized by sparse population, poor communication and relatively limited resources. It is the poorest and least developed zone. In Nigeria for example, the Middle Belt covers two-fifths of the total area of the country but has a population which is less than one-fifth. Throughout West Africa, this zone contributes very little to the export trade but it has vast areas of land awaiting settlement and in Nigeria it is already a food surplus zone. The future of this zone appears to lie in the expansion of food-crop production and fortunately, climatic and soil conditions permit the cultivation of both the root crops of the coastlands and the grains of the Sudan. The decision to locate the Nigerian

Iron and Steel Mill Complex near Ajaokuta in this zone is likely to attract a number of other industries and thereby bring about considerable industrial development in this part of the Middle Belt.

North of the Middle Belt lies the Sudan zone which has a relatively dry climate, largely because of its interior location. The main concentration of the cattle population occurs in this zone which is also the main groundnut and cotton producing area. This is the home of the cattle Fulani, the Shuwa Arab and nomadic Tuareg as well as the settled Hausa and Mandingo farmer. This zone saw the rise of several empires during the pre-colonial period, the more prominent of which included Mali, Songhai, Ghana and Sokoto-Gwandu—see Fig. (iii), p. xiv.

Finally, there is the coastal zone of the Gulf of Guinea which is a zone of intense exploitation of forest resources and of large-scale expansion of tree crops by peasants and also on commercial plantations. The characteristic features of the exterior sector also apply to this zone, which is generally considered to cover approximately the same area

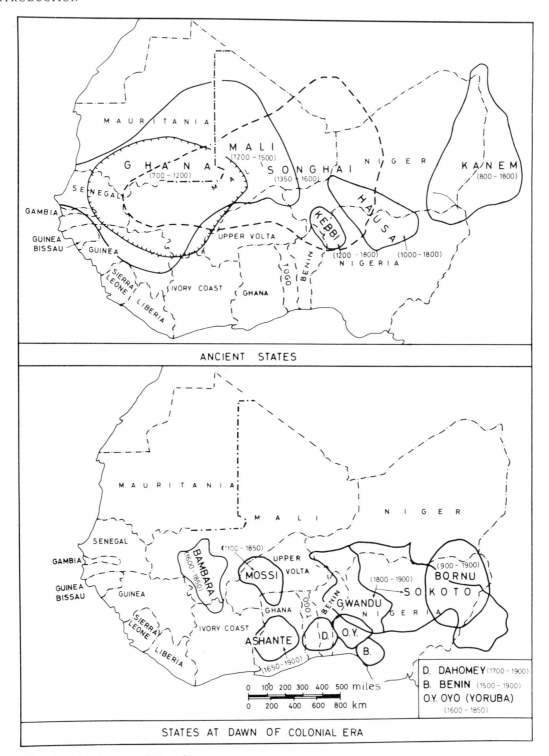

FIG. (iii)—*Pre-colonial empires of West Africa*

as the exterior sector. It follows that the interior sector is approximately made up of the Middle Belt and the Sudan zones.

West Africa forms a part of Low Africa (see Fig. (iv), p. xvi). Compared with eastern and southern Africa, it has a rather low elevation which is characterized by remarkably monotonous plains and plateau surfaces. The general elevation of Low Africa is below 600m (2,000ft) as compared with over 900m (3,000ft) in High Africa. With the exception of the Jos Plateau and the Guinea Highlands, tropical high-plateau surfaces which attracted white settlement in East and southern Africa do not exist. West Africa has therefore remained a black man's country and has not experienced the problems posed by European and Asian settlers in High Africa (East, Central and southern Africa). The local economy has therefore been developed largely by the Africans themselves, although non-African enterprise is also important, particularly in the French-speaking countries of Senegal, Ivory Coast and Niger Republic.

Its low elevation notwithstanding, West Africa exhibits the characteristic features of a plateau continent. Remnants of erosion surfaces which are common in High Africa occur in the Jos Plateau and the highlands of Adamawa; while the rivers are characterized by waterfalls and rapids. Lagoon-fringed and surf-beaten coasts, similar to those along the coasts of East and southern Africa, are common.

Like the rest of tropical Africa, West Africa experiences a serious problem of water shortage during the dry season. This is particularly true of the landlocked interior sector, where the cattle Fulanis have to move from one area to another in search of water and grazing. Excessively dry conditions along the desert borderlands caused the death of thousands of cattle and loss of crops during the dry season of 1972–3. The resultant famine became so severe that supplies had to be flown into the West African Sudan from the coastal areas as well as from Europe and America. There is therefore a great need to dig wells and build dams across local streams to provide water for irrigation as well as for animals and for domestic use.

Although West Africa is the most densely populated of the major geographical regions of Africa, it has shared with the rest of the continent the unpleasant experience of both the Arab and the European slave trade. The sparse population of the Middle Belt districts has been attributed largely to extensive depopulation during wars waged for the purpose of obtaining captives to be sold into slavery. The rise of large indigenous cities in the Sudan has also been attributed to the need for defence during the period of the slave trade. Along the coast, the slave trade brought about the proliferation of primitive posts and trading forts. Several fishing and salt-making settlements were also transformed into powerful trading city states, the best known of which included Bonny, Brass, Opobo Town, Duke Town (Calabar) and Lagos.

The colonial period, which lasted about 60 years, also left its imprint on the West African scene. French or English is the official language of the countries of West Africa, some of which are still economically tied to the apron strings of France or Britain, as the case may be. Educational institutions and the aspirations of most educated young people are still largely influenced by French and British ideals. But remarkable changes can be expected and are already taking place. Contact between neighbouring countries like Nigeria, Benin, Niger and Togo is increasing, though Benin still imports goods like cigarettes from France rather than from Nigeria. Economic cooperation will increase with the years and will provide the right atmosphere towards a political union of most, if not all, the states of West Africa.

The last fifty years have witnessed remarkable changes in the economy and society at a rate much greater than at any other period in the history of West Africa. Export of industrial crops has largely replaced subsistence agriculture, while the traditional system of communal land tenure is giving way to individual landholding. The large extended family in which the young men were economically dependent on the elders is giving way to the nuclear family headed by young men. Respect for traditional rulers remains but the powers and authority of such rulers have since been transferred to the law courts, while the sweeping reforms of the present military regimes have virtually removed the remaining vestiges of indirect rule.

Visible evidence of some of these changes includes the replacement of high forest vegetation by man-made forests of rubber, cocoa and oil palms. New towns have grown up to serve the new economy while newer residential areas of old cities like Kano and Zaria show a striking contrast with the older residential districts. In most rural areas, however, there appears to be little break with the past. The nomadic cattle Fulani still wanders about with his herd in search of water and grazing, and in parts of the far north, the camel, horse and donkey remain the only reliable forms of transportation during the rainy season. Rural house types show little or no sign of change from descriptions made two or three centuries ago.

Labour migration has been on the increase throughout West Africa and is characterized by movements from rural areas to the ports or min-

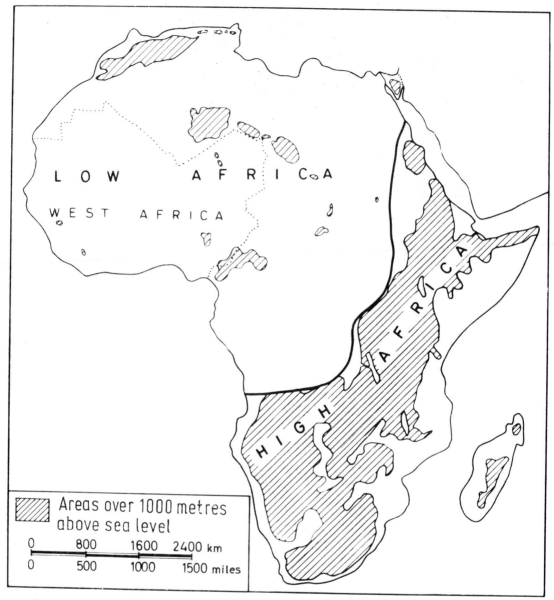

FIG. (iv)—High and Low Africa

ing towns as well as to centres of intensive exploitation of forest resources and expansion of plantation agriculture. Migrant tenant farmers such as the strange farmers of Gambia and Senegal, the migrant cocoa farmers of Ghana and the migrant food farmers of Nigeria constitute an increasing class of rural to rural migrants. The indication today is that more and more people will continue to migrate into the growing urban areas, many of which have become important industrial centres. A radical transformation of the rural economy is considered to be overdue, but is unlikely till the existing traditional land-tenure systems and farming methods change.

Part I

A Systematic Study of West Africa

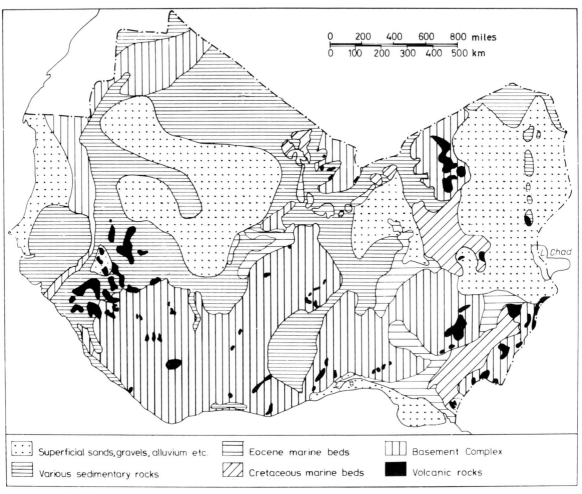

Superficial sands, gravels, alluvium etc. Eocene marine beds Basement Complex

Various sedimentary rocks Cretaceous marine beds Volcanic rocks

L. Chad

FIG. 1.1—Simplified geological map

PLATE 1—Rocky landscape in the Jos Plateau, Nigeria

SECTION A: THE PHYSICAL BACKGROUND

Chapter 1—Relief, Land Forms and Drainage

TYPES AND DISTRIBUTION OF MAJOR ROCK GROUPS

The relief, some land forms (including valley shapes), surface drainage, and the soils of a given area are often influenced by the character and disposition of the rocks in the area. For this reason, it is important to grasp the following basic facts about the geology of West Africa. A simplified geological map is presented in Fig. 1.1 and should be compared with the relief map (Fig. 1.2, p. 4).

Old hard rocks which underlie almost the whole African continent outcrop over vast areas of the south and the Middle Belt. These ancient rocks are crystalline in character and are usually referred to as Basement Complex rocks. They consist of igneous rocks like granite, and basalt as well as metamorphic rocks like quartzite, schist and slates. In such areas as the Chad Basin, the Benin lowlands and western Senegal, where vast stretches of sedimentary rocks occur, the Basement Complex has merely been covered up by varying depths of these relatively younger rocks. Mineral fuels such as coal, petroleum and gas are found in areas where these sedimentary rocks are of considerable depth but other minerals such as tin, diamond and manganese are associated with areas of old hard rocks.

Some of the highest land areas and the most rugged relief in West Africa are associated with sandstones, which are old sedimentary rocks, found mainly in the region of Guinea Republic and eastern Senegal. Old sandstones also occur in the Volta Basin of Ghana while the Udi-Igalla Plateau region of Nigeria consists of much younger sandstones. A more recent group of sedimentary rocks consisting of superficial sands, gravel and alluvium of marine, riverine or eolian (wind) origin occur in the Chad Basin, the region of the Inland Niger Delta and along much of the coastline.

In several areas including the Jos Plateau, the Adamawa Highlands, and the Air Mountains, volcanic intrusions have cut through sedimentary and

basement rocks to form regions of bold relief. Evidence of recent volcanic activity also occurs in the Biu Plateau, the Benue Valley and at Dakar, but the only active volcano is Mt Cameroon (3,069m or 10,000ft) which is located just outside West Africa.

RELIEF AND LAND FORMS

Africa is usually referred to as a plateau continent although it is actually made up of several plateau surfaces. A relief map of the continent (Fig. iv) reveals that on the basis of elevation, there are two Africas: High Africa in the east and south, and Low Africa in the north and west. West Africa is therefore a vast low tableland but like the rest of the continent, it is characterized by a narrow coastal plain, a narrow continental shelf, a number of plateau surfaces and immature drainage. Three major relief areas are distinguished and these are: 1) the lowlands or areas not more than 305m (1,000ft) above sea level, 2) the interior plains which make up most of West Africa, and 3) the highlands.

1. The lowland areas

Lowlands occur along the coast as well as in the Chad Depression and the inland Niger Delta. Along the coast, the lowlands are very narrow except in Senegambia, the Ivory Coast and south-eastern Nigeria where they stretch inland for 160—240km (100—150 miles). Contrary to what may be expected, the coastal lowlands are not featureless plains but consist of rather undulating landscapes. In some areas such as around Conakry, Accra, Ijede near Lagos and Fourah Bay in Sierra Leone, the land rises from the sea in high cliffs. A considerable proportion of the coastline is smooth, surf-beaten and harbourless, but extensive lagoons occur in most areas where the coast trends in an east to west direction as in Sierra Leone, the Ivory Coast and western Nigeria. The few inlets through the coast

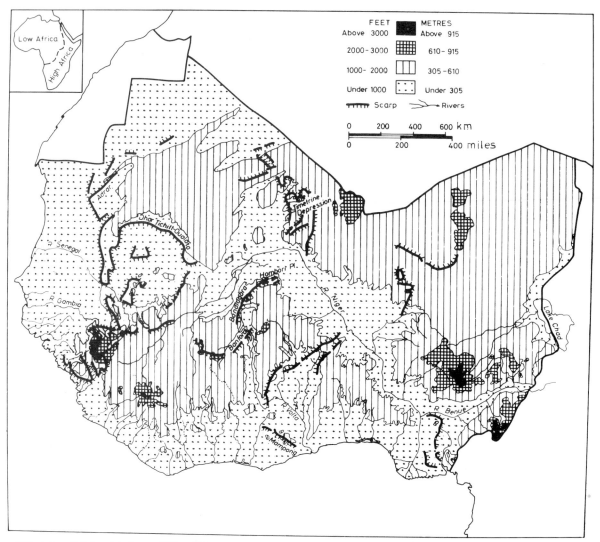

FIG. 1.2—Relief and drainage of West Africa

appear in the drowned estuaries of the Gambia, Conakry, Freetown and Calabar areas. Numerous islands appear along the coasts of Guinea, Sierra Leone and Nigeria.

Mangrove swamps also occur in the Niger Delta which is characterized by numerous ox-bow lakes, high levees and meandering water channels. Abandoned beach ridges (Fig. 1.3) constitute the dominant landforms of the outer perimeter of the delta while the islands of solid earth in the region of Port Harcourt provide evidence of drowning of this section of the coast.

Coastal dunes, usually parallel to the shore and rising to over 30m (100ft), occur in Senegal and Mauritania, particularly in the stretch between Dakar and Port Etienne. River courses have been interrupted by the dunes, behind which form a string of lagoons and marshes called *seyane* in the St Louis area. Much of the coastal lowland, which in these two countries has a width of about 320km (200 miles), is masked by sand dunes. In the more humid south, the coastal dunes are fixed and covered with scrub but north of Nouakchott, the dunes become mobile and the landscape more open.

The two main interior lowland areas of the Chad Basin and the inland Niger Delta are areas of inland drainage, the latter of which now, has an outlet into the sea through the middle Niger Valley. The uniformity of the landscape is striking, particularly during the rainy season when vast areas of both regions become completely inundated. High but fixed sand dunes occur in the area west of Lake Chad and are thought to have been formed during a period of greater aridity when desert conditions prevailed as far south as latitude $11\frac{1}{2}°$N. The most prominent landforms of the Chad Basin, however, consist of the 305m (100ft) high Bama-Maiduguri sand ridge which is 480km (300 miles) long and the much smaller 3m (10ft) Ngelwa sand ridge, which follows the present shore of the lake. The higher ridge, which has been cut in several places by rivers, represents a former extent of Lake Chad. In some places, this ridge splits into two or three close parallel ridges.

2. The wide plains

The rise from the coastal plains to the interior high plains is through a series of steps, each of which marks the end of one and the beginning of another cycle of erosion. The rivers descend these steps in rapids and falls. Each plain surface is an erosion surface; and is usually undulating but rather open and monotonous, especially in the drier savanna land of the Sudan.

Plains developed on rocks of the Basement Complex may be distinguished from the younger surfaces such as the Cross River plains which are developed on sedimentary formations. They are both products of sub-aerial erosion as distinct from plains of deposition such as those of the Chad Basin or the Niger Delta.

Inselbergs or erosional survivals appear here and there all over these plains. It is important to note that these land forms are found both in areas of the Basement Complex as in Western Nigeria or central Hausaland and in areas of sedimentary rocks such as the Udi-Igalla Plateau of eastern Nigeria. Inselbergs occur both in the high forest belt as well as in the drier savanna lands. They are characterized by very steep sides and are usually dome-shaped except where a capping of lateritic ironstone gives rise to flat-topped inselbergs. Inselbergs occur singly or in groups and may be found in various stages of disintegration (plates 1,2).

The origin of inselbergs is still a subject of controversy between geomorphologists, but the more

FIG. 1.3—*Typical land forms*

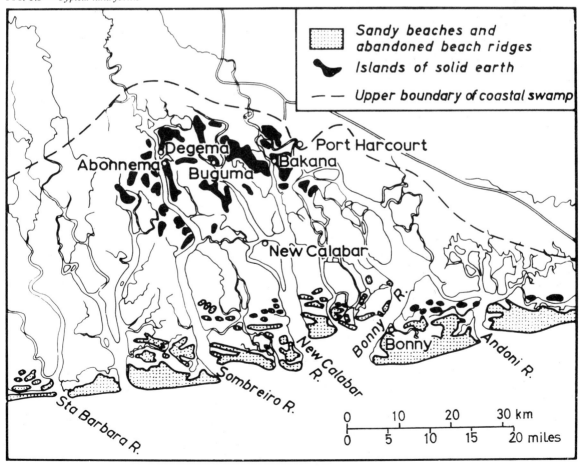

PLATE 2—Weathered inselberg on the Jos Plateau, Nigeria

reasonable arguments are those which attribute the formation of inselbergs to slope retreat or to sub-surface exhumation of rocks. In several parts of West Africa, these isolated hills provided a refugee outpost for settlement during the period of the slave trade.

A number of other interesting land forms occur in the scarplands of south-eastern Nigeria. These include the Enugu escarpment which rises abruptly for 200m (600ft) above the Cross River plains, the limestone caves at Ogbunike near Awka and Agulu Lake which was formed by sandbank blocking the mouth of a tributary stream. The beautifully carved though destructive erosion gullies at Nsudde, Agulu and Nanka constitute one of the most impressive landscapes anywhere in West Africa.

3. The highlands

In areas of old sandstone such as the coastal areas of Guinea Republic or the Mampong area of Ghana, large masses of resistant rocks stand out to form extensive highland areas. Other highlands occur in areas where the country rock has been breached by large masses of igneous intrusions such as are to be found in the Jos Plateau, the Adamawa Highlands and northern Guinea. The main highland areas are therefore the Jos Plateau, 1,220m (4,000ft) the

Cameroon-Adamawa Highland, the Biu Plateau, 700m (2,300ft), the Togo-Atakora Mountains of Ghana, 300—460m (1,000—1,500ft) and the Hombori Mountains, 450m (1,500ft) of the Niger bend. In the far north, that is in the heart of the desert, the Air Mountains, 450m (1,500ft) and the Ahaggar and Tibetsi Highlands, 450m (1,500ft) are the major highland areas. The most important highland areas of the west are the Futa Jallon-Guinea Highlands, 750—920m (2,500—3,00ft) and the Sikasso Highlands, 450m (1,500ft).

These highlands form the source of many prominent rivers, the headwaters of which have dissected much of the land. It is in those highland areas where there is evidence of recent volcanic activity that some very interesting land forms appear. In the Jos Plateau and the Bamenda Highlands for example, there are numerous volcanic cones which have well preserved craters, some of which contain crater lakes. A long period of laterization during which the lava flow from these cones was buried under a capping of iron-stone, followed by surface erosion, has given rise to numerous flat-topped hills or mesas on the Jos Plateau. The other type of hills found in the Jos Plateau consists of granitic inselbergs in various stages of disintegration. Finally, there are some large mining dumps which have since been overgrown with grass, and now appear like natural hills.

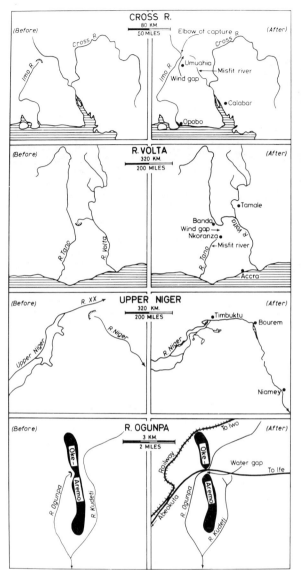

FIG. 1.4—Examples of river captures

DRAINAGE CHARACTERISTICS AND VALLEY FORMS

A major watershed running west-east from Senegal and broken only by the lower Niger Valley below Lokoja, separates the Senegal and Niger-Benue systems from rivers flowing directly into the Gulf of Guinea. Like most watersheds on the African plateau, this major divide is ill-defined in some places and consists of gently sloping surfaces rather than prominent hills or ridges. The Niger, 4,180km (2,600 miles) is by far the longest and most important river. It has a peculiar course in that it rises a few kilometres from the coast at the Futa Jallon, but flows inland towards the desert before bending towards the coast at Tosaye to enter the sea in Nigeria. In the past, the Niger flowed into an inland drainage basin in the region of the inland delta but was captured and diverted southwards by the lower Niger (Fig. 1.4). (see plate 3.)

Rivers such as the Bandama, the Volta and the Okpara which flow directly into the sea have steeper gradients and are extending their head-waters inland at the expense of the inland-flowing streams. This process has given rise to several river captures particularly since the watersheds are not high. The capture of the upper Niger by the lower Niger at Goa is one good example. Other clear cases of major captures include the capture of the Enyong Creek by the Imo River, the capture of the Black Volta and the capture of the Upper Gongola which formerly flowed into Lake Chad. Some of these are shown in Fig. 1.4.

In West Africa, river captures have had the effect of depriving the drier interior of the little water which it has. The wetter coastal areas sustain the more aggressive streams which have or are in the process of capturing rivers flowing inland to join the Niger or into Lake Chad. The imminent capture of the Logone by the upper Benue may be cited to show the potential danger of river diversion through capture in a drier area such as the central Sudan. Lake Chad receives about three-quarters of its waters from the Shari-Logone and is sure to be greatly reduced in size if this capture is not prevented. Current irrigation projects aimed at expanding cotton growing and the settling down of the nomadic cattle Fulani will be adversely affected.

Unlike other African rivers, the Benue, which is the largest tributary of the Niger, is not hampered by rapids and waterfalls throughout its course within Nigeria. The Benue owes this unique characteristic to the fact that below Yola, its valley is cut through sedimentary rocks. The river is therefore navigable below Yola for as long as the water level remains high. Unfortunately, however, like other West African rivers the Benue suffers from extreme seasonal fluctuations in volume; a fact which hampers navigability during the dry season. The rivers are fullest in the months of July and August, when vast areas of the surrounding lowlands may be flooded. As soon as the dry season sets in, the volume of water decreases while the smaller rivers may be completely dried up.

The interior plains are characterized by very open valleys, but gorge-like valleys dominate such highland areas as the Futa Jallon and the Adamawa Highlands. Valley-in-valley forms in the Jos Plateau and several other districts provide some evidence of rejuvenation which is also responsible for some of the rapids and falls along West African rivers.

PLATE 3—The Lokoja confluence of the Niger and Benue Rivers

FIG. 1.5—The course of a hypothetical West African river

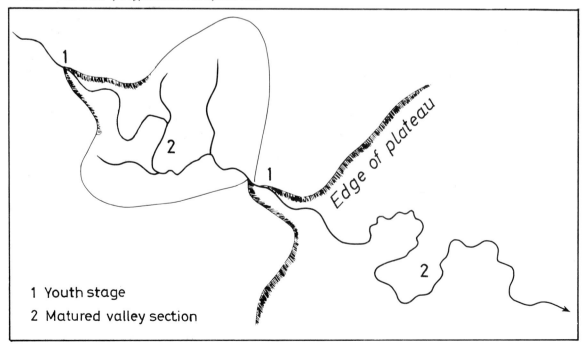

1 Youth stage
2 Matured valley section

PLATE 4—Elmina, Ghana

The alternation of sections of 'youth' with steep sided V-shaped valleys and 'matured' sections with open flat-bottomed valleys is another interesting characteristic of West African rivers. The Niger for instance flows through narrow valleys in the Futa Jallon into the open Macina plains of the inland Niger Delta and then cuts through another gorge-like section at Say. Below Say, the valley opens up but is constricted again at several other points including Kainji, Jebba, Itobe and Onitsha, before reaching the sea. A bottle-neck topography (Fig. 1.5) results.

Dry valleys are common even in such wet parts of West Africa as south-eastern Nigeria, but it is in the northern savanna lands that they are most numerous. Unlike the seasonal streams which carry running water during the rains, these dry valleys may contain no streams for several decades. In the drier savanna lands, they are usually easy to recognize owing to the gallery forest vegetation which these valleys support. Their origins have been attributed to river action in a period of more humid climate. In parts of Bornu and Mali, many of these dry valleys were formerly occupied by inland flowing streams which have since been diverted through river capture by rivers flowing into the Atlantic Ocean.

Chapter 2—Climate, Climatic Regions and Water Needs

PLATE 5—Trade season Basse under water

INTRODUCTION

It is important to know the difference between elements of climate and factors of climate. Elements of climate consist of those physical properties and conditions of the atmosphere which make up the weather at any time. Climatic elements include:

—the temperature of the air
—the direction and speed of the wind
—the humidity of the air
—the amount of precipitation

These elements are the results of a combination of a number of determining causes called factors of climate. These include:

—latitude or position relative to the equator
—continentality or distance from the sea
—altitude
—ocean currents
—the prevailing winds

Since West Africa lies wholly within the tropics, the full influence of the sun is felt over the whole area all through the year. As a general rule the

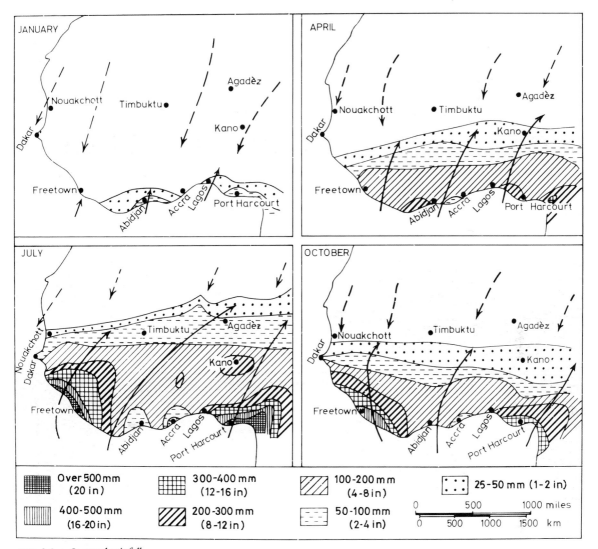

FIG. 2.1—Seasonal rainfall

climate of a place like Freetown or Timbuktu is determined largely by its distance from the sea. Thus, Freetown, which lies on the coast receives the full influence of the rain-bearing South-west Monsoon and therefore records a total annual rainfall of 3,505mm (138in.) spread over eight months of the year. Timbuktu, on the other hand is hot and dry for most of the year, because it is located about 1,300km (800 miles) away from the sea.

In West Africa, we talk of the dry season and the wet season; not summer, autumn, winter or spring! Can you make out why rainfall, rather than temperature, determines the seasons of the year in West Africa? The thoughtful student can see that rainfall is by far the most important element of climate in this part of the world. In most areas, the success or

failure of agriculture depends on the amount, distribution and reliability of the rainfall. It is also a fact that in many rural areas, rain water remains an important source of water for both man and beast.

RAINFALL DISTRIBUTION AND SEASONS

Important facts about the rainfall which can be verified from Table 2 (p. 14) and Figs. 2.1—2.4 (pp. 11—13, 15) include the following:

(a) The coastal areas, with the exception of the Accra dry belt receive most rain. There is a general decrease inland in the amount of rain

11

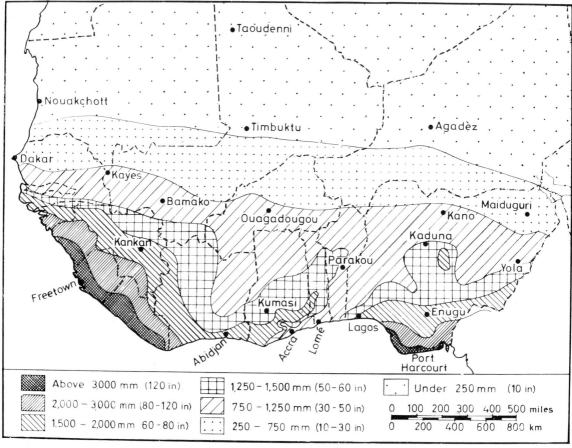

FIG. 2.2—Mean annual rainfall

from about 3,050mm (120in.) per annum along the coasts of Sierra Leone and Liberia, and the Niger Delta, to under 250mm (10in.) in the areas north of latitude 15°N.

(b) Relief effect resulting in higher total annual rainfall for inland areas like the Jos Plateau and the Togo Highlands. The high annual total rainfall of 10,000mm (400in.) for Debunscha which is situated at the foot of the Cameroon Mountain is clearly a result of the relief effect of that mountain.

(c) The Accra dry belt raises many questions for the geographer. Refer to Fig. 2.2 and notice that the rainfall increases immediately north of the belt.

Reasons given to explain the occurrence of this belt include the following:

(i) the alignment of the coast in a direction parallel to that of rain-bearing winds, in contrast for instance to the situation along the Sierra Leone coast where the south-west winds meet the coast at right angles.

(ii) the upwelling of cold water resulting from the meeting in this neighbourhood of the cold Benguella current and the warm Guinea current cools the winds passing over the water and thereby causes fogs instead of rain along the coast.

You may come across a few other explanations, but it is well to bear in mind that the matter has not yet been satisfactorily settled.

(d) The length of the rainy season decreases as one moves inland, away from the coast. Most areas in the forested south have about seven months with at least 100mm (4in.) of rain, as compared with less than three months in the far north. Make a careful study of Table 2. You will find that the rains start much earlier in the south (about March) and end later (October), but in the north the rains start in May and end in September.

(e) The south has a two-maxima rainfall regime in which the wettest months are June and October, while the west and north have a one-maximum regime with September as the rainiest month. It follows that there are two seasons in the north and west: the rainy season and the dry season. In the south, however, the August break in the rains makes it possible to recognize four seasons. These are:

—the long rainy season (March-early August)
—the short dry season (August)
—the short rainy season (September and October)
—the long dry season (November-February)

OTHER ASPECTS OF THE RAINFALL

There are several facts about the character of the rainfall such as its reliability and intensity which cannot be readily read from maps or tables.

You will probably know that the rainfall figures in Table 2 are averages for many years. Considerable annual variations occur in most stations, particularly in the north where annual variations of up to 50 per cent are common. Considerable delays in the onset of the rains resulting in delayed cropping or scorching of seeds planted in expectation of the rains occur even as far south as Ondo in western Nigeria. At the same time it is also common for the rainfall to be so heavy as to cause destructive floods which may wash out newly planted seedlings. (See plates 5,7.) The onset of the rainy season is usually heralded by fierce storms which often cause damage to crops and the roofs of thatch houses. A night storm may blow down tree trunks across roads, thereby impeding traffic for many hours. The rain comes in sharp thunderstorms during which as much as 35mm (1½in.) may fall in one hour. Towards the middle of the rainy season, the intensity of the rain decreases so much that along the coast, it may rain in drizzles throughout the day.

FIG. 2.3—Precipitation effectiveness

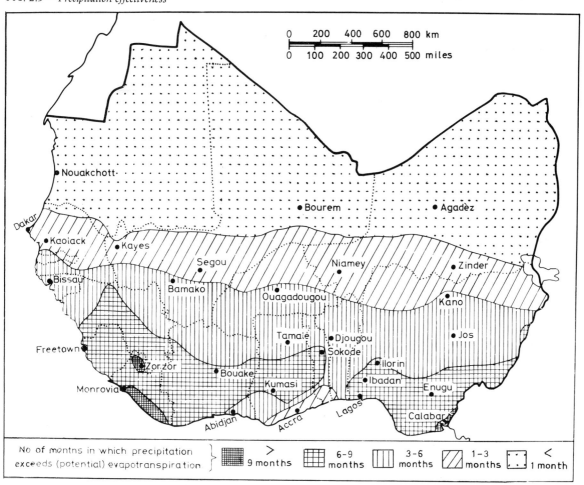

Table 2—Temperatures (°C) and rainfall (mm) for selected stations

Station	Elements	Jan	Feb	Mar	April	May	June	July	Aug	Sept	Oct	Nov	Dec	Year	Climatic type
CONAKRY 4.9m (16ft) 9°31′N.	Temp. Max.	31	32	32	32	32	31	28	28	29	30	31	31	31	Monsoon
	Temp. Min.	23	23	24	24	24	24	23	23	23	23	24	24	23.5	
	Rainfall	2.5	2.5	10	22.5	155	550	1,278	1,038	673	367	120	10	4,228.5	
WARRI 6m (20ft) 5°31′N. 5°44′E.	Temp. Max.	31	33	33	33	31	30	28	28	29	30	32	32	31	Sub-Equato-rial
	Temp. Min.	22	22	23	23	23	22	22	23	22	22	22	22	23	
	Rainfall	32.5	52.5	132.5	225	270	372.5	385	295	427.5	317.5	110	35	2,655	
BOUAKE 338m (1,110ft) 7°41′N. 5°02′W.	Temp. Max.	33	34	35	35	33	31	29	29	30	31	32	33	32	Wet-Tropical
	Temp. Min.	21	22	22	22	22	21	21	21	21	21	21	21	22	
	Rainfall	10	37.5	102.5	145	132.5	150	80	115	205	130	37.5	25	1,170	
TAMALE 194m (637ft) 9°24′N. 5°59′E.	Temp. Max.	36	38	38	37	34	32	31	30	31	33	35	34	34	(Tropical) Guinea Savanna
	Temp. Min.	18	21	23	23	23	22	22	21	21	22	21	21	22	
	Rainfall	2.5	7.5	55	80	117.5	137.5	137.5	202.5	222.5	92.5	17.5	5	1,077.5	
JOS 1,289m (4,230ft) 9°52′N. 8°54′E.	Temp. Max.	28	30	31	32	29	27	24	24	26	28	28	28	28	Highland
	Temp. Min.	14	15	18	19	18	17	17	17	17	17	21	14	17	
	Rainfall	2.5	2.5	27.5	85	200	222.5	325	287.5	210	40	2.5	2.5	1,407.5	
DAKAR 32m (105ft) 14°39′N. 17°25′W.	Temp. Max.	28	28	28	27	28	31	31	31	31	31	31	28	29	Senegal Coast
	Temp. Min.	18	18	18	18	20	23	25	24	25	24	23	20	22	
	Rainfall	0	0	0	0	0	30	87.5	260	142.5	42.5	5	0	567.5	
KANO 472m (1,549ft) 12°02′N. 8°32′E.	Temp. Max.	30	32	36	38	37	35	31	29	31	34	34	31	33	Sudan Savanna
	Temp. Min.	13	16	19	22	24	23	22	21	21	20	17	14	19	
	Rainfall	0	0	2.5	7.5	67.5	112.5	200	310	127.5	12.5	0	0	840	
KAYES 56m (183ft) 14°24′N. 11°26′W.	Temp. Max.	35	38	41	44	43	40	34	32	33	35	38	34	37	Sahel
	Temp. Min.	17	19	22	25	28	26	24	23	23	23	18	18	18	
	Rainfall	2.5	0	0	0	25	95	157.5	237.5	185	42.5	0	0	745	
NOUAKCHOTT 20m (66ft) 18°06′N. 15°59W	Temp. Max.	29	31	32	32	34	33	32	32	34	33	32	28	32	Desert Coast
	Temp. Min.	14	15	17	18	21	23	24	24	24	22	18	13	19	
	Rainfall	0	2.5	2.5	0	2.5	2.5	10	100	22.5	10	2.5	2.5	157.5	
AGADEZ 520m (1,706ft) 16°59′N. 7°58′E.	Temp. Max.	28	33	38	42	44	44	41	39	41	41	34	32	38	Desert
	Temp. Min.	10	12	16	21	25	24	23	23	23	20	15	12	18	
	Rainfall	0	0	0	0	5	7.5	50	92.5	17.5	0	0	0	172.5	

Source: R. J. Harrison Church, *West Africa*, Longman, 1974.

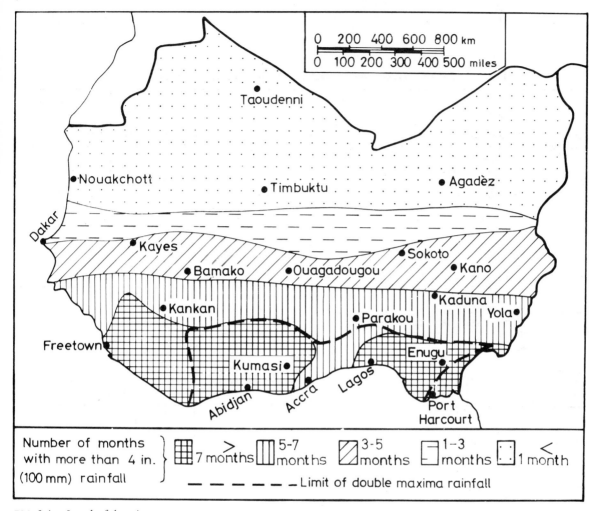

FIG. 2.4—Length of the rainy season

TEMPERATURE

Study the temperature figures in Table 2 and take a close look at Fig. 2.5 (p. 16). You will find that:

1) Temperatures remain high throughout the year and for each station there is little seasonal variation. In the south, the mean daily temperature remains around 27°C (80°F) throughout the year except during the rainy season when the temperatures are cooler; owing to (a) the cooling effects of the rains, and (b) the fact that cloud cover curtails the amount of insolation.

2) Along the coast of Mauritania, Senegal and Gambia there is a curious situation in which the wet season's mean daily temperatures are higher than the dry season's temperatures. You should go through the temperature figures for Dakar to confirm that this is so. The dry season's low temperatures are thought to be caused by the cooling effect of the cool Canary current and the sea breezes blowing across it.

3) Higher day temperatures are recorded in the interior, except in highland areas such as the Jos Plateau, the Guinea Highlands and the Mambila Plateau, all of which have lower temperatures compared with the surrounding lowland.

4) The diurnal range increases with distance from the sea. This is partly a result of clearer skies in the far north and the absence of the moderating influence of the sea. In January, when the harmattan dominates the climates of the north with its cooling effect, the pattern of diurnal variation is more complicated.

5) The mean daily temperatures for January decrease northwards. Thus, in the west, Conakry has a mean temperature of 27°C (80°F) compared with 23°C (73°F) for Dakar. The figures for the eastern district stations of Zungeru and Zinder are

15

30°C (85°F) and 26°C (78°F) respectively while the figures for the central stations of Tamale and Timbuktu are 27°C (81°F) and 21°C (70°F) respectively. Locate these towns on a sketch map of West Africa and write the figures beside each town. Study your map carefully and you will notice that it is erroneous to say that in West Africa the interior is always hotter than coastal areas. It is true, however, that in July, the temperatures increase northward; the mean temperatures for Conakry and Dakar being 25.5°C (79°F) and 28°C (82°F) respectively. The July figures for the other stations are Tamale 26.5°C (78°F), Zungeru 26°C (78°F), Zinder 28.5°C (83°F) and Timbuktu 31°C (88°F).

WINDS AND OCEAN CURRENTS

You have probably noticed that wind is both an element as well as a factor of climate. It is the south-west wind that brings most of the rain that falls in West Africa. It is also true that the length of the rainy season in any area depends largely on the duration of the influence of south-west winds in the area.

Two air masses dominate the climate of West Africa: the Equatorial Maritime air mass which is represented by the moisture laden South-west Monsoon, and the Tropical Continental air mass which is represented by the dry and dusty North-east Trades or the harmattan.

The meeting point of both air masses is called the Inter-Tropical Front (ITF). The ITF moves north and south according to whether the South-west Monsoon or the North-east Trades is dominant.

Note that the ITF rarely reaches the coast, and that since rain falls only in areas lying south of the front, several sections of the coast have rain almost all through the year.

The ITF begins to move northwards in February at which time the North-east Trades starts to retreat, giving way to the advancing South-west Monsoon. By July most areas south of latitude 20°N. are under the influence of rain-bearing winds from the south. In August the ITF reaches its inland limit and remains stable for a few weeks before starting to move towards the coast. Around January when the ITF is near the coast once more, the dominant wind over West Africa is the North-east Trades.

The harmattan

The harmattan is a cold, dry and very dusty wind which begins to blow in November. Its influence along the coast rarely lasts for more than two weeks; but in the north it blows for about three months.

FIG. 2.5—*Mean daily temperatures (seasonal)*

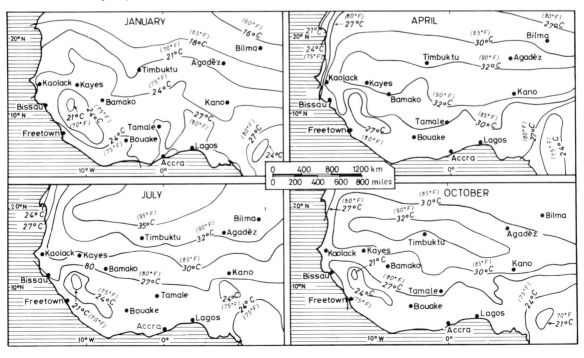

PLATE 6—Typical rainy season cloud formation in the Sahel dry zone, Senegal River Delta

Some of the unpleasant features associated with the harmattan include.
—cracked lips, skin and furniture
—the spread of dust all over the house
—widespread epidemics of cerebrospinal meningitis.
Its velocity, like that of the South-west Monsoon is between 16–24km per hour (10–15 mph).

Other winds

Along the coast, the two seasonal winds are sometimes replaced by sea and land breezes. Sea breezes blow during the day from a much cooler sea surface to replace air expanding from a warmer land surface. Their effect is felt most between 3–5 p.m. Land breezes, on the other hand, blow from land to sea between the hours of 10 p.m. and 8 a.m. The effect of sea breezes is usually restricted to a maximum of 16km (10 miles) from the coast.

Ocean currents

The currents washing the coast of West Africa are the cold Benguella current, the Guinea countercurrent and the cool Canary current.

As a factor of climate, ocean currents influence climatic conditions in an area through the winds blowing over them. Winds blowing over a warm current are usually moisture laden while winds blowing over cold currents usually have a cooling effect on the coast and bring about the formation of fogs rather than rain.

Both the fogs occurring along the coast of Mauritania and the desert conditions which prevail along this coast are attributed to the influence of the cool Canary current. The dry climate along the coast of Accra is also thought to be caused, at least partly, by conditions created as a result of the meeting of the cold Benguella current and the warm Guinea current.

RELATIVE HUMIDITY

What makes the climate of West Africa so unpleasant is its high relative humidity rather than high temperatures. The relative humidity is the ratio between the amount of water vapour actually held in the air and the maximum possible amount at that temperature. It is a measure of the dampness of the atmosphere and is usually expressed as a percentage.

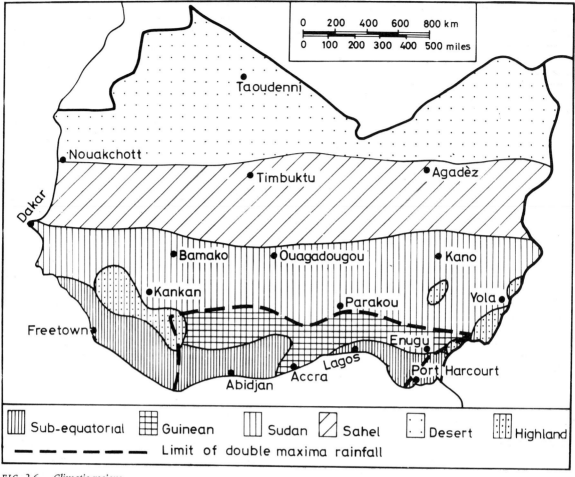

FIG. 2.6—Climatic regions

As a general rule, the relative humidity is highest in the mornings and evenings, the minimum value being about midday. Refer to Table 3 and notice that stations nearer the coast have higher relative humidity and that the relative humidity is always higher during the rainy season. The main reason for this is that for most of the year, the coastal area is under the influence of the south-west wind which has a relative humidity of about 100 per cent.

CLIMATIC CHANGES

About fifty years ago, there was widespread fear that the climate of the northern part of West Africa was becoming drier and that the Sahara was advancing southwards. In 1932, a forestry commission was set up to investigate the situation. The report concluded that there was no evidence to support the fear and stated that the climate of West Africa has not changed since the days of the

Roman Empire. The widespread severe drought of 1973 which affected the sahel region of northern Nigeria, Senegal, Niger, Upper Volta, Mali and Mauritania has re-awakened the fears of the southward advance of the Sahara Desert. During this great drought thousands of cattle died of thirst and relief had to be flown to the drought affected areas. It is relevant to observe, however, that there was an unusually abundant rain in 1974 resulting in very good harvests in some areas, but in extensive floods in other areas.

CLIMATIC REGIONS

Figure 2.6 is a simplified map of the climatic regions of West Africa. The six climatic regions into which the area is divided are: 1) sub-equatorial, 2) Guinean or wet-tropical, 3) Sudan, 4) Sahel, 5) desert or Saharan, 6) highland.

Table 3—Mean relative humidity (percentages). Observations at 8.00 a.m. & 1.00 p.m.

Station	Jan	Feb	Mar	Apr	May	June	July	Aug	Sept	Oct	Nov	Dec	Year	Location
CONAKRY	89	90	85	83	85	89	93	94	94	92	88	89	89	Coastal
	65	65	63	64	70	77	84	87	82	74	67	73	73	
LAGOS	98	97	98	98	98	98	97	97	97	98	98	98	98	Coastal
	62	64	65	73	78	82	79	78	77	77	70	69	73	
DAKAR	67	76	84	87	84	83	81	86	87	86	78	67	80.5	Coastal
	43	45	53	58	59	63	67	73	72	67	51	44	58	
BOUAKE	80	86	85	86	89	91	91	92	92	92	90	84	88	Southern Uplands
	38	44	48	55	62	66	69	71	71	67	61	49	58	
JOS	33	40	45	66	83	92	95	97	96	86	51	40	69	Interior High Plateau
	14	17	18	24	46	62	71	76	63	45	21	17	39	
KANO	37	33	31	42	63	74	88	94	92	80	48	43	60	Sudan
	13	12	12	19	32	46	60	71	61	36	15	12	32	
KAYES	32	31	29	30	46	70	83	88	89	85	57	42	57	Sahel
	16	14	13	14	25	42	64	70	67	58	24	20	36	
ZINDER	21	19	16	20	44	53	68	76	68	40	25	29	40	Desert
	12	12	10	10	20	28	48	56	44	22	18	20	25	

Source: *French West Africa, Volume II: the Colonies*, British Naval Intelligence Handbook Series.

1. Sub-equatorial

Regions with this type of climate have a high annual rainfall of over 1,520mm (60in.), with every month having at least 25mm (1in.) of rain. Except for the Cross River-South Cameroon area, where the rainfall is heavier and more typical of the equatorial type, there is a marked two-maxima regime. Temperatures are uniformly high and are similar to those in the true equatorial type, except that both the diurnal and annual range are greater. High relative humidity of about 90 per cent in the morning is characteristic.

2. Guinean or wet-tropical

This region has a clearly marked dry season (November—March) and a wet season with maxima rainfall in June and September. The rainfall is between 1,000 and 1,250mm (40 and 60in.) Relative humidity is about 80 per cent in the morning except in the dry season (which lasts for four months) when the figure drops to 70 per cent.

3. Sudan

Sudan climates have a shorter rainy season (about five months) than the Guinean type. The annual total rainfall is 500 to 1,000mm (20 to 40in.), but there is considerable variation from year to year. The onset of the rains is rather unreliable and may lead to crop failure. Both the diurnal and the monthly temperature range are much greater than in the regions already described. The relative humidity is low, particularly in the dry season, rising from about 40 per cent in January to 70 per cent in July.

4. Sahel

This type of climate is found in the Niger Republic, Mali and Mauritania. It has rainfall of between 250 and 500mm (10 to 20in.) which comes during the three wet-season months of June, July and August. Mean annual temperatures of over 38°C (100°F) are common during the rainy season while the harmattan keeps down the dry season temperatures to about 32°C (90°F). High diurnal and annual temperature ranges are characteristic.

5. Desert or saharan

The desert or Saharan climates occur in areas with less than 250mm (10in.) of rain. There is no rainy season, since the little rain that falls can come in any month of the year. In certain areas it may not rain for several years.

PLATE 7—Floods at Abeokuta, Nigeria

PLATE 8— Irrigated sugarcane fields at Bacita

6. Highland

The saying that mountains make their own climate is very true of the highlands of West Africa. In all cases the highland effect consists of lowering the temperature but increasing the rainfall compared with the surrounding plains. The climate of a particular highland area, such as the Jos Plateau is therefore a modified type of the climate of the climatic belt in which the highland is located. For this reason, the climate of the Jos Plateau is considerably different from that of the Guinea Highlands or the Bamenda Highlands.

WATER RESOURCES AND THE WATER PROBLEM

In much of West Africa drinking water for man and beast is poor in quality and inadequate in quantity. Since cropping depends mostly on rainfall, a delay in the rains often results in loss of crops and famine while long droughts may cause extensive starvation, mass migrations of people to urban centres, where water is available, and loss of thousands of herds of cattle. This is what happened in 1973. The relief supplied to drought victims was enormous in monetary terms. In Nigeria, the Federal Government gave ₦13 million to the drought-affected states, that is in addition to aid provided by various agencies within and outside the country. The long term solution to the drought problem is large-scale development of irrigation projects and rural water supplies through damming rivers and tapping the underground water resources by digging wells.

Rainfall is by far the most important element of climate in West Africa (as in other tropical areas) as far as agriculture is concerned. This is particularly so since the use of irrigation is not widespread, even in areas of very variable rainfall and high rates of evapotranspiration like the Sudan and Sahelian zones. West Africa experiences great seasonal and spatial variations in rainfall, but much smaller variations in evapotranspiration rates. Precipitation effectiveness or the water balance (that is difference between the amount of water received from rainfall and loss due to evapotranspiration) is an important index for assessing the agricultural potential of an area. Since areal variation in evapotranspiration is small, the number of months in which rainfall exceeds potential evapotranspiration (Fig. 2.3) is highly correlated with the total annual rainfall (Fig. 2.2) as well as with the number of months with more than 100mm (4in.) of rainfall (Fig. 2.4). The map of precipitation effectiveness (Fig. 2.3) provides a fair picture of the availability of water for agriculture in West Africa and is an important guide in planning agricultural development (including irrigation projects) in the region.

Those parts of the coastal areas which receive rainfall throughout the year have more water than they need. Often such areas are drained by numerous rivers and creeks and the water problem in such areas consists of how to control floods, and how to improve the quality of drinking water which constitutes a major source of health hazards in the coastal swamp areas.

In the high forest and Guinea savanna zones, villages located many kilometres away from rivers and streams depend largely on rainwater for their domestic water supplies. During the rainy season the water problem is largely one of the poor quality of the water collected through ponds or pits dug for the sole purpose of trapping water. In the dry season, the problem becomes one of acute water shortage. Long hours are spent in travelling to fetch water from the nearest stream which may be located from 1–10km (1–6 miles) from the village. As far as farming is concerned, the rainfall is fairly reliable but occasionally there is a delay in the onset of the rains. In such a case crops planted in anticipation of the early rains may be scorched by excessive heat and will have to be replanted. Irrigation is desirable especially in the Guinea zone where the Bacita irrigated sugar-cane estate and the Badeggi rice irrigation project are (Plates 8, 9). For most of these two zones, however, the water needs for local staple crops are adequately met by the rainfall. The more pressing need is to provide boreholes for villages located far from streams as in parts of the Udi Plateau and the Ishan Plateau of Nigeria.

It is in the Sudan and Sahelian Zones, where the water needs exceed the water supplies from rainfall, that man, beast and crops suffer most from inadequate water supplies. The rainfall in such areas is usually less than 750mm (30in.), spread over only three to five months in the year. Settled cultivators in these zones have always supplemented crops from upland or rainy season farmlands with crops grown along fadama (river floodplains) or dry season farmland. In some places, a rudimentary form of irrigation is practised and since about 1960 a number of large irrigation schemes have been undertaken. The cattle rearers in these zones adjust to the water situation by leading a nomadic life. During the dry season, most of them move to the wetter south or riverine floodplains and the Chad Basin where water and grazing are available, but return to their home districts during the rainy season. The quality of domestic water supplies in this region is also poor.

In the savanna (Guinea and Sudan) and Sahel regions of West Africa, irrigation is necessary to ensure sufficient water for crops during the rainy season as well as to permit double-cropping during the dry season. Fortunately, surface water is available in the region of Lake Chad and the inland Niger Delta as well as along the Niger and Benue Rivers. Vast areas are, however, handicapped by lack of surface drainage during the dry season when many rivers dry up completely or exist as disconnected pools. Extensive areas are also known to have considerable reserves of underground water and in parts of Bornu and Kano Emirates, these reserves have been tapped for centuries. There is a need to intensify the search for more groundwater parti-

PLATE 9—Sugarcane plantation

cularly in the areas of Basement Complex rocks which cover a very large proportion of the water-deficit areas of West Africa. In view of the high rate of evapotranspiration in these dry areas, and in view of the high cost of building dams, and laying pipes, the feasible way to provide water for man, beast and irrigation is to construct more concrete-lined boreholes. Boreholes are also considered more suitable for the needs of the rural people who live in small villages which are separated from one another by distances of around 16km (10 miles) or so. Large-scale projects involving the creating of man-made lakes would then be restricted to the valleys of the major perennial rivers.

Chapter 3—Vegetation, Soils and Soil Erosion

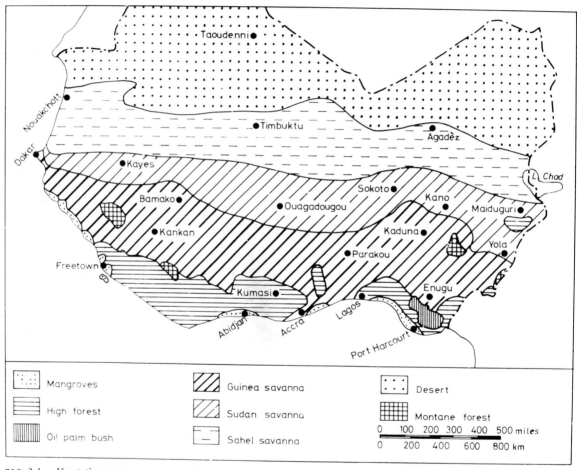

FIG. 3.1—Vegetation map

GENERAL CONSIDERATIONS

Take a close look at Fig. 3.1 and notice that the main vegetation belts are arranged in a west-east direction. The reason for this is that rainfall is by far the most important factor influencing the natural vegetation of West Africa. This fact is best confirmed by comparing the map of annual rainfall (Fig. 2.2) with the vegetation map (Fig. 3.1).

Other factors which influence the vegetation of West Africa are man, altitude, and soil conditions. We shall examine briefly how these factors operate.

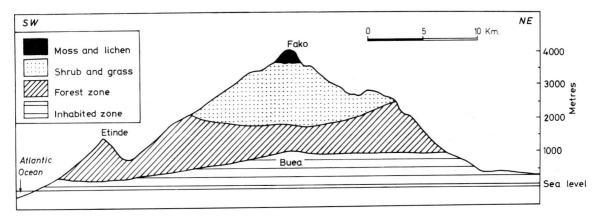

FIG. 3.2—Vertical zonation of mountain vegetation

The human factor has worked mainly through the clearing and firing of bush in preparation for cultivation, through over-grazing and through bush firing for hunting. Several woodlands have also been destroyed through the cutting of trees for firewood, yam sticks and building poles. So great has been the influence of man that today, vast areas of high forest have been replaced by secondary vegetation.

Altitude is an important factor which modifies the vegetation of highland areas. The vertical arrangement of vegetation belts in the Cameroon Mountains is shown in Fig. 3.2. Study this diagram carefully and compare it with the map of vegetation belts. The high altitude grassland of the Bamenda Highlands provides good cattle grazing in an area where the surrounding lowland supports forest vegetation.

River floodplains and other areas which are waterlogged for several months do not support forest vegetation. Rather, grass vegetation is typical of such areas. This is why grassland vegetation occurs in some areas such as the Sobo Plains of mid-western Nigeria, which are located in the rain-forest belt. Areas with lateritic soils which are located in the forest belt also support grassland vegetation because the compact nature and impermeable character of laterite does not support tree growth. Gallery forests found along dry valleys or along the valleys of seasonal streams in grassland areas are also caused by soil conditions. Usually soils along these valleys retain more moisture compared with soils in the nearby uplands, hence the greater concentration of trees along such valleys.

THE VEGETATION TYPES

The vegetation of West Africa falls into seven main types. These are: 1) swamps and other coastal vegetation, 2) tropical rain forest, 3) Guinea (or derived) savanna, 4) Sudan savanna, 5) Sahel savanna or thorn scrub, 6) Saharan, 7) montane.

1. Swamps and other coastal vegetation

Along the coast, groves of coconut palms with a light undergrowth overlook the waters of the Atlantic Ocean. In several areas such as Popo Island (south of Badagry) and Bonny Island, the extent of this vegetation belt has been increased as a result of the establishment of coconut plantations.

An extensive stretch of salt-water swamps in which mangroves make up the main vegetation appears immediately behind the coconut corridor. As shown in Fig. 3.1 the belt of mangrove swamps is not continuous but is to be found in most areas where the coast is aligned in an east-west direction. The width of these swamps varies from less than 1.5km (1 mile) in the Lagos area to over 30km (20 miles) in the Sapele area.

Plate 10 (p. 24) shows a typical mangrove area. The tallest trees, exceeding 21m (70ft) appear in the centre of the islands or peninsulas that characterize this area, although the densest growth of entangled roots and branches is found along the banks of the numerous water channels. Mangrove wood makes excellent fuel which burns even when the wood is fresh. The wood is not readily attacked by termites and is used for building, mining props and railway sleepers. The bark and fruit is rich in tannin and in the past the bark was sometimes burnt to produce salt.

Further inland, beyond the reach of tidal water, mangroves give way to freshwater plants. The most important of these plants is the raffia palm from which palm wine is obtained as well as raffia for the crafts industry. House building materials obtained

PLATE 10—Mangrove swamp area in Nigeria

PLATE 11—Giant tree ferns in Fernando Po

from the raffia palm include palm fronds used as rafters as well as for constructing the walls, piassava for tying up the wall framework and the leaves which are used for making roofing mats. Oil palm trees and a few rain forest trees such as iroko and the oil bean tree also grow in freshwater swamps.

2. Tropical rain forest

Refer to the vegetation map and notice the major break in this vegetation belt in the region of the Accra plains, extending east to Badagry. The belt is an area of dense, evergreen forest of tall trees, with an undergrowth of lianas and other climbing plants which may become so entangled as to make penetration almost impossible. The tallest trees are over 36m (120ft) high; but there are two other distinct layers of trees—a medium layer of trees measuring about 30m (100ft) and a lower layer of trees below 15m (50ft). In areas where the forest has remained untouched for several decades, the top canopy may become so closely interlocked as to prevent completely the rays of the sun from reaching the ground.

In that case the ground remains damp and almost completely void of undergrowth. See plate 11.

The rain forest is rich in economic trees such as iroko, mahogany, sapele wood, and walnut; but the stands of each species are widely scattered, thereby making exploitation expensive. Exploitation is also made difficult by the fact that many trees have trunks whose bases are fluted by winged buttresses rising up to 3 m (10 ft) from the ground. In many districts, however, inadequate transportation is the main factor restricting timber extraction. See plate 12.

In areas such as the eastern states of Nigeria where there is great demand for farmland, the rain forest has since been replaced by the oil palm bush. As the name implies, the oil palm, an important economic crop which is usually preserved when the bush is fired in preparation for farming, is the dominant tree. Areas with high rain forest vegetation are now limited to forest reserves.

3. Guinea savanna

The Guinea savanna or the tree savanna as it is sometimes called is the most extensive vegetation belt in West Africa. It consists of a mixture of trees and grass, with trees being very numerous in sparsely settled areas. In the south where the rainfall can maintain a forest vegetation, the Guinea savanna is usually described as derived savanna, since it is a product of the continuous destruction of high forest by farmers. The northern part of the Guinea savanna is, however, a product of local climatic conditions since the rainfall there is too small to support high forest vegetation.

Tall grass and other tall herbaceous growth form a continuous cover over large areas. The more important trees include the fan palm, shea-butter, dry-zone mahogany and the tamarind. These trees grow very long tap roots and have thick barks which serve as protective covers from the annual dry-season fires. All trees in this vegetation belt shed their leaves in the dry season when water is very scarce. (See plate 13.)

Gallery forests are a characteristic feature of the vegetation of this belt. These are areas of greater tree density usually called fringing forests since they are found along water courses where the soil is usually moist. They are usually low and continuous, covering no more than 12m (40ft) on each bank.

4. Sudan savanna

There are fewer trees, while the grass becomes shorter as compared with the Guinea savanna. This is the cattle belt of West Africa and bush fires are more common. The fires which sweep across vast areas towards the close of the dry season are usually caused by cattle

PLATE 12—*Women and children carrying timber in the rain forest near Kumasi, Ghana. Firewood is an important item in village economies*

rearers, whose aim is to hasten the sprouting of fresh grass for feeding their animals.

A wide variety of acacia trees appears all over the Sudan savanna, which is sometimes called acacia grassland. Other important common trees include the shea-butter, the African locust bean, the silk cotton and the baobab. These fire-resistant trees usually have burnt and twisted stems, and few of them exceed 12m (40ft) in height.

Traces of the natural vegetation, consisting of a greater stand of trees, are found along water courses and along uncultivated hill slopes. Villages are usually embedded in tree groves and in general, an island of woodland in the open grassland or *kurmi* as the Hausas call it, represents a village or hamlet or the site of an abandoned settlement.

5. Sahel savanna or thorn scrub

This is an area of thorn bushes and small trees which grow under dry conditions. The vegetation is rather

25

PLATE 13—Guinea savanna landscape near Jalingo, Nigeria

scanty and even during the rainy season the grass cover never forms a continuous carpet. Rather large areas of bare sand separate tufts of short grasses and trees. See plate 14.

The characteristic tree is the acacia, of which several varieties grow. Some of these trees, especially *Acacia Senegal*, produce gum Arabic, which is an important item of trade. A few date palms begin to appear while large groves of dum palms are very common.

6. Saharan

Semi-desert and desert vegetation appear in areas having less than 250mm (10in.) of rain per annum. The southern part of the Sahara has a considerable cover of low grass and other annuals during the months of July to September, when almost all the rain falls. A few thorny scrubs grow in some localities. Most of the landscape, however, consists of bare surfaces of sand, pebbles and rocks.

True desert conditions exist in the far north of Mali and Niger Republic as well as in Mauritania. Although there may be no rain for several years, the desert is not without its grass and tree vegetation. Desert vegetation is, however, restricted to the oases and to areas where the water table is near the surface. The oases support a permanent vegetation of dates and permanent settlement where crops like wheat and millet are grown under irrigation. Perennial shrubs and small trees grow in areas with underground

PLATE 14—Savanna with Acacia Raddiana, *east of Dagana, Senegal*

watercourses. Such plants usually have thorns instead of leaves. The Sahara also has a vegetation of grass and herbs which begin to grow immediately after a rainstorm and live for only a few weeks.

7. Montane

Just as highland areas have higher rainfall, but lower temperatures than the surrounding lowlands, their vegetation also differs with increase in altitude. The vertical zonation of vegetation on the Cameroon Mountains which lies just on the eastern boundary of West Africa is presented in Fig. 3.2. The other highland areas of West Africa are generally not high enough to exhibit clearly the remarkable effects of altitude on vegetation such as is found in the mountains of East Africa.

But although West African highlands are not high enough to produce the whole range of montane vegetation, the relief effect is quite obvious in the Obudu Hills, the Bamenda Highlands, the Jos Plateau, the Man Mountains and the Guinea Highlands. The lower slopes of highlands located in the forest belt, such as the Bamenda Highlands, the Obudu Hills and the Guinea Highlands are covered with forest vegetation. The upper slopes and the plateau surfaces, where these occur, have a grassland vegetation, which normally supports a cattle population, thanks to the fact that the tsetse fly does not thrive in these

highland areas. Highland areas like the Jos Plateau which are located in grassland regions have a grassland vegetation at the base, forest vegetation on the windward slope and grass vegetation on the plateau surface. Can you explain why this is so?

Transhumance, that is, the seasonal movement of animals and men up and down the slopes of upland areas which is characteristic of mountainous areas like the Alps and the Himalayas, is also practised in West Africa. Fulani cattle-rearers usually go up the Jos Plateau, the Bamenda Highlands and the Guinea Highlands during the rainy season but descend to the river valleys during the dry season.

SOILS

Study the generalized soil map in Fig. 3.3 and compare it with the maps showing the climatic regions (Fig. 2.6) and vegetation (Fig. 3.1) of West Africa. You can see that the relationship between climate and soil type is very close. Climate is therefore an important factor in soil formation. Other factors of soil formation are:

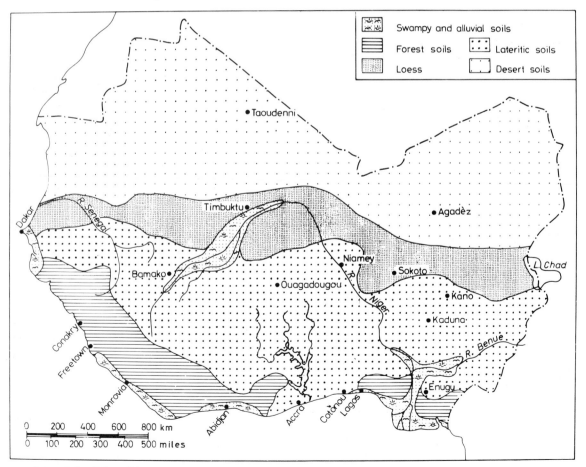

FIG. 3.3—Soils of West Africa

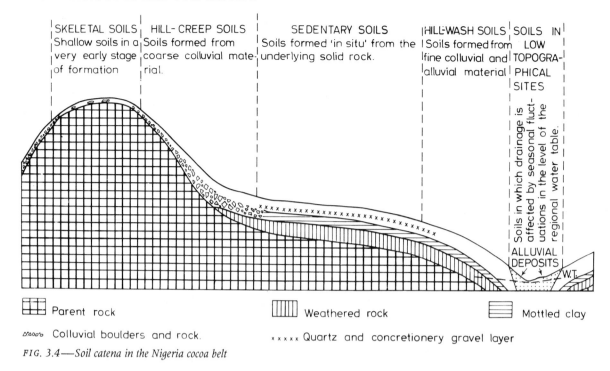

SKELETAL SOILS | HILL-CREEP SOILS | SEDENTARY SOILS | HILL-WASH SOILS | SOILS IN
Shallow soils in a | Soils formed from | Soils formed 'in situ' from the | Soils formed from | LOW
very early stage | coarse colluvial mate- | underlying solid rock. | fine colluvial and | TOPOGRA-
of formation | rial. | | alluvial material | PHICAL
| | | | SITES

Soils in which drainage is affected by seasonal fluct-uations in the level of the regional water table.

ALLUVIAL
DEPOSITS
W.T.

▦ Parent rock   ▥ Weathered rock   ▤ Mottled clay

◿◿◿ Colluvial boulders and rock.   ×××× Quartz and concretionery gravel layer

FIG. 3.4—*Soil catena in the Nigeria cocoa belt*

1) The parent material from which the soil is for-med. This may consist of hard rocks or sand brought by wind or running water. The parent material usually determines the physical ap-pearance and the chemical composition of the soil.

2) Relief or slope, which affects not only the rate of soil formation but also the water content and the rate of soil loss through erosion. On very gentle slopes, soils tend to be marshy or poorly drained while steep slopes have very thin soils. Deep soils are usually formed in undulating areas.

3) Plants and animals which, when they die, add considerable organic matter to the soil. The work of worms and burrowing animals is important in mixing up organic remains in the soil.

Soil catena

The term catena is used to describe the arrangement of soil types developed along a sloping hillside, from the top of the hill (water divide) to its base (valley). Fig 3.4 illustrates a catena arrangement in the cocoa belt of south-western Nigeria. You will notice that on top of the hill, where erosion is slight, deep soils are formed. Lateritic soils form on gentler sections of the slope which are affected by fluctuations in the water table. Sandy loams characterize the lower slopes while poorly drained clayey soils form in the valley.

MAIN SOIL GROUPS

Fig. 3.3 shows that there are five major soil groups. It is important to realize that there is a considerable variety of soil types within each group and that the map presents a very generalized picture. The five groups recognized are: 1) coastal swamps and alluvial soils, 2) rain forest soils, 3) lateritic soils, 4) loess soils of the far north, 5) desert soils.

1. Coastal swamps and alluvial soils

Along the coast the soils are sandy and impoverished through leaching, a process whereby clay particles and soluble salts are continuously carried down into the ground by percolating rain-water. This is the main reason why the sandy beaches and ridges fronting the sea are not cultivated. A more extensive area of swampy soils which support mangrove vegetation separates the coastal sands from the waterlogged silts of the freshwater swamps. This area suffers from an oversupply of water from rain and rivers. In the coastal areas of Sierra Leone and Guinea, these soils are used for growing swamp rice.

2. Rain forest soils

Soils in this group are usually rich in humus derived from heavy leaf fall in the forest. Unfortunately the soils are highly leached because of the heavy rainfall.

Under cultivation, forest soils soon lose their fertility which is concentrated in a thin top layer. This is why it is necessary to rest the soil under bush fallow for several years.

Apart from supplying humus, the forest also protects the soil from erosion. Lateritic soils which are more common in drier areas of savanna woodlands occur in areas which have been cleared of forest for several years. Parent materials are however responsible for the large variety of soil types in this group. The black soil of the Accra plains owes its dark colour not to decayed vegetable matter, but to the mineral content of its parent material. Indeed, unlike most black soils, it is not fertile.

3. Lateritic soils

Laterite soils form along gentle slopes or plateau surfaces, stripped of tree cover (Fig. 3.5). A marked dry season alternating with a wet season is a necessary condition for formation. During the wet or rainy season mineral salts, mainly compounds of iron and aluminium are carried down into the ground by leaching. At the same time the rise in water table during this season helps to cause an upward migration of iron and aluminium salts. The result is a concentration of these salts in a restricted zone. In the dry season the soil waters are brought to the surface by

evaporation leaving behind insoluble compounds of iron and aluminium in slag-like concretions. This is laterite. Under plant cover it is soft and heavy, but when exposed to the atmosphere it becomes so hard that it appears as a rock. It is this quality that makes laterite suitable for making dirt roads as well as for building walls of houses. Occasionally, laterite may be rich enough in iron or aluminium to form the ore for these minerals.

Much of West Africa is covered with lateritic soils but the major areas are located outside the forest belt and south of the desert-Sahel boundary. They are cultivated where better soils are not available.

4. Loess soils

A fairly broad belt of chestnut steppe soils extend from northern Senegal, through Mali, northern Upper Volta, southern Niger and northern Nigeria to the shores of Lake Chad. These soils are developed in a grass environment and are similar in texture to the prairie soils of North America. The parent materials consist mostly of loess or fine sand brought down by wind from the Sahara Desert. These soils are generally fertile, but are not fully utilized because of the low rainfall in the areas where they occur.

As the vegetation becomes thinner in a northward direction, these soils change colour from dark brown

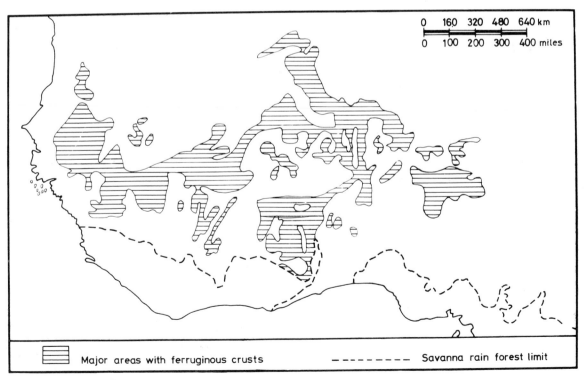

FIG. 3.5—Lateritic soils

to light brown, indicating a decrease in the humus content. Thus while the southern loess soils of northern Nigeria support good crops of cotton, maize and rice, the sandier lighter soils of the desert borderlands seem more suitable for groundnut and millet cultivation.

5. Desert soils

Desert soils occur over most of Niger Republic, Mali and Mauritania. Since weathered material in the desert is redistributed by wind and occasional sheet-floods, the parent material for soil formation is often sorted out into rocky areas, dune areas with sandy materials and playa floors with silt and clay. Since there is little rain-water for downward leaching, calcium carbonate and soluble salts usually accumulate within the upper horizon of desert soils. It is important to realize that although the presence of salts is common in desert soils, there are some desert soils which are not saline. Since many crops including cotton, millet and guinea corn cannot thrive well on saline soils, major irrigation projects are usually restricted to areas with non-saline soils. In West Africa, as in many other arid areas, it is the shortage of water, rather than the presence of salts in the soils, that is the major limiting factor to cropping.

SOIL EROSION

Soil erosion takes place when the rate of soil loss far exceeds that of soil formation. This is accelerated erosion as distinct from natural erosion. It is usually started off as a result of human interference through farming, grazing or road making. The steepness of the slope and the torrential character of the rainfall are other important factors which help to increase the rate of soil erosion.

There are two types of soil erosion: sheet erosion and gully erosion. Sheet erosion, by wind or running water, takes place on gently undulating surfaces which have been stripped of much of their vegetation. This type of erosion is particularly common in the plateau surfaces of savanna and Sahel regions. The soil loss may expose the roots of grasses.

The most spectacular and probably the most destructive type of soil erosion is gully erosion. Some of the areas which have been badly affected by gully erosion include the over-farmed districts of Awka, Udi and Nsukka in south-east Nigeria, the slopes of the Futa Jallon and the districts around Sokoto and Ouagadougou. In the Awka and Udi districts of Nigeria gully erosion has destroyed so much farmland that the local people have had to migrate to farm in other parts of the country. Some gullies in these

PLATE 15 — Gulley erosion at Agulu, Nigeria

districts started when rain-water became concentrated along footpaths leading to springs, where the people fetch water for drinking and other domestic use. Poor methods of farming, such as making mounds or ridges along the slopes of a hill instead of along the contours have had the same effect as footpaths in initiating gullies.

Plate 15 shows some gullies at Agulu in south-east Nigeria. Study this photograph carefully and note that areas made useless for farming include not only those where the gullies occur but also those areas where the sand removed from the gullies is deposited.

SOIL CONSERVATION

The aims of soil conservation are to retain the fertility of the soil and to retain the soil structure and thereby prevent soil destruction by soil erosion. A system of farming in which no fertilizer is used impoverishes the soil and weakens the soil structure, thereby making it less resistant to soil erosion. In West Africa soil fertility is regained by leaving the land under bush fallow for many years. But in areas where there is great demand for farmland, the fallow periods have been reduced from over ten years in the past to about three years. Here bad cases of soil erosion are found.

Efforts to check erosion and help the soil to regain its fertility include the following:

—preventing any form of cultivation in areas now affected by gully erosion

—building of soak-away pits by the wayside, so that rain-water is trapped and prevented from washing away the soil

—the planting of fast-growing shrubs like *acioa baterri* (*icheku* in Ibo or *akan* in Ibibio) and the cashew tree; the heavy leaf fall from these plants is expected to supply humus to the soil.

SECTION B: PEOPLES AND SOCIETIES

Chapter 4—The Peoples and their Ways of Life

GENERAL COMMENTS

The 121 million people who live in West Africa (1974) belong to many ethnic groups, the most numerous of which include the Yorubas (11 million), Ibos (9 million), Hausas (12 million) and Fulanis (5 million). Each group speaks a different language of which more than 300 types have been distinguished and in the past, most linguistic groups had very little contact with other neighbouring groups. Today, ethnic consciousness is still very strong and, in Nigeria for example, the generality of the people still think of themselves first as Yorubas, Ibos or Tivs rather than as Nigerians. In many countries of West Africa the main unifying factors today are the official language which is either French or English and the economic interdependence of the various peoples which has grown during the last 70 years. (See Fig. 4.1.)

West African peoples fall into two broad groups, namely: 1) the peoples of the north, and 2) the forest Negros. The northern peoples include the Hausas, Fulanis, Moors and Tuaregs, all of whom came into West Africa from across the Sahara Desert. Most of these peoples profess the Muslim faith and until the beginning of this century their trade and cultural contacts were mainly with peoples of the Arab world, rather than with the nearby forest peoples. A considerable number of these northern peoples, notably the Fulanis, Tuaregs and Shuwa Arabs are nomadic cattlemen, who spend the dry season away from their home districts, in search of water and grazing for their cattle (Fig.

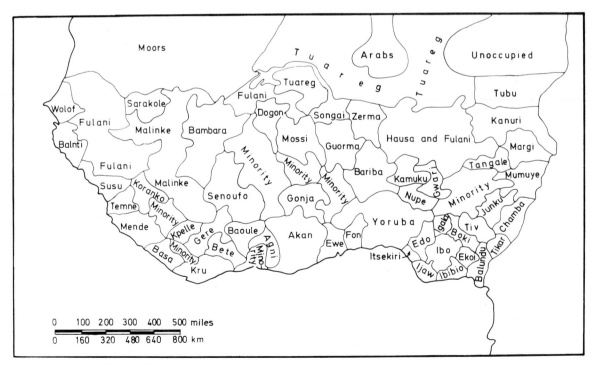

FIG. 4.1—Peoples of West Africa

PLATE 16—*Yoruba woman from one of the western states of Nigeria*

4.2, p. 34). Increasing number of Fulanis and Shuwa Arabs have, however, settled down to practise some elementary form of mixed farming.

The most prominent settled cultivators amongst the northern peoples include the Wolofs of Senegal, the Bambaras of Mali, the Mossis of Upper Volta and the Hausas of Nigeria. Most of these settled cultivators live in large towns and farming villages, and are usually organized into large traditional political units which are still ruled by traditional chiefs. Their typical mud huts with grass thatch, or flat mud roofs in the far north, present a great contrast to the tents of the nomadic cattlemen.

With the exception of the Akan peoples of Ghana and the Yorubas and Ibos of Nigeria, the Middle Belt and the coastal forests are inhabited by relatively smaller groups consisting of settled cultivators. The predominant religion amongst these groups is traditional religion which features the worship of various idols, but since about 1910, an increasing number have adopted the Christian faith. Political organization varies from the large forest kingdoms of Ashanti, Benin and Yoruba to the largely fragmented groupings in the Middle Belt and Iboland where the village-

group is the largest traditional political unit. Along the coast, groups such as the Ijaws of the Niger Delta and the Efiks of Calabar were organized into small city states of which the most famous were Bonny, Opobo and Duke Town.

Since the beginning of the colonial period, there has been increasing contact between the forest peoples and the peoples of the far north, a development which started during the pre-colonial period religious wars, when some of the northern peoples tried to spread Islam by force of arms. Today northern religions and ways of life have penetrated into parts of the forest belt and there has been considerable inter-marriage between the various groups. Most ethnic groups, however, maintain several distinctive characteristics as shown below in the sections which give brief accounts of the major ethnic groups that inhabit West Africa.

THE MOORS

Although the Moors number just about half a million, they occupy a vast area of desert and semi-desert country in Mauritania, northern Mali and the northern borders of Senegal. They are divided into many small rival tribal groups. Moors are predominantly Muslims and their society is organized into four classes or castes in which 1) the warriors and 2) learned religious men (or *marabouts*) form the ruling class. The other two social classes are 3) the artisans (or *zenaga*) and 4) the serfs (or *harratine*) who consist of freed slaves and their descendants.

The Moors lead a nomadic life, their main occupation being animal rearing, but a few of the *harratine* settle permanently in villages where they grow millet and other crops. Camels are the most important animals kept, but sheep and goats are also kept by most families. Milk and milk products are the main items of food and most of their household equipment such as mats and rugs (and even clothing) are made from animal hair, wool and skins. The majority of Moors live in tents which they pitch together in small groups. (See plate 17, p. 33.)

THE TUAREGS

The Tuaregs (sing. Targui) who number about half a million people live mainly in Niger Republic and in the region of the Niger bend in Mali Republic. They are generally tall and well-built. The men wear sleeveless cotton shirts, loose trousers, a turban-like head cloth and a veil covering the whole of the face below the eyes as protection against sun rays and

PLATE 17 —Young Moor from Akjoujt, Mauritania

PLATE 18—Tuareg nomads near Mopti, Mali

sand-storms. Most Tuaregs marry one wife each, un-like most other Muslim groups and their women have much freedom and are not required to wear veils as many other Muslim women do. Tuareg society, like that of the Moors is organized into classes or castes which include the nobles, the mallams or learned men, the artisans and the serfs.

Most Tuaregs are still pastoral nomads who move about with their herds and flocks of camels, sheep, goats and a small number of cattle, in search of water and grazing. Each clan or group has a fixed and defi-ned grazing territory and like the Moors and Fulanis, they rarely kill their animals for meat. Since about 1910, an increasing number of Tuaregs have settled down as farmers who combine cattle-rearing with grain cultivation. These farmers live in grass huts or permanent houses of stone and cement, unlike the nomads who live in skin tents. Their food consists of milk, butter, cheese, millet, couscous and dates.

The Tuaregs lead a hard life in difficult surround-ings which provide very poor pasture for animals and few opportunities for earning a living. Like other nomadic groups, the struggle for grazing rights and water-points has often resulted in long quarrels and bloody conflicts which have made ethnic unity vir-tually impossible. (See plate 18.)

THE FULANIS

Although the Fulanis (5 million) are less numerous than the Yorubas, Hausas and the Ibos, they are by far the most dispersed people in West Africa and the word *peul*, which is the name the Fulanis call them-selves, means 'scattered'. Their main concentrations are in Senegal, Guinea Republic, Mali and Nigeria (Fig. 4.2, p. 34). Before the colonial period, the Fulanis founded and ruled the Muslim empires of Macina and Sokoto-Gwandu and today in Nigeria, most of the emirs of the northern states are Fulanis.

On the basis of their occupations and mode of life, the Fulanis fall into two groups, namely the Cow Fulani and the Town (or settled) Fulani. The Cow Fulani leads a simple nomadic life and is very much attached to his cattle. This group rarely intermarries with other peoples and it is amongst the Cow Fulani that the purest members of their ethnic origin are to be found. They are usually very tall and commonly live in small tents or low temporary huts built of straw and tree branches. Most Cow Fulanis are Muslims who also practise some form of traditional religion. Cattle are a form of capital and are rarely slaughtered. Rather the Fulani depends very much on cattle milk for food. The cattle are used to pay bride price, although many Fulanis now sell their cattle for cash.

The Town Fulanis on the other hand lead a settled life in the city or village and have largely intermarried

33

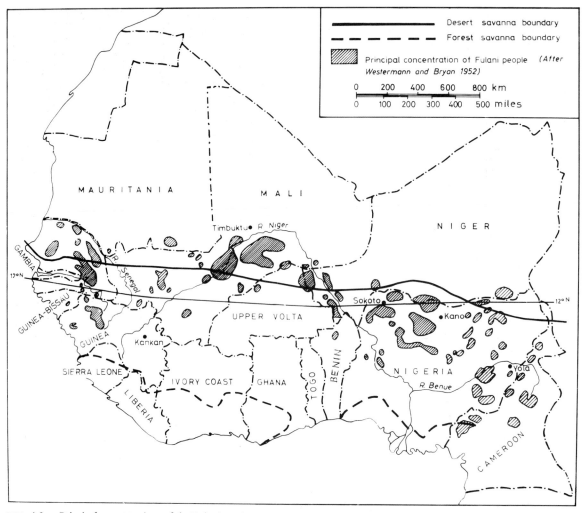

FIG. 4.2—*Principal concentrations of the Fulani people*

with people of Negro stock. The settled Fulanis who live in small villages cultivate a variety of crops including guinea corn, millet and rice, while those who have cattle usually place the animals under the care of the Cow Fulani. Those who live in the cities include learned mallams, government employees and artisans. An increasing number of Cow Fulanis have also settled down in the Guinea Highlands and the Jos Plateau where they practise some elementary form of mixed farming. (See plate 19, p. 35.)

THE WOLOFS

The Wolofs, who number about 650,000, are the most prominent group in Senegal. They are also found in Gambia. They are generally tall and handsome, and like the northern peoples described above, their society is organized into castes which include the aristocrats, artisans and descendants of slaves. Most Wolofs are Muslims and as a warrior group, used to look down on farm work until about 1886 when a Muslim prophet taught that agriculture was holy work. (See plate 91.)

Today most Wolofs are settled farmers whose main farm crop is groundnuts. Wolof farmers, however, rely heavily on migrant labour from Mali and Guinea to work on their groundnut farms. They live in small villages of round thatched mud houses, and since their county is very dry, both their villages and farmlands are located near to river valleys and other moist depressions behind the coastal sand dunes.

THE MANDINGOS

The Mandingos who are also called Mandes are one of the oldest settled groups of agriculturalists in West

Africa. They number about 3 million and settle in the area extending from southern Mali to northern Ivory Coast. Mandingo sub-groups include the Sarakole of Mali and Senegal (about 400,000), the Malinke of Mali, Senegal and the Ivory Coast (about 1,000,000) and the Bambaras of Mali and Ivory Coast (about 1,400,000). The ancestors of the Mandingos are thought to have settled in the region of the inland Niger Delta several thousand years before Christ and it was their descendants who established the famous ancient empire of Mali (see Fig. iii). (See plate 20.)

As agriculturalists, the ancient Mandingos developed from local wild plants a wide range of food crops including yams, millet, guinea corn, water melon and rice. Today, in addition to farming, many Mandingos have prospered as traders and fishermen on the Niger. The western sub-groups such as the Sarakoles and Malinkes are mostly Muslims while the Bambaras are still predominantly animists. The Dioula sub-group live in small groups all over the western part of West Africa and as prominent traders their economic role in West Africa is comparable to that of the Hausa trader in the eastern part of West Africa.

PLATE 20—Mandingo woman at Kayes, western Mali

PLATE 19—In a Fulani village, Nigeria

THE MOSSIS

The Mossis of Upper Volta number about 2 million and inhabit one of the few very densely populated districts in West Africa. They are a pure Negro people who live in small villages of cylindrical mud-brick huts with conical roofs of straw thatch. Their territory is poor and farmland is inadequate, resulting in the emigration of about 500,000 Mossis to work in the plantations of Ivory Coast and Ghana.

Most Mossis are farmers who cultivate millet, maize, bananas, yams and rice on the naturally infertile soils of their home district. Other crops grown on Mossi farms include beans, tobacco and onions. Riverine fishing is also important. Many people supplement their income from gathering forest products and crafts-making.

Before the colonial period, the Mossis had developed a most complex and efficient political system which has been largely preserved in spite of the French policy of direct rule. There is still one supreme ruler, the Morho-Naba who lives in Ouagadougou and according to Mossi tradition, his authority is absolute. He is supported by a number of important state officials who together constitute the nobility. Members of the ruling class are all Muslims while the vast majority of the common people are animists, some of whom have since been converted to Christianity.

THE KRUS

The Krus are more commonly referred to as Krooboys or Krumen (a corruption of 'crew men') and are found in scattered fishing villages along the coasts of eastern Liberia and western Ivory Coast. They number about 450,000 and are best known for their skill as daring seamen and fishermen. They are a true negro people with strong and well-built bodies. Young Krus have featured prominently as seamen in European cargo and mail boats plying the West African route. They are also generally employed in the loading and unloading of ship cargo.

At home, the Krus live in small villages consisting of wooden huts raised on piles (similar to Ijaw huts in the Niger Delta and the Lagos creeks area). They are organized into clans each of which has a council of headmen. Apart from fishing, the Krus specialize in canoe building and the cultivation of rice and cassava. Limited opportunities for employment at home have resulted in the emigration of many Krus to establish fishing colonies along the coast from Dakar (Senegal) to Douala (Cameroon).

PLATE 21—Hausa people dancing

THE HAUSAS

About 14 million Hausas live in Nigeria and Niger Republic, although the number of West Africans who speak Hausa is probably more than 18 million. As a group, the Hausas have a mixture of Negro, Fulani and Tuareg blood resulting from generations of intermarriage with the Fulanis who conquered the ancient Hausa states and the neighbouring Tuareg peoples of the desert margins. Before the Fulani Jihad of the early nineteenth century, when the Fulanis seized power in the fourteen Hausa states, most Hausas were animists. The Fulani conquerors enforced the adoption of Islam and today most Hausas profess the Muslim faith. (See plate 21.)

Hausa economy has always featured the intensive cultivation of guinea corn, millet, maize and beans. The Hausas are also well known as successful itinerant traders who deal in various crafts, including leatherwork, cloth and imported goods. In Nigeria, the Hausas are largely responsible for organizing the trade in cattle and kola nuts between western Nigeria and the northern states of Nigeria. Many Hausas also own herds of cattle, but these are usually left under the care of Cow Fulanis.

The Hausas live in large towns as well as in small agricultural villages which like the towns were usually, in the past, surrounded by a defensive wall. In the cities of the far north, such as Katsina and Kano, the Hausas build flat-topped mud houses, but further south, their huts are covered with conical roofs of grass thatch. Can you explain these differences in house types and the building materials?

THE YORUBAS

The Yoruba-speaking peoples of West Africa numbered about 11 million in 1973 and are concentrated in the Ogun, Oyo, Ondo, Kwara and Lagos states of Nigeria as well as in the south-eastern districts of Benin. Yorubas claim a common descent from Oduduwa who lived at Ife and from where the people dispersed all over western Nigeria and beyond. During the period of the slave trade, many Yoruba slaves were taken to Brazil and Cuba, two countries in which the worship of traditional Yoruba gods is still common. (See plate 16.)

Amongst African peoples, the Yorubas are best known for the large size of their traditional towns which include Ife (130,000), Ibadan (627,000) Oshogbo (209,000), Ijebu-Ode (68,500), Ogbomosho (319,800) and Ilesha (166,000). These towns still have a large proportion of farmers, although the concentration of people into such large units has encouraged trade and crafts industry on a large scale. Lack of planning, the winding nature of the narrow streets and the absence of drains have contributed to the extremely filthy surroundings which are characteristic of Yoruba towns.

In Yoruba society, farming is a man's job while the women are mainly traders and craft workers. Trade in foodstuffs and manufactured goods is controlled by women, but men dominate the trade in cocoa, which is the main export-crop produced by the Yorubas. It is largely the income derived from cocoa that has made the Yoruba territory the most developed part of Nigeria.

The worship of traditional gods like Ogun (god of iron), Shango (god of thunder) Oshun (god of River Oshun) is still very common even amongst those Yorubas who profess the Christian or Muslim faith. There are more Muslims than Christians, particularly in the northern Yoruba districts of Ibadan, Ilorin and Kabba.

THE IBOS

The Ibos are generally characterized as an energetic and individualistic people. They number about 9 million and form the indigenous population of Imo and Anambra States and parts of the Bendel State of Nigeria. Unlike the Yorubas, who are organized

PLATE 22 — *Ibo girl*

into large kingdoms and who live in large towns, the Ibos live in villages which in the past formed the largest effective political unit amongst them. Often the village is named after an ancestor who is thought to have established the settlement. Except amongst the western and riverine Ibos, who live in compact villages, Ibo settlements consist of dispersed compounds scattered about the territory owned by a particular village.

Central Iboland has a large population concentration of more than 325 persons per sq. km (850 per sq. mile). Farmland is scarce and since the people are predominantly farmers, many of them have had to migrate to farm in other parts of Nigeria. Many others migrate to trade or work for wages in the towns. Trading plays a very important part in Ibo economy and is largely controlled by men, unlike in Yorubaland where trading is dominated by women.

Iboland was virtually untouched by Fulani warriors who posed as the apostles of Islam, and so remained an area of traditional religions until the period of British rule when many people adopted Christianity. The ready acceptance of Christian teaching was to prove a great asset in the development of skilled and semi-skilled workers of Ibo origin. Thus at Independence in 1960, Ibo civil servants and technicians were to be found controlling positions of influence all over Nigeria. It was during the Nigerian Civil War (1967–70) that the Ibos became well-known outside Nigeria for their role in organizing the Biafran rebellion.

The ethnic groups discussed in this chapter are representative of the peoples of the far north, the Middle Belt and the forest belt. Their traditional ways of life show a remarkable adaptation to local environments. The imposition of colonial rule and the adoption of Christianity resulted in marked changes in traditional ways of life. Amongst other things, the authority of chiefs who, amongst some groups, formerly held the power of life and death, declined, while some secret societies were proscribed or went underground. Road and railway construction, together with the monetization of the economy and the growth of towns resulted in increased inter-group contact but the strong attachment to one's village of origin remains, and most people who live and work in cities aim to build a house in their villages of origin.

Finally, there is a small group of very influential people of non-African origins who live and work in West Africa. The most influential group consists of European administrators, professionals, missionaries and merchants. Most of them are French and British who numbered about 100,000 and 40,000 respectively in 1960. In Senegal, Ivory Coast and Togo for example, the French settled permanently as shopkeepers, garage-owners, plantation owners and professionals but in Nigeria and Ghana, most Europeans served in the colonial service and in commerce. Since independence the number of Europeans has declined greatly, except in the Ivory Coast where the number of French settlers has increased. In Nigeria and Ghana, the civil service and retail trade are now manned by Africans, but not so in Senegal or Ivory Coast.

The other influential group of non-Africans is made up of Lebanese, Syrians and Indians who settled in the larger towns as shopkeepers, wholesale traders and industrialists. There were probably about 20,000 of them in West Africa in 1960. In 1969 and 1970, many Lebanese and Syrians were forced to close down their businesses and leave Ghana in compliance with that country's Aliens Act which restricted many businesses to Ghanaian citizens. The 1972 Indigenization Decree of Nigeria which came into effect in 1974 has had the same effect of displacing many Indians, Lebanese and Syrians from some occupations.

Chapter 5—The Population of West Africa

The total population of West Africa was about 121 million in 1974 of which over 71 million lived in Nigeria. In this chapter we shall consider the distribution of the population, the labour situation and the general pattern and types of migration. The grouping of the predominantly rural population of West Africa into villages and the increasing rate of urbanization are also considered briefly.

DISTRIBUTION OF POPULATION

A few important facts about the population of West Africa appear to be obvious after a careful study of the population density map (Fig. 5.1). The first of these

facts is that vast areas of West Africa are very sparsely populated, having less than 23 persons per sq. km. (60 per sq. mile). Such areas include the Chad Basin, the Cross River district, western Ivory Coast, eastern Senegal and much of Mali. At the same time, there are a few restricted areas in Iboland, Ibibioland (both in south-eastern Nigeria) and the Mossi area of Upper Volta which support over 230 persons per sq. km (600 per sq. mile).

The second fact about the distribution of population in West Africa is the occurrence of vast areas of low density population in the Middle Belt, which is the area lying approximately between latitudes $7\frac{1}{2}°$N. and 12°N. This low density zone is particularly noticeable in Nigeria where it separates the coastal areas of

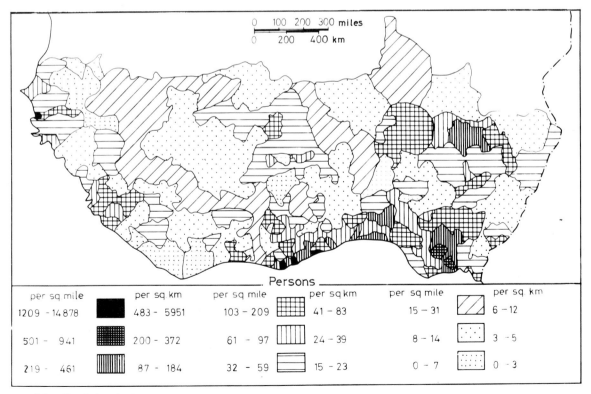

per sq mile	per sq km	per sq mile	per sq km	per sq mile	per sq km
1209 – 14878	483 – 5951	103 – 209	41 – 83	15 – 31	6 – 12
501 – 941	200 – 372	61 – 97	24 – 39	8 – 14	3 – 5
219 – 461	87 – 184	32 – 59	15 – 23	0 – 7	0 – 3

FIG. 5.1—Population density

dense population from the northern high density districts of Sokoto and Kano. In Nigeria, the Middle Belt occupies about 38 per cent of the total area of the country but supports only about 20 per cent of the population. This may be compared with the coastal areas and the Sudan zone which cover 20 per cent and 42 per cent of the total area respectively, but support 45 per cent and 35 per cent of the population respectively.

A few isolated pockets of high population density occur in the Middle Belt districts of Tivland, the Jos Plateau, the Mandara Hills area and north-eastern Ghana. With the exception of Tivland, these Middle Belt high-density areas are associated with hilly districts which offered considerable protection for people during the slave raids of the pre-colonial periods.

FACTORS INFLUENCING THE DISTRIBUTION OF POPULATION

The factors which influence the distribution of population in West Africa are mainly historical and physical conditions of climate, relief, drainage and availability of water supplies. The sparse population of the Middle Belt for example is greatly due to the large-scale depopulation of this region during the period of the slave trade. During this period, many towns and villages were completely destroyed in the inter-tribal wars and slave raids, and in many districts the entire population was carried away into slavery or driven to seek refuge in inaccessible hill areas. The Middle Belt suffered very much from both the Sudanese Kingdoms which supplied slaves to Arab slave traders as well as from the coastal chiefs who raided the area for slaves which were sold to European slave dealers.

The few pockets of dense population in the hilly areas of the Middle Belt also originated during the period of the slave trade. Such hilly areas as the Jos Plateau and the Mandara Hills provided shelter to fleeing refugees and although many people have since descended to live on the plains, there are still many villages located on the hills.

In the sudan zone which lies north of the Middle Belt, the main centres of population concentration are the districts which were ruled by powerful chiefs who were able to provide protection and good government to their people. The fortified city of Kano which is located in a rich agricultural district therefore attracted thousands of people from the neighbouring districts. The concentration of people around Sokoto and the Mossi capital of Ouagadougou also came about in the same way.

The areas of high population densities in south-eastern Nigeria are more difficult to explain, particularly since these areas have some of the poorest soils in West Africa. Slave wars were rare in this part of West Africa because the slaves were obtained largely through the medium of a bogus god called the Long Juju as well as by sales of social undesirables such as stubborn children, thieves and adulterers.

Most of the coastal areas of high population densities are more recent and are a result of port development and increasing migration of people to work in factories and other establishments located in the port-towns, some of which also serve as capital cities for the various countries. Other opportunities which have attracted people to these coastal areas include tree-crop production, mining and timber exploitation.

Although history is a very important factor which helps to explain the present population map of West Africa, the drainage characteristics and complete lack of water for use by man and animals are also important. The vast swampy areas of the Niger Delta and the coastal lagoons have always been sparsely populated and so have the vast arid areas of Niger, northern Mali and the Lake Chad Basin. The ravages of sleeping sickness and river blindness have also made large areas of the Middle Belt and the forest belt unsuitable for human settlement.

THE LABOUR SITUATION

Since most of West Africa is sparsely populated, there has always been a shortage of wage labour particularly in Liberia, Ivory Coast, the cocoa belts of Ghana and Nigeria and in the Middle Belt. At the beginning of the colonial period, the shortage of labour led to the use of prisoners and forced labour for building roads, railways and ports, particularly in the French-speaking countries of Senegal, Mali and Ivory Coast.

The situation today is one in which many rural districts experience great difficulty in recruiting labour to work in the mines and tree-crop plantations, while the rapidly growing urban centres suffer from serious unemployment of young school-leavers who have migrated from rural areas. There are, however, some rural areas where shortage of farmland has created a labour surplus situation. It is such areas that export population to the mines and rich agricultural districts of the coastal belt.

Most West African countries still depend largely on highly skilled labour from Europe and North America. This is more true of the French-speaking countries of Senegal and Ivory Coast where the schools, factories and the civil service are still largely

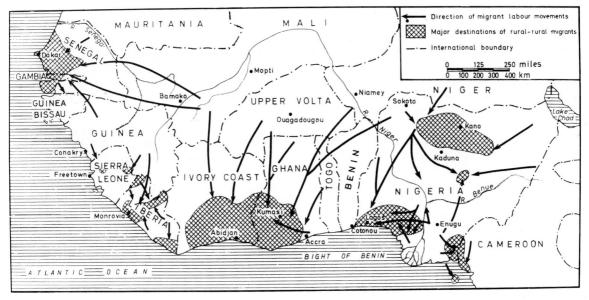

FIG. 5.2—Patterns of migration

manned by French people. Nigeria and Ghana have the largest number of highly trained indigenous personnel, an increasing number of which is trained in local universities and technical institutions.

Types and pattern of migrations

Pre-colonial period slave raids and inter-tribal wars caused large-scale movements of people away from the war zones and it was during this period that much of the forested part of Yorubaland was settled. These cases of forced migrations, including the use of forced labour during the early colonial period, have since given way to voluntary migrations from one part of West Africa to another.

Recent migrations feature movements across international boundaries as well as internal migrations within each country and within the territory occupied by each ethnic group. An increasing number of people, especially young school leavers, migrate to look for jobs in the rapidly growing port-towns and administrative capitals of Dakar, Abidjan, Accra, and Lagos, which are also important industrial, educational and commercial centres. Other industrial towns such as Port Harcourt, Warri, Kano and Kumasi also attract many migrants. A vast majority of those who leave rural areas, however, migrate into other rural areas of the coastal belt where they work in the mines or in the tree-crop plantations and timber concessions of the forest belt. There is also a large number of self-employed migrants who settle in rural areas as tenant farmers or in towns as petty traders and artisans.

The general direction of migration is towards the more developed coastal areas where the ports, industrial centres, tree-crop plantations and mines provide greater opportunities for employment (Fig. 5.2). The sparsely settled agricultural districts of southern Ivory Coast attract thousands of migrants from Upper Volta and Mali and every dry season, thousands of Hausas from Sokoto Province migrate to work as wage-earners in the cocoa belts of Ghana and south-western Nigeria. Hundreds of Nigerians also migrate to work as labourers in the cocoa plantations of the Equatorial Guinea island of Fernando Po.

Self-employed migrant tenant farmers include the *nevatanes*, or strange farmers, from Mali and Guinea, who settle as groundnut farmers in Senegal and Gambia. In the Nigerian cocoa belt where the local Yoruba people pay more attention to cocoa production, hundreds of Ibos, Igbiras and Urhobos have moved in to grow food crops for sale to the urban population as well as to those cocoa farmers who do not grow enough food for their families. Urhobo migrants in particular specialize in harvesting and processing oil palm fruits for oil.

Most of those who migrate in search of farmland, originate from very densely populated areas which suffer from acute shortage of farmland. Migrant fishermen who may be found along the coast from Dakar to Douala form another group of self-employed migrants.

The free movement of wage-labour and of self-employed migrants suffered a considerable set-back following the expulsion of 800 Nigerians from

41

PLATE 23—Old Idanre, a hill settlement in Nigeria

Cameroon in 1967, 100 Ghanaian fishermen from Sierra Leone in 1968 and the large-scale expulsion in 1969/70 of 300,000 Nigerians, 250,000 Upper Volta citizens, 150,000 Niger Republic citizens and about 100,000 other aliens from Ghana.

There is also a considerable seasonal movement of cattle rearers in search of water and grazing for their cattle. The Fulanis for example move towards Lake Chad and the Niger–Benue valleys every dry season, returning to their home districts in the drier

PLATE 24—New Idanre, Nigeria

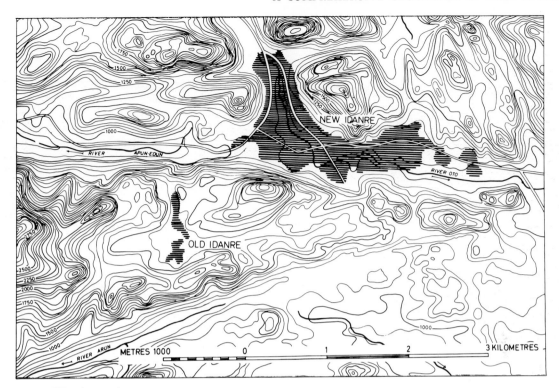

FIG. 5.3—Old and New Idanre

Sudan zone or going up to the tsetse-free uplands of the Bamenda Highlands and the Jos Plateau during the rainy season.

Brief mention should be made of the downhill migration of settlements since about 1910. Many hill villages in Benin, Nigeria and Guinea which were built on inaccessible but defensible sites have since moved down to the surrounding plains. Some of these settlements such as Idanre, Semorika and Aku in Nigeria still have a small population on the old hill-village site while the majority of the people live in the newer village on the lowlands. In almost all cases, the new settlement on the plain is better planned and more hygienic, but its greatest asset lies in the fact that it is located along a road suitable for motorized transport and is therefore more accessible than the old hill village (Fig. 5.3 and plates 23, 24).

Finally, the increasing number of West African workers in Europe deserves some attention. These workers consist of two categories: the unskilled and semi-skilled labourers, who form the vast majority of migrants from the French-speaking countries; and a smaller number of highly qualified graduates. Emigration of highly trained manpower, or a brain-drain, is caused partly by the poorer salaries paid in West Africa, although there are several other causes, including the difficulty of securing suitable employment, and the very high

cost of living in the capital cities of West Africa where most of the people in this category prefer to settle. The desire to earn higher wages is also responsible for the large-scale emigration of Senegalese and other French-speaking West Africans to work as labourers in France, Belgium and Germany.

The emigration of West Africans to Europe is however not a recent phenomenon, but one which started on a small scale even before the colonial period. During the colonial period thousands of West African students went to study in Europe and many of them who could not make the grade refused to return home while some of those who were successful also settled in Europe, largely to obtain full French citizenship in the case of French-speaking West Africans. These colonial-period migrants were mostly intellectuals as compared with the large numbers of poorly educated French-speaking West Africans who have migrated to Europe during the last ten years, that is during the first decade of independence of West African states. The inability of the young West African states to provide jobs for their increasing working population and the demand for labour in the building and public works sector of the European economy have encouraged this migration. Improvements in transportation and communications have also helped to accelerate the migration of West Africans to Europe in recent years.

RURAL SETTLEMENT AND HOUSE TYPES

More than 90 per cent of the population still live in rural settlements consisting of small hamlets and villages. Nucleated settlements in which the huts are built quite close to one another are common except amongst the Tivs and some Ibo and Ibibio groups of Nigeria. The Abakaliki Ibos in particular live in compounds which are scattered about the entire territory of the village so that each person has a considerable area of farmland around his compound (Fig. 5.4).

In both the forest belt and the open savanna areas, the nucleated village settlement appears to have been adopted for security reasons. In the grassland areas in particular, most villages were surrounded by walls which were pierced by slits through which defenders could shoot arrows and throw spears at the invader. Today the walls no longer exist and many villages have tended to become dispersed as villagers move out to settle and farm outside the former village walls. Along the coast and on hill tops, nucleated villages appear to have been a result of limited building space.

Amongst the Tivs who live in scattered huts, each compound is enclosed by a fence of mats or live sticks,

FIG. 5.4—Types of village settlement

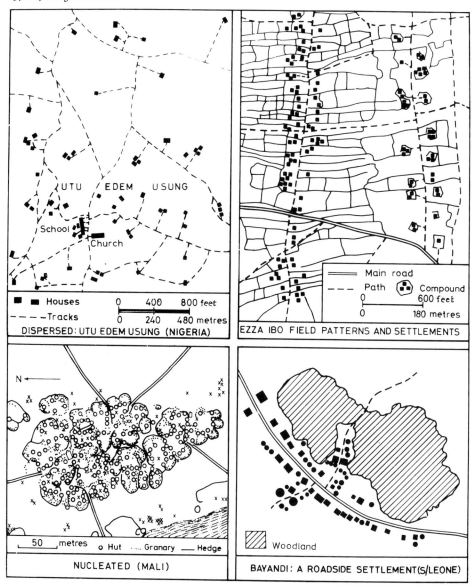

DISPERSED: UTU EDEM USUNG (NIGERIA)

EZZA IBO FIELD PATTERNS AND SETTLEMENTS

NUCLEATED (MALI)

BAYANDI: A ROADSIDE SETTLEMENT (S/LEONE)

PLATE 25 —Homestead at Bauchi, Nigeria

PLATE 27 —Old Bussa (now under Kainji Lake)

PLATE 26 —A walled compound in the palm belt of Nigeria

but in the south, compounds are usually surrounded either by fences of live sticks or by walls of mud or concrete. Each compound houses a man and his immediate family as well as some relations. Large extended-family compounds were common in the past but these are now being replaced by much smaller units. As a general rule, the surroundings of each compound, including the frontage and back-yard of the huts, is cultivated with various crops including maize, vegetables and yams. This is the class of farmland usually called the compound land, as distinct from the main or distant farmland. The shapes and sizes of compounds found in parts of West Africa are shown in Fig. 5.5 (p. 47). (See plates 25, 26, 27.)

The inhabitants of a village often claim a common ancestor after whom the village is normally named. The huts are arranged in an orderly way such that people who are more closely related in blood tend to live much closer together. The common meeting centre is the village square which sometimes serves as the village market. Amongst most ethnic groups, the rural market is held once every four days or once every eight days.

Plate 28 shows a rural landscape at Ozubulu (near Onitsha) in Nigeria. There is a complete dispersal of compounds all over the village territory. This is an area with a population density of over 385 persons per sq. km (1,000 per sq. mile). Farmland is very scarce and since the compound land is cultivated every year, this area can be regarded as being under permanent cultivation. (See p. 46.)

Road building has brought about the growth of street or ribbon villages (Fig. 5.4). Many villages which were bypassed by roads linking important towns have since moved to the roadside to take advantage of motorized transport.

Although water supply is an important consideration in the choice of settlement sites, many villages are not located near the river banks. The open character of Sudanese river valleys which are affected by periodic floods is partly responsible for this situation. In many cases, however, it appears that the people give preference to nearness to farmland rather than to water supplies. The result is that in areas where rivers are few and far between, some villagers have to travel distances of up to 8km (5 miles) to the nearest streams to fetch water. During the rainy season, most people depend on rain-water collected from house roofs or from wayside pits specially dug for the pur-

45

pose; but during the dry season, when the pits and the seasonal streams dry up, water is very short.

Grassland peoples such as the Mossi, Nupes and Tivs build round huts of mud with grass thatch while others, like the Songhais, build semi-circular huts made of skin or matting on a framework of branches. In the drier Sahel region, rectangular earth huts of mud walls and flat mud roofs are common but in the rainy forest belt, the rectangular huts, which consist of mud on wattle framework, have steeply sloping roofs of mats or grass thatch. The coastal people who live in rather swampy surroundings, usually raise their huts on piles as a protection against floods.

URBANIZATION

Unlike the rest of Africa south of the Sahara, West Africa has a large number of indigenous urban centres which are essentially pre-industrial cities in character. The main concentration of these urban centres is in Yorubaland in western Nigeria where the largest towns include Ibadan (627,000), Ife (130,000), Oshogbo (209,000), Ilesha (166,000) and Ijebu-Ode (68,500). All these towns are located in the Guinea savanna

PLATE 28—Aerial view of Ozubulu showing the complete dispersal of settlement

PLATE 29—Ibadan, Nigeria, seen from Mapo Hall

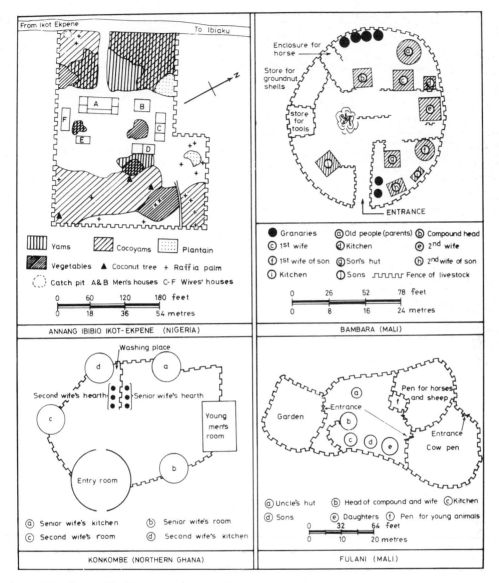

From Ikot Ekpene   To Ibiaku

Yams
Cocoyams
Plantain
Vegetables ▲ Coconut tree + Raffia palm
(:) Catch pit A&B Men's houses C-F Wives' houses

0   60   120   180 feet
0   18   36   54 metres

ANNANG IBIBIO IKOT-EKPENE (NIGERIA)

Enclosure for horse
Store for groundnut shells
Store for tools
ENTRANCE

● Granaries ⓐ Old people (parents) ⓑ Compound head
ⓒ 1st wife ⓓ Kitchen ⓔ 2nd wife
ⓕ 1st wife of son ⓖ Son's hut ⓗ 2nd wife of son
ⓘ Kitchen ⓙ Sons ⌐⌐⌐ Fence of livestock

0   26   52   78 feet
0   8   16   24 metres

BAMBARA (MALI)

Washing place
d   a
Second wife's hearth   Senior wife's hearth
c
Young men's room
Entry room
b

ⓐ Senior wife's kitchen   ⓑ Senior wife's room
ⓒ Second wife's room   ⓓ Second wife's kitchen

KONKOMBE (NORTHERN GHANA)

Pen for horses and sheep
ⓐ
Entrance
Garden
ⓑ
Entrance
ⓒ ⓓ ⓔ
Cow pen

ⓐ Uncle's hut ⓑ Head of compound and wife ⓒ Kitchen
ⓓ Sons ⓔ Daughters ⓕ Pen for young animals

0   32   64 feet
0   10   20 metres

FULANI (MALI)

FIG. 5.5—Types of family compound

belt, with the exception of Ijebu-Ode, which like Benin City and Kumasi are located in the forest belt (Fig. 5.6, p. 48). (See plate 29.)

The oldest towns in West Africa, however, are found in the drier savanna zone, which has a longer history of stable government and which had better developed transportation and inter-group trade during the precolonial period. The more famous of these towns include Timbuktu (6,000), Kano City (295,400), Zaria (166,000) and Katsina (91,000). In recent years, those towns like Timbuktu and Katsina, which depended much on the trans-Sahara trade for their growth, have declined in importance and are still losing population to the new industrial centres of the coastal belt.

Another set of old towns appears along the coast. Many of these coastal port-towns, including Bonny, Calabar, Warri, Ouidah, Abidjan and Dakar, started as small native fishing villages but grew to become important trading ports during the period of the slave trade. There were more than twenty of these slave ports along the coast of Ghana. During the colonial period, some of these coastal towns were selected as the administrative capitals and major ports for the various territories and today many of them have grown to become major industrial and commercial centres. At the same time many others, including Burutu, Forcados and Opobo Town, have declined to assume their original role as fishing villages.

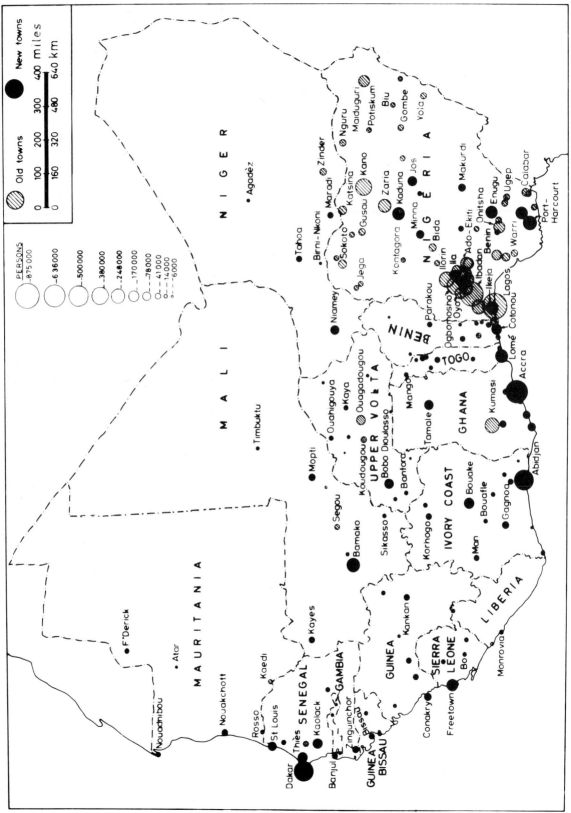

FIG. 5.6—Distribution of urban centres

PLATE 30—Part of Tema township, Ghana

Finally, there are many new towns which were built during the colonial period to serve as mining centres, ports or administrative centres. These new towns include the ports of Port Harcourt, Tema, Conakry and Freetown and the mining towns of Enugu (coal), Jos (tin), Tarkwa (gold) and Obuasi (gold). The roads and railways also created new towns such as Kafanchan, Nsawam and Kindia (in Guinea) and increased the importance of older towns like Parakou (Benin), Aba (Nigeria) and Bouake (Ivory Coast). Kaduna was built specially to serve as the capital of the former Northern Nigeria while existing villages such as Ikot Ekpene (Nigeria), Goa (Mali), Koudougou (Upper Volta) and Thies (Senegal) which were selected to serve as provincial or divisional capitals grew up to become important market and educational centres. (See plate 30.)

Beginning from the end of the Second World War, but particularly since the early 1960s, the coastal towns and some of the inland administrative centres have witnessed large-scale immigration of people in search of jobs in industry, commerce and the civil service. The rate of growth of towns like Dakar, Abidjan, Accra, Lagos and lately Warri, Enugu and Calabar has been so great that these towns now experience serious problems of congestion in housing and of inadequate public transport and water supplies. The rate of urban unemployment is high and so is the rate of organized crime. It is these problems of rapid urbanization that have occasioned the frequent but ineffective call for people to return to the land. It appears that the influx to the cities will continue until living conditions in the rural areas improve.

Chapter 6—Land Rights and Agricultural Land Use

Land is the main source of livelihood for the peoples of West Africa, about 80 per cent of whom still depend almost exclusively on agriculture. It is not surprising therefore that the people have developed a very strong attachment to the land, particularly in the districts where their ancestors lived. In this chapter we shall discuss some traditional ideas about land, the changes which are taking place and the effects of these on the pattern of agricultural land use. We shall end by examining the case for land reforms as a necessary step to modernizing West African agriculture and the problems facing land reform schemes.

Land which is in use is owned by someone and the owner could be an individual, a family, a clan or village or even a society such as the church. In West Africa, there is no unclaimed land even in the most sparsely settled areas or uninhabited swamps such as those of the Niger Delta. Rather every portion of land is claimed by one ethnic group or the other. Each country is made up of many ethnic groups each of which occupies a separate and contiguous territory. The ethnic group in turn is made up of many clans each of which consists of villages or village-groups. It was the clan and the village-group which owned land in the past and still do so today in some areas. In other areas, new systems of land ownership have emerged and in this chapter we shall discuss the following three systems: 1) traditional land tenure systems, 2) collective land tenure, 3) individual land tenure.

TRADITIONAL LAND TENURE SYSTEMS

Traditional land tenure systems in West Africa are commonly referred to as communal tenure and although there are minor differences in operating the system in different areas, the basic ideas governing the system are broadly similar. The most fundamental and common idea about the traditional land tenure systems is that the land belongs to the community which may be a village, village-group or the clan. The right of the individual to use the land derives from his membership of the community and all aliens are excluded except when given special permission to use the land by heads of families in the clan. For members of the community, title to land is purely usufructuary and land which is no longer in use by the individual reverts to the community. Outright sale of land is prohibited since the land is regarded as belonging not only to the living, but also to dead ancestors buried therein and children yet unborn. Under this system, each member of the community is entitled to as much land as he wishes to cultivate.

In general the village community is a closely-knit group of blood relations who claim common descent from an ancestor whose name the village normally bears. Each village has a defined territory while a number of related villages constitute a clan. The close relationship between genealogy and territoriality is striking, (see theoretical model Fig. 6.1, p. 51).

Under the traditional system of communal land tenure, the land is cultivated under the block-farming system in which the village territory is divided into a number of blocks each of which is farmed for about two years before being left under fallow, while the villagers move on to farm the next block. The fields therefore rotate about a fixed settlement and the duration of the rotation cycle depends on the number of farmers and the size of the territory. As the population of the village increases, the demand for farmland also increases and initially, this leads to a shortening of the duration of fallow periods. In some areas all plots within a block under fallow revert to the community and are re-allocated to any member when that block comes under cultivation again; but in many other areas, families go back to cultivate the same plots when the block is due to be farmed once again.

Today, the communal system of land tenure is restricted largely to the sparsely settled areas such as the Cross River district and the Benin division of Nigeria, western Ivory Coast and much of Liberia. In the more

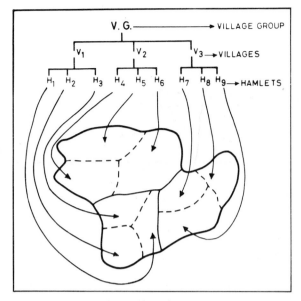

FIG. 6.1—Territoriality and genealogy

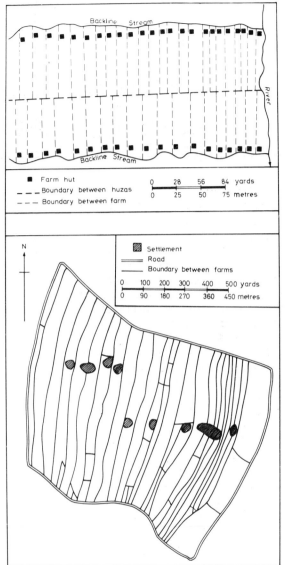

FIG. 6.2—Huza field system in Ghana

densely settled areas which experience acute shortage of farmland, the system has since broken down. A modified system of communal land tenure also exists in areas formerly under Muslim rulers who placed all conquered land under the care of designated vassals. Under Muslim law, the villagers continued to cultivate their land unmolested but had to pay tribute to the rulers.

COLLECTIVE LAND TENURE

Collective land tenure is not common in West Africa and may be considered to be a major modification of traditional systems of land holding. It has come about partly because of shortage of farmland in some areas, thereby forcing farmers to migrate to other areas and partly because land is now being sold outright in some areas, even to non-members of the village or clan. Unlike the village community, the collective group does not necessarily consist of blood relations, but of farmers whose common aim is to acquire land for cultivation. This system is best developed amongst the Krobo people of Southern Ghana and works as follows.

A group of people form themselves into a 'company' with a leader who is appointed by the group to meet the village chief of the land-owning group and negotiate the purchase of some farmland. When the price of the land is settled, the leader pays for it from money collected from members of the group. A stream or footpath is chosen as a baseline and where none of these exists a straight line cut through

the property near the boundary serves as a baseline. The land is then divided into equal lengths along the baseline and shared out in proportion to the amount contributed by each member of the company. If for example a member whose total contribution was ₦10 is given one baseline length called a 'rope', then the member who contributed ₦20 will receive two 'rope' lengths, and so on. Fig. 6.2 shows an example of shared-out collective land or *huza* in southern Ghana.

It is significant that once the land has been shared out, each member assumes outright ownership of his individual share of the land and the company is dissolved. The owner of a strip is at liberty to sell his land

PLATE 31 — *Hills and ridged land for dry-season vegetables, northern Nigeria*

whenever he wishes to do so and unlike the migrant tenant farmer, he can plant any crop including tree crops, since he has freehold title on the land. Often each farmer builds his house near the frontage of his strip of land giving rise to a linear pattern of settlement which is known as *huza* by the Krobos.

INDIVIDUAL LAND TENURE

In the more densely populated areas which experience great pressure of population on farmland as well as in areas of rapid expansion of tree-crop production, the communal land tenure system has largely been replaced by individual title to land. Village heads and elders have found it increasingly difficult to meet individual demands for farmland in the congested districts of Iboland for example, with the result that people have tended to farm a piece of land for longer periods than is necessary and to claim outright title to such land. People who are short of money have even sold their land to those in need of more farmland. In this part of West Africa the spread of individual title to land therefore appears to be a result of the declining authority of local chiefs and the wide adoption of a money economy in place of the traditional

barter system of the pre-colonial period. In most cases, however, land can only be sold to members of the same village or clan and not to aliens who, by definition, include members of other clans of the same ethnic group.

Tree-crop production for export, which in West Africa is dominated by small-scale cultivators, has been a major factor in the replacement of communal tenure by individual title to land. Amongst many ethnic groups in West Africa tree crops such as coconuts, cocoa, the African pear and the oil palm belong to the man who planted them or to his descendants. If a man plants a grove of coconuts on land 'shown' to him by his grandmother for example, it is only the crops that belong to him, not the land. At the same time the *de jure* owner of the land cannot claim ownership of the tree crops and is obliged to buy them if he wishes to remove the trees from his land. It is to prevent this situation of *de facto* ownership of land by tree-crop planters who have no title to the land that many people refuse to allow migrant farmers to cultivate tree crops on land leased to them. For the same reason village elders do not normally allow people to establish large tree-crop farms on communally held land, and in order to avoid the risk of having their tree crops cut off when a piece of community land is demanded for public use, tree-crop farmers usually prefer to purchase their farmland outright.

EFFECTS OF LAND TENURE ON LAND-USE PATTERNS

We have seen that under the traditional system of communal land tenure, the block-farming system was adopted as a satisfactory device for controlling land use so as to preserve soil fertility under a system that made little or no use of manure. Only a section of the village territory was cultivated at one time while the other sections lay under various stages of fallow. The spread of individual title to land in some areas and the local laws of property inheritance which have since been extended to include land inheritance has resulted in extreme fragmentation and dispersal of farm holdings in such areas. As an extension of the original idea that every member of the community is entitled to some area of farmland, a man is now expected to allocate part of his farmland to his grown-up male children. Often this results in the fragmentation of his fields and the dispersal of farms allocated to each son.

In parts of eastern Nigeria where individual land tenure has resulted in extreme fragmentation and dispersal of farmland, and where many people prefer to build a house on one of their farm plots, an interesting pattern of land use has emerged. Dispersal of settlement in such areas has resulted over the years in the gradual colonization of the entire village farmland and since the immediate surroundings of the dwellings are cultivated every year, a patchy form of permanently cultivated areas is now typical (see Fig. 6.3 and plate 28).

The strip fields pattern of the *huza* system of southern Ghana is largely a product of the land tenure system. It is also a result of the attempt to share collectively acquired land, with the view to ensuring that each member of the group has a fair share of the total land. Thus, where the land borders on water, the strip method of sharing ensures that each member receives some portion of land fronting the water and portions located along the valley slope and hill crest where applicable. This enables each farmer to have within his holding a wide range of soil types. Fig. 6.2 shows a typical *huza* field system and the associated pattern of settlement.

See also plate 31.

THE CASE FOR AND THE STRATEGY FOR LAND REFORMS

The need for land reforms in West Africa has long been recognized as a necessary step towards improving agriculture in the region. But so far, no government has been bold enough to carry out the necessary

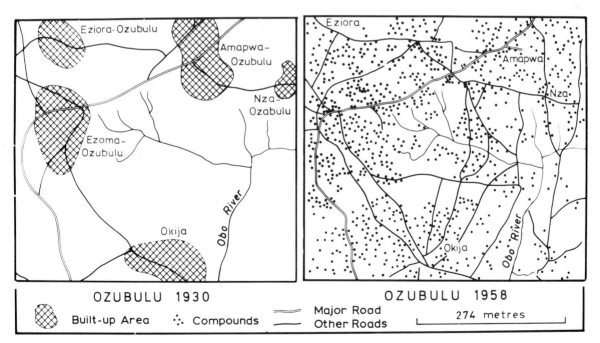

OZUBULU 1930

OZUBULU 1958

274 metres

Built-up Area   Compounds   Major Road   Other Roads

FIG. 6.3—Dispersal of compounds—Ozubulu

PLATE 32—Trainee farmer learning to plough at Yendi, Ghana

Hence the need for land reforms that will enable farmers to own economically viable units of land.

In West Africa, where a situation in which the land is owned by a few wealthy landlords does not exist, land reforms will take the form of (i) allocating communal land in large enough units to members of the community who wish to farm as well as to non-members of the community who will be required to lease or purchase outright the land allocated to them; (ii) consolidating and relocating farmland.

We have pointed out that the communal land tenure system persists in most sparsely settled areas where people usually live in closely nucleated settlements. In such areas land reforms will result in scattered compounds since farmers will have to live on their land so as to be close to their place of work. Social isolation will be the result but there will be considerable economic gains. Fortunately the practice of living in isolated farm camps is not new, since it is well established in the tree-crop producing areas of the south as well as in food-crop producing areas of the Middle Belt. Many migrant tenant farmers in the sparsely settled areas of southern Nigeria and the groundnut growing areas of Senegambia also live in isolated farm camps.

A land reform unit of the Ministry of Agriculture should supervise the scheme which will consist of dividing the land into regular plots of between 12–16 hectares (30–40acres). Indigenes of the village territory need not pay rent but land should also be made available to citizens from other parts of the country who wish to settle and farm. Such settlers will have to pay rent as is being done at present by migrant tenant farmers. In this way, it will be possible to provide a large enough area of land for each person who wishes to farm. It will also be possible to guarantee the migrants security of tenure over the land while at the same time not disinheriting the indigenous people.

The greatest difficulties in carrying out land reforms in West Africa are likely to be experienced in those congested districts where people are scattered all over the village territory, cultivating four or more scattered plots every year, each plot rarely measuring more than 0.2 hectare ($\frac{1}{2}$ acre). In such districts, consolidation and re-allocation of farmland will involve abandoning some family compounds, and this is not likely to be popular.

See plate 32.

reforms which are bound to meet with stiff opposition from a people who have a great emotional attachment to land. At present, farming income remains low because the average farmer produces very little surplus for sale. One reason for this situation is that the farmer can only cultivate a small area of land each year, still using the primitive hoe and matchet. Mechanization is seen as a possible means towards increasing farm output and fighting rural poverty but mechanization requires large and contiguous farms, not fragmented and dispersed holdings.

SECTION C: RESOURCES AND ECONOMIC GROWTH

Chapter 7—Food-crop Production and Animal Husbandry

In West Africa, as in other developing areas, agriculture is the main source of livelihood with about 80 per cent of the people engaged in farming. Detailed accounts of recent developments in agriculture will be given for various countries but in this chapter we are concerned only with the general features of farming in West Africa. Agricultural practices and crops vary from one zone to another, but West African farmers have much in common. Farm implements for example remain primitive and still consist of the hoe and the matchet.

GENERAL COMMENTS

Size of farms

Field sizes are small by any standard. In the forest belt few farms exceed 0.8 hectares (2 acres) but farm sizes of 2–4 hectares (5–10 acres) are common in the open savanna land. Smaller fields of about 0.2 hectares (½ acre) are more usual in the densely settled areas. It is therefore not surprising that many foreigners refer to West African farms as gardens. It is important to point out that in any given year, one farmer may cultivate three or four separate fields which are located at distances of 2–11km (1–7miles) from one another.

The small size of farmlands is caused by several factors. First, the amount of work, including bush-clearing and weeding, which the farmer can do using the primitive hoe and the matchet is very limited. He therefore cultivates the area of land that he can cope with, given the labour available to him. We may recall here that often the farmer spends several hours walking to and from the farm, thereby losing part of the time that could have been used in productive work on the farm. In parts of the forest belt where land is still plentiful, the small size of farms is caused by difficulty in clearing the forest. In the very densely settled areas of Iboland, Mossi territory and the Kano district, the small sizes of farm plots is

caused by shortage of farmland resulting from increasing pressure of population. The small area of land available along the *fadamas* (river floodplains) of the Savanna belt also explains why the dry-season farms located along these river valleys are usually smaller than the wet-season (or main) farmlands located on the interfluves. Finally, in the yam-growing districts, the amount of seed yam available to a farmer may be a factor influencing the size of his farm.

Nature of farms

In the distant past, farming was largely for subsistence, but today, most full-time farmers in West Africa produce for the market. Even some of the part-time farmers who combine farming with other occupations like tailoring, carpentry, bricklaying and even teaching sometimes sell part of their crop. The change from a largely subsistent to a market economy has come about because of the need for cash to pay taxes and school fees, as well as for buying an increasing range of goods in the local market. In areas where farmers rarely produce enough food to feed themselves, additional income for food and other expenses comes from tree crops like the oil palm, cocoa and rubber or from collecting forest products like firewood and snails. The expansion of tree crops has indeed tended to lead to a neglect by farmers to produce foodcrops with the result that areas like the cocoa belt of Nigeria have to import part of the food requirements of the rural population.

In the past, when land was plentiful, shifting cultivation, which involves the building of a new settlement whenever the farmer migrates to cultivate a plot, was common. It is still practised today in a few areas. In most areas, however, the system of farming is called the rotation of bush fallow, a system in which cultivated fields rotate round a fixed settlement. Bush fallowing in many districts came about as a result of increasing demand for farmland. In other areas the creation of forest reserves, where no

PLATE 33 —— *Maize plantation*

one is allowed to farm, restricted the area of farm-land available and forced the people to adopt the method of bush fallowing.

Fallow periods of up to 15 years are still common in very sparsely settled areas, but in the densely settled areas of south-eastern Nigeria and the Mossi country of Upper Volta, the land lies fallow for no more than four years after two years of cultivation. Permanent cultivation is even practised in the crowded areas of eastern Owerri Province and the central districts of Kano State. This is made possible by the intensive use of household manure.

Classification of farmland

Two classes of farmland are recognized. These are the distant or main farmland (*oko egan* in Yoruba) and the home plot or compound-land (*oko etile* in Yoruba). The compound-land is an area of intensive and per-manent cultivation where crops like yams, maize, okro and fruit trees are cultivated. The distant farmland is usually greater in size than the com-pound-land, but little or no manure is applied to distant farmland, except perhaps in the Kano district.

Although the above classification of farmland applies to the far north, farmlands in the drier savanna are usually classified as upland or wet-season farms, and *fadama* or dry-season farms. Upland farms are much larger in area and may be considered as the main farmlands. They are cropped during the rainy season when guinea corn, millet and potatoes are grown. *Fadama* farms are located on river floodplains which are usually so small in extent that many villagers do not possess *fadama* farms and are obliged to migrate to work in distant areas during this season. Crops of the *fadama* include tobacco, rice and sugarcane which are all planted soon after the annual flood subsides. The main areas of flood-land cultivation are shown in Fig. 7.1. In areas like the Gungawa district of the Kainji Lake Basin, some rudimentary form of irrigation is practised on the floodplains. (See plate 33.)

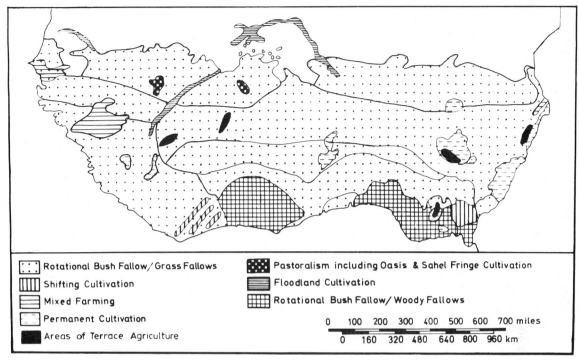

FIG. 7.1—Farming types of West Africa

Market gardening

The development of market gardening in the suburbs of large towns is another feature which is common to all the zones. Around the coastal port-towns of Lagos, Accra and Abidjan; in the suburbs of the Middle Belt towns of Jos and Kaduna as well as around the Sudanese towns of Kano and Bamako, farmers now grow crops like lettuce, cabbages, carrots and potatoes. The rapid expansion of market gardening around these cities shows that, like farmers all over the world, the West African farmer responds very readily to local market conditions. An increasing number of relatively well-to-do local people have kept up the demand for these crops which were formerly imported from Europe. This demand is met not by increased imports but by local farmers who have adopted these new crops.

Other types of farming

Farming types shown in Fig. 7.1 have all been briefly discussed. Other types are 'terrace' cultivation and mixed farming. Terrace agriculture is practised along the slopes of highland areas like the Jos Plateau, the Guinea Highlands and the northern parts of the Mandara Mountains. Another area of large-scale terrace farming is around Maku in Iboland. This type of farming was more widespread in the period of the slave trade when hill-top dwellers were afraid to descend to cultivate the surrounding plains.

Cattle-rearing is restricted to the far north owing to the occurrence of the tsetse fly in the south. But in the north, the cattle population is almost exclusively in the hands of nomadic groups like the Tuaregs and the Fulanis. The fact that cattle-rearing and arable farming are not carried out by the same people has been a serious handicap to the development of mixed farming in West Africa. In some districts, however, there is an arrangement whereby cattlemen graze their cattle on fallow bush in return for so many measures of millet or guinea corn. The droppings of cattle during the period of grazing usually constitutes the only manure applied on such land.

The occurrence of hunger periods during the planting season is another characteristic feature of farming in West Africa. The hunger period occurs partly because of the inability of some farmers to produce enough food to last throughout the year, partly as a result of crop failures and partly because of poor storing facilities.

FARMING REGIONS AND THE MAIN FOOD CROPS

Agricultural zones, like climatic and vegetation zones, run roughly from west to east. Along the coast

PLATE 34—*Yam stacks*

Abakaliki, and in the Nupe area of Nigeria. Other important crops grown throughout this zone are cassava, maize and cocoyams. Beans, bananas and groundnuts are also grown for food. (See plate 34.)

A predominantly grain zone in which cattle-rearing is very important lies immediately north of the root-crop zone. Millet, guinea corn, sweet potatoes and groundnuts are the main food crops. Crop failures caused by droughts are common in this zone, and north of the 12°N. parallel the growing season is so short that farmers cultivate a quick-maturing variety of millet. Irrigation is necessary for the expansion of food production as well as export crops such as groundnuts and cotton. Existing irrigation projects in this zone include the inland Niger Delta rice and cotton estates, the Sokoto rice and tobacco farms and the Ebeji irrigation scheme on the southern shores of Lake Chad. Mixed farming is possible and is being encouraged. (See plate 35.)

Little or no farming takes place north of latitude 15°N. which marks the beginning of a zone with a rainy season of less than three months. The northern part of the Inland Delta Irrigation Scheme lies in this

PLATE 35—*Experimental rice farm at Nimbe, Nigeria*

cultivation is highly restricted and in most areas uneconomic. Mangrove swamps in Sierra Leone have, however, been cleared and cultivated with swamp rice. A similar exercise may turn the Niger Delta into an important food-surplus zone. At present, plantains, bananas and the coconut are the most important crops of the coastal areas, where fishing rather than farming is the main economic activity.

The root-crop zone, much of which lies within the forest belt, has an eastern or yam sub-zone and a western or rice sub-zone (Fig 7.2 opposite). The dividing line between the zones of rice and yam culture is the Bandama River in the Ivory Coast. Yams can thrive throughout the zone and so can rice. Indeed, since about 1950 rice production has become important in parts of the yam sub-zone following the large-scale expansion of rice cultivation in

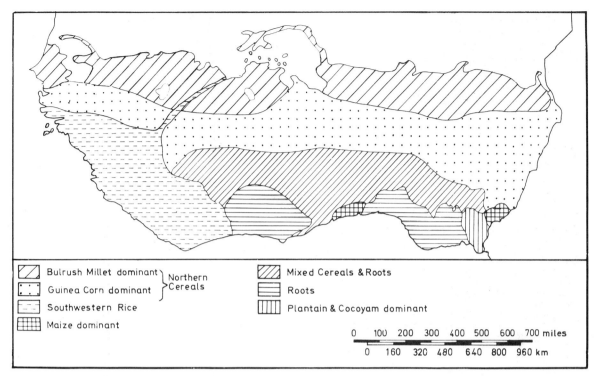

FIG. 7.2—Crop regions

Legend:
- Bulrush Millet dominant ⎫ Northern
- Guinea Corn dominant ⎬ Cereals
- Southwestern Rice
- Maize dominant
- Mixed Cereals & Roots
- Roots
- Plantain & Cocoyam dominant

0 100 200 300 400 500 600 700 miles
0 160 320 480 640 800 960 km

zone and is the most extensive cultivated area. Millet, wheat and barley are grown in small patches along waterways and in the oases of Adrar des Iforas.

West Africa has only a few indigenous food plants and almost all the staple food crops now grown by the people were introduced during the last two hundred years. Guinea corn, bulrush millet, upland rice, some varieties of yams, beniseed and the oil palm are native

PLATE 36—Cattle

Table 4—Crops introduced into West Africa before 1900

	Root crops	Cereals	Legumes	Others
From Tropical America (by the Portuguese)	cassava, sweet potatoes	maize	lima beans	tomato, pawpaw, cotton, pineapple, tobacco, guava, groundnut, avocado pear, cocoa, pepper
From Asia (by Muslim pilgrims)	certain yams cocoyams	swamp rice	peas	cotton, mango, banana, coconut, egg-plant, lime, plantain, sugarcane
From north-east Africa and Arabia	—	—	—	okro

to West Africa; and so is the kola nut. But such important crops as the cassava, sweet potatoes, groundnuts and maize were introduced from Asia and the Americas by the Portuguese (see Table 4). Other new crops include pawpaw, pineapple, some varieties of yams, rice and cotton, tobacco, cocoa and para rubber. Groundnut was introduced first into Senegal as a food crop but gradually spread eastwards and is today the most important export of Senegal and northern Nigeria.

PLATE 37 —Argungu fishing festival, northern Nigeria

FARMING PRACTICES IN THE FOREST BELT

The farming calendar for Eket (Table 5) gives a good idea of how the farmer in the forest belt spends the year. Preparation of farmland starts from December through to early March and the aim is to fire the bush before the first rains come. Yam mounds and, in some rare cases, ridges are made, mounds of about 1.5 m (5 ft) high being common in swampy areas such as parts of Abakaliki. Yams and maize are planted soon after the first rains, although many farmers usually plant these crops before the first rains. This is risky because a delay in the rains may be disastrous; but seeds planted after the first rains may also be scorched if no more rain falls for another week or two.

Yam is the crop of the man in Table 5 and after it has been planted by the combined labour of the man, his wives and children, the farmland is divided into smaller units and allocated to the wives who cultivate maize, okro, melon and other green vegetables. During the months of April and May when the plants are fully grown it is difficult to penetrate the farm. One good aspect of mixed cropping is that the thick vegetative growth protects the soil from erosion by rain-water. Mixed cropping also provides a sort of insurance against the failure of a particular type of crop.

Weeding the farm is done by women and children, except in areas like Yorubaland where farming is the work of men while women engage in trade and crafts. The harvest season is as busy as the planting season. Maize is harvested in June and the first yam harvest is in July. Cocoyams may be planted by women after the maize harvest, cassava after the first yam harvest. In the second year of farming, cassava is the only crop on the plot. An increasing number of farmers now

Table 5—Farming calendar for Eket district (forest belt)

Season	Month	Agricultural activity	Comments
Long Dry Season	December	Clearing of new farmland. Yam harvest continues. Storing of yam in barns.	Slack period in farming. Collecting of forest products.
	January	Clearing and burning of farmland. Digging yam holes in main farmland.	
	February	Preparation of compound-land. Yams, maize, okro planted on compound-land and main farmland.	
Long Rainy Season	March	Yams planted on main farmland. Planting of melons and fluted pumpkins.	Peak demand for labour in the farms.
	April	Cocoyams and cassava planted. Yam vines staked and trained. Weeding. Fresh maize and other vegetables harvested from compound-land.	
	May	Fresh maize harvested. Weeding. Planting cassava. Staking and training of yam vines.	
	June	Weeding. Harvesting dry maize.	Hungry season.
	July	Weeding.	
Short Dry Season	August	Topping early yam (New Yam Festival). Training yam vines. Weeding. Planting of second maize and other vegetables.	
Short Rainy Season	September	Topping early yam. Planting cassava. Weeding.	
	October	Yam harvest begins.	Peak demand for labour.
Long Dry Season	November	Yam harvest. Building yam barns. Storage of yams.	Slack period farming.

plant cassava as a first crop on the land, particularly in areas with short fallows, where yams do not normally give good yields.

FOOD FARMING IN THE GRASSLAND AREAS

Compared with the forest belt, less effort is required in preparing farmland in open savanna country. Often no bush clearing is involved as the farmer simply sets the parched grass fields ablaze during the dry months of the harmattan. Planting is on both ridges and mounds in the Middle Belt but in the far north or Sudan grassland region, ridges replace the mounds of the south. The farming calendars for Oyo and Kano in Tables 6 and 7 are representative of farming activities in the Guinea and Sudan grassland areas. (See pp. 62, 63.) (See also plate 31.)

Guinea corn, usually interplanted with millet, is the first crop planted on a newly prepared farm in the far north. Cassava is planted on the same fields after the grains have been harvested. Cotton and ground-nuts are usually planted by themselves and so are swamp rice and tobacco which are grown on *fadama* land.

ANIMAL HUSBANDRY

Cattle-rearing is important only in the Sudan zone which is relatively free from the tsetse fly which carries a deadly cattle disease. Horses and donkeys are also restricted to the north but sheep, goats and

Table 6—Farming calendar for Oyo (Middle Belt)

Season	Month	Agricultural activity
Short Rainy Season	October	Harvesting of guinea corn and yam.
Long Dry Season	November	Preparation of guinea corn plot for yam cultivation. Planting of early yam.
	December	Yam planting continues. Harvesting of cotton, beans and cowpeas.
	January	
	February	Late yam planting. Preparation of land for early maize cultivation.
Long Rainy Season	March	Planting of early maize. Late yam planting.
	April	Planting of early maize, okro and cowpeas. Planting of early tobacco.
	May	Planting of guinea corn.
	June	Weeding. Harvesting early maize and early tobacco.
	July	Topping early yam. Planting of late tobacco.
Short Dry Season	August	Harvesting of early beans and cowpeas. Preparation of land for late maize, beans, cowpeas and guinea corn.
Short Rainy Season	September	Planting of late maize, guinea corn and beans. Harvesting late tobacco and yam.

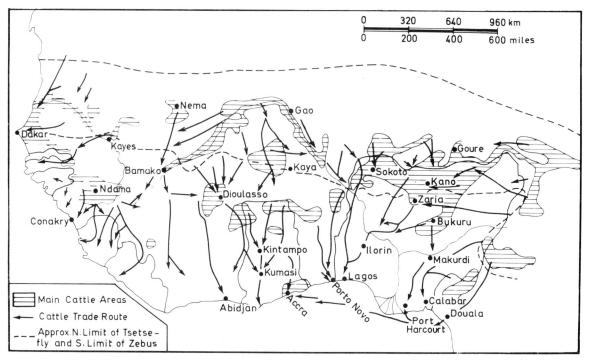

FIG. 7.3—Main livestock areas and cattle trade routes

Table 7—Farming calendar for Kano district (Sudan Savanna)

Season	Month	Agricultural activity	Comments
Dry Season (harmattan)	January	Cleaning of previous year's farms—millet and guinea corn stalks collected for house and fence construction. Cassava harvest starts.	
	February	Bush cleaning continues.	
	March	Distribution of manure from Kano City and other settlements to the farms. Donkeys carry back firewood as return cargo.	
	April	Spreading of manure on farmland and making of ridges. Harvesting tree crops like tamarind (*tsamiya*), locust beans (*dorowa*) and the silk cotton tree.	
Rainy Season	May	Guinea corn and millet planted immediately after first rains. Animals now moved inside stalls and fed on collected fodder or grazed under supervision on uncultivated land.	Very busy planting month
	June	Ridge-making for groundnut cultivation. Groundnuts planted. Weeding.	
	July	Weeding. Cowpeas planted.	
	August	Cowpeas planted. Weeding and repairing ridges. Beginning of millet harvest.	Severe floods may result in loss of crops.
	September	Millet harvest. Grass cutting for animal fodder. Planting of cassava.	
Dry Season	October	Groundnut harvest. Drying of groundnuts.	
	November	Guinea corn harvest. Shelling groundnuts and sale of groundnuts. Cowpeas harvest.	
	December	Groundnut sales continue. Collection of groundnut leaves for fodder during dry season. Animals let out to graze on farmland.	Slack season begins.

poultry are to be found all over West Africa (Fig. 7.3). Two types of cattle are found, the zebu cattle of the far north and the humpless cattle of the southern Sudan. The zebu is mostly owned by the Cow Fulani who still migrate with their cattle according to the season of the year. There is no attempt at improving the breed and usually cattle are not sold until they are past their prime. The main cattle consuming centres are in the coastal areas and a large proportion of cattle is transported on the hoof. Veterinary services are provided along the main cattle routes but the animals arrive in the south rather emaciated.

An increasing number of settled cultivators now keep cattle which are placed in the care of nomadic rearers, with the exception of two or three heads kept around the homestead all the year round to supply milk and manure. Homestead cattle are fed with corn stalks. (See plate 36.)

A type of dwarf cattle called Muturu, which is immune to trypanasomiasis, the disease transmitted by the tsetse fly, is kept in the forest belt. This animal is eaten in only a few areas, but in other areas it is kept for sacrificial purposes.

Large flocks of sheep and herds of goats are kept in the north. The animals are bigger in size and more hairy than their southern counterparts. Further north sheep and goats are usually driven in herds to graze in the fields, whereas in the south the few goats kept by a family are to be found tethered to a shed and are fed with forage brought in from the bush every day. As in the case of cattle, the main consuming centres for goats and sheep reared in the north are in the south.

Most farming families keep chickens, but virtually no attention is paid to the birds, which are left to roam about and fend for themselves. In recent years, however, many farmers have established modern poultry farms to provide eggs and chickens to the growing wage-earning population in neighbouring urban centres.

Chapter 8—Production and Marketing of Cash Crops

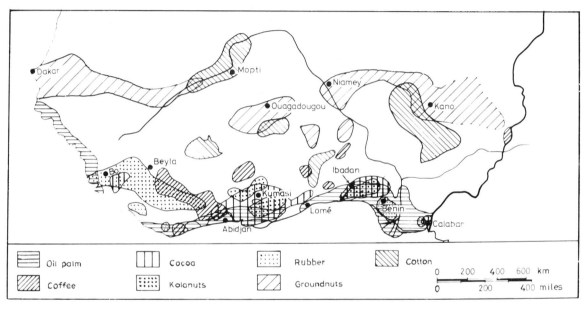

FIG. 8.1—*Major export crops*

Legend:
- Oil palm
- Coffee
- Cocoa
- Kolanuts
- Rubber
- Groundnuts
- Cotton

With the exception of the oil palm and kola nut, the major cash crops of West Africa were introduced from other parts of the world. These crops include groundnuts from South America, cotton from Asia and South America and cocoa from Brazil. Local varieties of cotton have been cultivated for several centuries all over West Africa. Most farmers, however, now cultivate superior varieties which the various governments have introduced from North America and East Africa. Indigenous rubber-bearing plants were also widespread in the forest belt, although today's rubber economy is based on para rubber, which was introduced from South America.

Fig. 8.1 shows the areas of production of these crops. The most productive zone is the coastal belt, followed by the Sudan. The Middle belt (see Fig. (ii), p. xv) produces very little for the export market. Differences in the climatic conditions between north and south (Chapter 2) account for the fact that tree crops, which are perennials are restricted to the south

while the northern and coastal savannas produce annual crops. The restriction of cocoa cultivation to the areas shown in Fig. 8.1 is caused by soil conditions since the climate of most of the south is suitable for cocoa production.

Since the Sudanese farmer plants and harvests his groundnuts or cotton in the space of twelve months or less, he is in a better position to adjust to changing market conditions, growing more when world prices go up, but producing more food crops for sale when the price of cotton or groundnuts is low. The tree-crop farmer is less fortunate in this regard. The cocoa farmer for example, who planted more cocoa during a boom in 1953, may find that the cocoa price has gone down considerably in 1959, when his first harvest is due. Experience has shown that the adoption, by farmers, of new crop varieties is more readily achieved with annual than perennial crops, and that the control of plant diseases is easier with annual crops.

In many parts of West Africa, the great emphasis

placed on the production of cash crops has often resulted in a neglect of food-crop cultivation. In Senegal where the main export is groundnuts, millet has since become a secondary crop and many local farmers now depend on imported rice. Most cocoa farmers in Nigeria have to purchase much of the staple food which was formerly grown by them; and this is true of many other farmers specializing in the production of cash crops. The food deficit situation in countries like Ghana, Ivory Coast, Senegal and Togo, which spend large sums of hard-earned foreign exchange on food imports, is caused largely by the emphasis on the production of cash crops for export. The major food items imported are rice, sugar and wheat, all of which can be cultivated, and are indeed cultivated in West Africa. Many countries are aware of the risk involved in neglecting the food-crop sector since a sudden stoppage of food imports, during a war situation for example, could result in food shortages. Efforts should therefore be made, as is being done in Ghana, to reduce the reliance on imported foodstuffs.

PEASANT VERSUS PLANTATION PRODUCTION

One important fact about export crops from West Africa is that production is concentrated in the hands of local farmers. It is also significant that most farmers readily adopted these crops with a view to improving their earning power. In Ivory Coast, however, African farmers in the Abengourou region (near Ghana) were compelled to cultivate cocoa as from 1912. This forced agricultural policy, adopted by the government of Governor Angoulvant, was prompted by the great success achieved by African cocoa farmers in neighbouring Ghana. At first the Ivory Coast farmer strongly resisted the order to grow cocoa, but later adopted the crop which has since spread throughout the south-east of the country.

In many other parts of the tropical world such as Zaïre, Malaysia and Brazil, crops like the oil palm, cocoa, rubber and cotton are produced in large plantations. Many plantations also existed during the colonial period in French-speaking West Africa as well as in the Cameroons and Fernando Po, but government policy in the English-speaking countries was against the plantation system, which was regarded as unsuitable for local social and economic conditions. It is interesting that this policy was reversed when Africans came to power in these countries. In Nigeria, for example, there were 42 large plantations in 1962, about 36 of which were established after 1951 when local politicians took over control of agricultural policy. Large plantations of rubber also exist

in Liberia which has been an independent country for about 100 years.

What is a plantation and what are its advantages, if any, over peasant-type production? A plantation is a very large estate measured in hundreds of hectares and involving the investment of large sums of money. The organization of labour and production is usually similar to that of a modern factory; and in so far as the quality and regularity of supply are concerned, the plantation is superior to peasant-type production. But in addition to a large area, the plantation requires a large and regular supply of relatively cheap labour. These two requirements cannot be obtained at one and the same place since a sparsely settled area with much land will be short of local labour. The plantation has in consequence come to be associated with migrant labour, which some economists consider to be wasteful and inefficient.

Most plantations produce only one or two crops. The 36,000 hectare (90,000 acre) Firestone rubber plantation is about the largest tree-crop plantation in West Africa. Other large plantations include the 6,400 hectare (16,000 acre) Calaro oil palm estate near Calabar, the 2,000 hectare (5,000 acre) cocoa plantation in Ikom, the 8,000 hectare (20,000 acre) rubber plantation at Ikot Mbo (near Calabar), and the 2,400 hectare (6,000 acre) Bacita sugarcane plantation near Jebba.

One reason why some countries now encourage plantation agriculture is that they believe that the plantation will help to arrest the increasing drift of people to the towns, by providing employment in rural areas. It appears, however, that the plantation cannot achieve much in this regard since the amount of skilled labour required in any plantation is small. It is also important to observe that although many governments now support the plantation system, the contribution of the plantation to agricultural exports has so far been insignificant, and is likely to remain so for some time. In Nigeria for example only 5 per cent of the 60,000 tons of rubber produced in 1961 and $3\frac{1}{2}$ per cent of the total palm oil exports for that year came from plantations.

General features of the main cash crops such as conditions favouring production are discussed below. It is important to realize that crops like groundnuts, cotton and palm oil are produced both for local consumption and for export. Figures given in respect of such crops usually represent the quantities exported, not total production.

THE OIL PALM

The oil palm is native to West Africa where it is rarely cultivated, but is normally found growing wild in

PLATE 38—Oil palm nursery, Nigeria

open forest country. Conditions favouring growth include a high temperature of not less than 24°C (75°F), and an annual rainfall of at least 1,270mm (50in.) spread over about eight months of the year. The tree grows under various soil conditions, including the swamps of the Niger Delta, in stream beds and in relatively infertile soils such as the acid sands of south-east Nigeria which is the most important palm oil producing area. (See plate 38.)

Oil palms growing wild in the bush are carefully preserved when the bush is fired in preparation for cultivation. Such palms usually grow to over 12m (40ft) high and begin to bear fruits as from the tenth year of germination. Cultivated palms on the other hand are much shorter, give heavier yields and begin to bear fruits during the sixth or seventh year of cultivation. (See plates 39a, 39b.)

Methods of production and ownership of palms vary with different ethnic groups. The cutting and pulping of boiled fruits is usually the job of the man, while women and children extract the nuts from the pulped mash and crack them for kernels. In the large modern plantations, all these processes are carried out simultaneously by giant oil mills, which extract up to 90 per cent of the oil content of the fruits as compared with 55 per cent by local methods. It is

PLATE 39a—Palm wine tapper climbing the palm tree

Table 8—Palm oil exports from West Africa (thousand tonnes)

	1909–13	1956	1958	1960	1962	1966	1968	1970	1971	1972
Nigeria	82.0	188.2	173.2	186.3	120.6	145.5	3.3	7.4	20.2	2.0
Benin	—	16.2	12.2	16.0	9.2	9.9	10.5	16.0	18.5	n.a.
Guinea	—	—	—	—	—	—	15.0	13.0	13.0	13.0
Togo	19.0	2.1	0.9	0.7	0.3	—	—	—	—	—
Ivory Coast	—	1.6	0.8	1.6	1.2	0.9	2.3	12.5	28.5	47.6
Total West Africa	101.0	208.1	187.1	204.6	131.3	156.3	31.1	48.9	80.2	62.6
Zaïre	2.0	151.3	163.6	167.1	151.1	—	—	—	—	—
Africa	121.0	372.0	363.1	391.5	308.5	—	—	—	—	—
World Total	121.0	575.5	596.7	617.4	542.4	—	—	—	—	—

Source: *United Nations Commission for Africa, Statistical Yearbook*, 1973, Part 2, West Africa.
Note the general decline in export tonnage in almost every country. There has also been a falling demand for palm oil in Europe.

estimated that about 50 per cent of the oil produced is consumed locally. Almost all the kernel is exported although many mills in Nigeria now extract kernel oil. The oil palm is sometimes tapped for wine, but the more tasty wine comes from the raffia palm.

At the beginning of this century, West Africa was the only exporter of palm oil, with Nigeria accounting for 68 per cent of the total export. The position changed just before the Second World War when the plantations of Indonesia and Malaya became the leading producers. This development shows the superiority of the plantation over peasant-type production in the oil palm industry. It was one of the factors which led to the adoption of plantation agriculture in parts of West Africa. Many hand presses and, later, pioneer oil mills were introduced to help improve the quality of palm oil produced by West African peasant farmers. The position today is that although Nigeria exports very little palm oil, she is still the leading producer of the commodity in West Africa followed by Benin and Ivory Coast. Nigerian production has, however, fallen very rapidly since 1969 and it is now feared that in view of the increasing demand for palm oil for food and industrial use, the country may have to import palm oil by 1980. The Federal Government budget of 1974 removed all restrictions on palm oil imports into the country in view of the rising price of oil for domestic use. (See Table 8.) Palm kernels and lately palm kernel oil are important in the export trade of Nigeria, Ivory Coast and Sierra Leone. Until about 1960, palm kernel oil was pressed almost exclusively in Europe and North America, where the oil is used for making margarine, cooking oil, paints and soap. In West Africa palm kernel oil is obtained traditionally by roasting the kernel and the oil is usually used as a pomade, for cooking or as medicine. Table 9 gives an idea of the export trade in palm kernels (see p. 68).

COCOA

Until recently, cocoa, which is grown mainly in the forest belt of Ivory Coast, Ghana and Western Nigeria, was produced entirely for export. A small quantity is now processed in Nigeria and Ghana to make cocoa bread, cocoa wine and beverages. The crop was introduced from South America and except for a few plantations in Ivory Coast and Nigeria, cocoa is

PLATE 39b—*Palm oil industry, East Central State, Nigeria*

67

Table 9—Palm kernel exports from West Africa (thousand tonnes)

Country	1956	1958	1960	1962	1964	1966	1968	1970	1971	1972
Nigeria	457	447	420	373	400	400	162	182	242	212
Sierra Leone	59	56	56	62	53	56	65	60	51	49
Benin	50	60	61	44	56	7	7	9.8	10.5	—
Togo	11	12	14	10	15	17	13	13	—	—
Liberia	—	—	15	—	—	12	12	13	17	5
Ivory Coast	12	17	16	11	13	9	9	18	19	20
Total West Africa	637	633	614	537	564	517	286	295.8	339.5	286
Zaïre	35	39	20	19	1	—	2	—	—	—
Africa	6	—	674	615	624	568	337	—	—	—
World Total	790	792	749	670	—	—	—	—	—	—

Source: *United Nations: Economic Commission for Africa, Statistical Yearbook*, 1973, Part 2, West Africa.

Note 1) The general decline in export tonnage.

2) The small tonnage for Zaïre is due largely to the fact that the Congo is the largest exporter of palm kernel oil in the world, (i.e. the bulk of the kernel is pressed for oil in Zaïre).

Table 10—Cocoa exports from West Africa (thousand tonnes)

Country	1908	1918	1928	1938	1962	1964	1968	1970	1971	1972
Ghana	12.9	67.4	223.3	261.6	429	387	335	367.3	341.0	412.2
Nigeria	1.4	10.4	50.0	97.5	198	197	209	196	272.0	227.5
Ivory Coast	—	0.4	14.5	52.7	108	124	121.5	143	145	159.2
Togo	0.08	1.6	6.3	7.6	11.1	14	14.3	30.5	27.2	27.1
Total West Africa	14.4	79.8	294	419.4	743	730	681	736.8	785.2	826
Sao Tome and Principe	28.6	17.3	14.6	12.7	10.6	8.7	11.0	—	—	—
Fernando Po	2.3	4.2	8.7	12.2	29.4	35.8	39.7	—	—	—
Tropical America	138.6	162.8	181.3	229.5	—	—	—	—	—	—
World Total	192.5	274.2	514.4	706.9	—	—	—	—	—	—

Source: *United Nations: Economic Commission for Africa, Statistical Yearbook*, 1973, Part 2, West Africa.

grown by local farmers in small estates of 1—6 hectares (2—15 acres). (See plates 40, 41.)

The progress of cocoa cultivation in West Africa provides a sharp contrast to that of the oil palm which, being indigenous, is rarely cultivated. In 1912, the bulk of the world cocoa came from the plantations of the New World but since 1936, the peasants of Ghana and Nigeria have overtaken the plantations and now produce two-thirds of the world's cocoa (Table 10). This is a remarkable achievement and a great credit to the initiative of the West African farmer. The quality of the bean remained poor for many years, however, until the farmers were given instructions on methods of fermenting and drying the beans. Cocoa is now the chief export of Ghana and western Nigeria and a very important one of Togo and Ivory Coast.

Conditions favouring growth and maximum yield include deep, well-drained soils which are rich in humus, an annual rainfall of about 1,270mm (50in.), and high relative humidity. A shade temperature of 27°C (80°F) is required and when young, the trees need shade and protection from sun rays and strong winds. This shade is usually provided by banana plants, which have become an important subsidiary crop in cocoa-growing districts.

Young cocoa trees begin to yield after five years and continue to produce for thirty-five years. The greatest threat to the cocoa industry is infection by two diseases called Black Pod and Swollen Shoot. Vast areas of cocoa have had to be destroyed in attempts to eradicate these diseases. In Nigeria, land which has been cleared of infected cocoa plants is often planted with kola.

PLATE 40—*Drying cocoa beans in experimental racks at Tafo Research Centre, Ghana*

PLATE 41—*Harvesting cocoa pods in Ghana*

PLATE 42—*Kola tree on the Lagos-Ife road, Nigeria*

KOLA

There are two main species of kola, *Cola acuminata* (*Abata*) and *Cola nitida* (*Gbanja* or *Goro*), both of which are native to the forests of West Africa. *Abata* is native to the area extending from Benin to the Congo Basin while *Gbanja* is native to the forests west of Togo. *Gbanja* is the kola of commerce and the most important producing area today is south-western Nigeria (100,000 tons). Ghana (14,000 tons), Ivory Coast (14,500 tons) and Sierra Leone (4,000 tons) are also important producers of kola. Kola exports from western Nigeria to the northern states is estimated at over ₦10 million per annum. The bulk of the kola is traded within West Africa where it is consumed mainly by people living in the savanna and desert areas. A small amount (probably less than 10 per cent) is exported to Europe and North America (plate 42).

RUBBER

Rubber is another forest crop. It is produced mainly in Liberia and Nigeria. Two rubber-bearing plants, the *Funtimia elastica* and the *Landolphia* grow wild in the forests and Guinea savanna of Nigeria while another native rubber plant, the *Kicksia elastica* is very common in the forests of southern Cameroon. On the world scene, wild rubber from the Amazon and Africa represented 99 per cent of the world's production in 1906 as compared with only 2 per cent in 1963. In West Africa today, as in other parts of the world, rubber cultivation is based on the para-rubber tree (*Hevea brasillensis*).

Para rubber grows best in regions having 1,770–2,030mm (70–120in.) of evenly distributed rainfall with not less than 50–75mm (2–3in.) in any month. A uniformly high temperature of about 27°C (80°F),

or more, with no month having less than 21°C (70°F) is essential. Gently sloping land with relatively fertile deep soils is necessary since rubber plants require well-drained soils.

Except in the Benin rubber belt where peasant production is predominant, rubber in West Africa is produced in large plantations in Liberia, Nigeria and West Cameroon. Rubber is the chief export of Liberia which is second only to Nigeria as the largest producer in Africa. See Table 11. (See plate 43.)

COFFEE

Coffee trees grow wild in many parts of the rain forest belt of West Africa including Liberia, Sierra Leone, the Ivory Coast and Cameroon. Today, the main areas of commerical cultivation are in the upland areas of these and other countries. The Ivory Coast, Cameroon, Guinea and Nigeria are the important producing countries. Varieties cultivated are *Coffee robusta*, by far the most widely cultivated variety, *Coffee arabica* and *Coffee liberica*.

Coffee is essentially an upland crop which does best where the average daily temperatures do not fall much below 21°C (70°F). An annual rainfall of 1,140–1,520mm (45–60in.) is adequate, but rainfall should be heaviest during the flowering and maturing season and slight during harvest so that the beans can be dried. Hill slopes and mountain sides provide adequate drainage conditions required by coffee plants which also need deep soils.

Initially commercial production of coffee in the Ivory Coast and Cameroon was strictly a European enterprise; and the crop was grown on plantations of about 280–400 hectares (700–1,000 acres). The situation in Ivory Coast has since changed and local African farmers who cultivate no more than two hectares

Table 11—Rubber exports from West Africa (thousand tonnes)

Country	1953	1959	1960	1961	1963	1966	1968	1970	1971	1972
Nigeria	21	41	—	56	64	71	53	59	51	41.2
Liberia	36	40	48	42	41	55	65	83	85	83
Ivory Coast	—	—	—	0.1	0.4	5.5	6.9	11	12	13
Total West Africa	57	81	48	98.1	105.4	131.5	124.9	153	148	137.2
Africa	79	118	140	149	—	—	—	—	—	—
World Total	1,668	1,861	2,060	2,037	—	—	—	—	—	—

Source: *United Nations: Economic Commission for Africa, Statistical Yearbook*, 1973, Part 2, West Africa.

Note 1) Export from Nigeria is decreasing while that from Liberia is increasing.

2) Liberia is now the leading exporter in West Africa (and indeed in Africa).

3) Nigeria is, however, the larger producer, but much of what is produced is consumed in local factories, hence lower export figures.

PLATE 43 — Rubber plantation in Ghana

PLATE 44 — Bagging groundnuts

(5 acres) of coffee per family now produce more coffee than European plantations. In 1956 for example, only 10,000 hectares (25,000 acres) out of a total area of 220,000 hectares (550,000 acres) under coffee in Ivory Coast belonged to European planters. In Nigeria, Guinea and Sierra Leone, the crop has always been in the hands of local people. Ivory Coast is the largest exporter of coffee in West Africa, and indeed in the whole of Africa.

GROUNDNUTS

The groundnut was originally grown as a food crop in the drier savanna lands but today it is the most important commercial crop of Senegal and Gambia and one of the most important exports of Nigeria. Groundnut and groundnut oil make up over 90 per cent of the export of Senegal by value and about 95 per cent of Gambia's export. Cultivation is entirely in the hands of African farmers and the rapid expansion of this crop, like that of cocoa, is a great credit to the adaptability and ability of the West African farmer.

71

PLATE 45—*Groundnuts pyramids at Kano; the groundnuts are stacked during harvest to await export*

Table 12—Groundnut exports from West Africa (thousand tonnes)

Country	1956	1958	1960	1962	1964	1966	1968	1970	1971	1972
Nigeria	455	521	337	538	553	582	648	292	137	106
Senegal	188	330	253	277	214	298	243	—	—	—
Niger	90	87	51	69	93	164	162	132	93	—
Gambia	37	64	34	59	31	38	31	34	33	—
Guinea Bissau	26	30	18	32	31	—	—	—	—	—
Mali	—	—	—	41	47	12	11	18	—	—
Total West Africa	796	1,032	693	1,016	969	1,094	1,095	476	263	106
Africa	1,034	1,226	910	1,282	1,308	—	—	—	—	—
World Total	1,497	1,378	1,088	1,399	1,392	—	—	—	—	—

Source: *United Nations: Economic Commission for Africa Statistical Yearbook*, 1973, Part 2, West Africa.
Note that climatic conditions, fluctuations in price paid to farmers, impoverished soils, transport cost and availability of wage labour account in part for the fluctuation in export figures, particularly in Senegal and Gambia.

In Nigeria, for instance, the export figure for 1911 was only 2,000 tons but in 1965/6 the figure had risen to over 970,000 tons. The actual amount harvested is far in excess of this figure since a considerable proportion of the crop is consumed locally.

Those who have travelled extensively in West Africa might have noticed that groundnuts are cultivated everywhere, from the sandy levees of the Niger Delta, through the floodplains of the Anambra Valley to the drier sandy plains of Niger Republic. The best conditions for commercial production are found in the light, sandy soils of the Sudan zone, with a rainfall of 640–1,000mm (25–40in.) and a marked dry season for drying the crops. Availability of good transportation is an important factor within this zone, outside which the crop is only produced for local consumption. See Table 12. (See plates 44, 45.)

COTTON

Cotton production is of increasing importance in Nigeria and Mali but compared with the Nile Basin or East Africa, cotton production in West Africa is insignificant. Cotton is not a new crop in West Africa where hand-woven cloth, made from locally grown cotton, has been produced for several centuries. Today, weaving is considered the most widespread cottage industry in West Africa. As in the case of rubber and rice, improved varieties of cotton, the most successful of which is the Allen 26 J, have been introduced and are fast replacing the older varieties.

Nigeria produces about three-quarters of the total amount of about 70,000 tonnes, most of this coming from the cotton belt extending from eastern Katsina Province to the north-western part of Zaria Province. In the inland Niger Delta region of Mali cotton is produced under irrigation. Smaller quantities come from Guinea and the Ivory Coast.

Ideal conditions for cotton production include a rainfall of 760–1,400mm (30–55in.), most of which falls during the growing season, abundant sunshine, a marked dry season when the bolls dry and are harvested. The soils must be rich and well-drained; in Zaria, the cotton belt is identified as the area having rich black soils. The introduction of improved varieties, the fact that the crop does not compete for labour with other crops during the planting season, and improved transportation are other factors which have made for rapid expansion of cotton in various parts of West Africa. The practice of inter-cropping cotton with groundnuts and other crops has been discouraged, since it is a contributory factor to poor yields. (See plate 46a.)

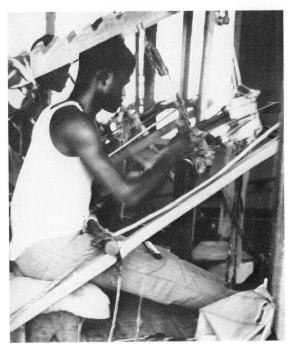

PLATE 46a—A Kente cloth weaver, Accra, Ghana

BANANA

Commercial production for export is restricted to the Cameroons, Guinea and Ivory Coast, where the crop is grown in large plantations. By far the largest producer is the Cameroons where production is concentrated along the coast. Banana, like the plantain, is of course a very common crop in West Africa and is to be found growing in most compound-lands in the forest belt. Bananas produced on compounds are however for home consumption and internal exchange, not for export.

The banana is a fast-growing plant which completes its life cycle within a year. It does best in low-lying but well-drained alluvial soils. Rainfall of 1,900–2,540mm (75–100in.), distributed so that there is no drought, is required but the crop has been found to grow in drier areas such as the cocoa belts of Nigeria and Ghana. In the Tiko plains of west Cameroon, some of the banana estates are irrigated and it is estimated that irrigated bananas yield about six tonnes of fruit more per hectare than non-irrigated bananas. (See plate 46b.)

MARKETING OF EXPORT CROPS

In the English-speaking countries of Nigeria, Ghana, Sierra Leone and Gambia all crops, with the exception of rubber in Nigeria, are marketed through

73

PLATE 46b—Picking bananas

rubber. Pan buyers who go from farm to farm to buy cocoa beans compare with those who move from compound to compound to buy measures of palm oil or kernel. Wayside buying sheds for groundnuts, palm produce and cocoa are common features of the rural areas in West Africa. Some producers load their produce on bicycles, donkeys and canoes and take it direct to the collecting points. Usually the profits made by these small-scale buyers are very small but many of them make some additional money from interest on money which they advance to needy farmers in anticipation of the next harvest.

Agricultural exports from the French-speaking countries still go mostly to France and consist principally of groundnuts, cocoa, coffee, cotton, palm produce and bananas. After the Second World War, during which many processing industries were established, many products from the French-speaking countries were no longer shipped in crude form. Rather, groundnuts have increasingly been exported in the form of oil, cake, or shelled nuts while coffee beans are processed and manufactured into Nescafé coffee in Ivory Coast. Fruit exports have also been largely replaced by fruit juices and preserves. The value of agricultural exports have thereby been enhanced and, in addition, transport costs have been considerably reduced.

Sociétés de Prévoyance (which started in 1910 as an organization aimed at protecting Africans against their habitual improvidence by creating grain reserves, but later became a credit institution) and co-operatives play a major role in both selling and storage of agricultural exports especially the marketing of groundnuts. Equivalents of the marketing boards of the English-speaking countries also exist in the French-speaking countries. The colonial-period Groupement National d'Achat des Produits Oleagineux (GNAPO) for palm produce, and the national cocoa-buying organization (GNAFCO), which determined the price of groundnut and cocoa imported in to France, were however based in France, not in the various French-speaking West African countries. In 1956, however, the Ivory Coast government set up a separate price-supporting *caisse de stabilization*, in order to counter a situation in which the income of cocoa farmers was drastically reduced as a result of a continuing fall in world cocoa prices. The *caisse de stabilization* merely fixed a buying price (70 CFA francs per kilo f.o.b. in Ivory Coast) for the season and established a fund from which cocoa exporters would be paid if world prices fell below a certain level and to which they must contribute if world prices rose above it. Unlike the marketing boards, the *caisse* made no provision for enforcing the payment of the fixed prices to the producer.

marketing boards established by the various governments. Each commodity marketing board appoints its buying agents and fixes the producer price for every crop season. The purpose of setting up these boards was to help ensure the stability of producer prices. It does this by setting aside some money in years when producer prices are high in the world market, and using part of this reserve to top up prices paid to the producer in years when world prices are very low.

From the time the crop leaves the farm to the time it gets into the hands of the marketing board at the port of export, it passes through several grades of middlemen. In general the process of trade is the same with cocoa, palm produce, groundnuts and even

Chapter 9—Internal Trade and Traders

During the pre-colonial period considerable trade took place between various communities inhabiting West Africa. In the grassland areas, trading often involved long-distance travel in which Hausa and Dioula traders featured prominently. Items of trade included local foodstuffs, salt, natron, cotton cloth, iron implements and kola nuts. European-manufactured goods which came into West Africa either across the Sahara to the important market centres of Kano, Timbuktu and Zinder or through the coastal trading port-towns of Lagos, Calabar, Dakar and Takoradi were also important. In return for European trade goods, West Africa exported slaves, gold, and leather goods to the countries of Europe. The medium of exchange in the far north was cotton cloth or salt but in the south, trade was both by barter and through the medium of cowrie shells which served as currency. The poor state of transportation as well as occasional inter-group warfare restricted the volume of trade until the early colonial period when the situation started to change.

The factors which encouraged trade during the colonial period include:
1) The introduction of cash crops, which resulted in some degree of specialization so that those farmers who concentrated on cocoa, groundnut and rubber production had to buy some of their food requirements.
2) The introduction of poll tax which had to be paid in cash.
3) Improved transportation following the building of roads, railways and bridges.
4) The end of armed civil conflicts following the imposition of French and British rule.

Since the beginning of this century, the pattern of trade, the trade goods and the organization of trade have changed considerably and are still changing. Some of these changes are discussed under the sections dealing with local trade in foodstuffs, trade in manufactured goods and crafts, and trade in agricultural exports. The character of the various trading groups such as the market women, the Syrian-Lebanese and the European trading firms are also discussed.

TRADE IN LOCAL FOODSTUFFS

The large amount of trade in local foodstuffs which has gone on for centuries shows that some West African farmers have always produced a surplus for the market. It is true that most farmers produce much of their food, but the need for exchange has always existed. Thus the people of the Niger Delta have always depended on basic foodstuffs from the hinterland people who, in turn, buy fish from the delta people. In the past the trade was largely by barter, a system of trade which has still not died out in the more remote villages, where people still buy things like snuff by offering the snuff dealer some quantity of green vegetables or fruits.

Increasing specialization in tree crop production and the increasing number of the non-farm population has resulted in a great boom in the trade in foodstuffs. Rural areas which do not produce enough food for the local population include the Nigerian cocoa belt, the Kano groundnut belt, the very densely populated areas of Iboland, Mossi territory and the mining districts of the Jos Plateau, Liberia and Ghana. The non-farm population is concentrated in the cities which like the rural food-deficit areas, depend on food imports from food-surplus rural areas.

All over West Africa, the women dominate the retail trade in foodstuffs. Men have, however, become prominent in the foodstuffs trade since 1950. The role of the men, who consist of food contractors to institutions such as hospitals, colleges and prisons, as well as wholesale dealers in certain food items like yams, gari, rice and onions is that of collecting and transporting the foodstuffs from remote rural areas to the major centres of consumption. Long distances are involved and the traders may spend several days away from home. Onitsha food traders, for example, hire lorries to evacuate yams purchased in Ogoja, rice from Abakaliki, and onions from the Kainji Lake Basin. The foodstuffs are usually cheap in these isolated areas. In general, housewives do not find it convenient to take part in this aspect of the trade. They therefore buy from the big dealers in units such as

PLATE 47 — *Market scene at Kaduna, Nigeria*

bags of rice, gari, beans and onions, which they retail to consumers in the cities and rural markets.

Rural markets meet periodically and housewives from the towns often travel to buy food more cheaply at these markets. Food crops produced in rural areas are also taken by the headload to be sold in nearby urban markets. Often the housewives who carry these foodstuffs to the markets are forestalled a kilometre or two to the market by women traders who buy the goods for resale at a small profit to urban consumers. The high price which the consumer pays for his food-stuffs is generally blamed on the large number of intermediaries between the farmer and the consumer. Often the cost of food in town is more than twice the price paid to the farmer who produced the item.

Another aspect of the trade in foodstuffs is the sale of cooked food, an occupation which is best deve-loped amongst the Yorubas of Nigeria and Benin. A wide range of cooked foods is sold in market places, building construction sites and along the streets in most Yoruba towns and villages. The food, which includes cooked rice, yam, moinmoin (from beans) and dodo (fried ripe plantain), is usually wrapped in special leaves and may be bought for as little as five kobo.

Another feature of the foodstuff trade and one which is also best developed amongst the Yoruba is the hawking of food items including yams, plantains and meat from house to house and along the streets. This type of trading is usually done by young girls and boys who carry their goods in small baskets or basins. House to house hawking takes place mainly in the mornings and evenings when people are at home. See plates 47, 48.

TRADE IN OTHER LOCAL PRODUCTS

Kola nuts and local handicrafts are two of the oldest trade goods in West Africa. Kola nuts are produced in the forest belt although the main centres of con-sumption are in the savanna and semi-desert regions of the far north, where there is at least one kola nut trader in every village. In Nigeria, the main produc-ing area is the Shagamu district, but before 1935, most of the kola nuts traded in West Africa came from the forests of Ghana, Sierra Leone and Guinea Republic. The trade is largely in the hands of Hausa traders who settle permanently in the producing areas for the purpose of buying, packing and transporting the nuts to the northern districts. In the past, kola nuts were transported mainly by rail, but today the dealers prefer road transport, which is more flexible.

In the consuming centres, the kola nuts are retailed by women and children, either at the market place or at sheds in front of dwelling houses. Children also hawk kola nuts from house to house.

In Nigeria, rich kola nut traders also engage in the cattle trade between the north and the south. Often the money realised from cattle sales in the south is invested in buying kola nuts which are sent back to the north in the lorries which brought down cattle, beans or onions from the north. The retail trade in beef is, however, usually in the hands of the local population who buy the live animals from Hausa dealers.

Itinerant Hausa and Dioula traders also specialize in craft products including leather poufs, shoes and sandals, blankets, perfumes, trinkets and wood carvings. Some of these traders may be seen displaying their goods outside international airports, major hotels and catering rest houses (motels) in the main cities of West Africa.

TRADE IN MANUFACTURED GOODS

Until the beginning of the Second World War, almost all the manufactured goods traded in West Africa were imported from Europe, North America, and the Asian countries of India, Japan and Hong Kong. The wholesale and retail trade in these goods was dominated by big European trading firms of which the most prominent were the Compagnie Française de l' Afrique Occidentale (CFAO), the Société Commerciale de l'Ouest Africain (SCOA), the United Africa Company (UAC), John Holt and Leventis. There were also a large number of Indian, Syrian and Lebanese companies including K. C. Challerams, J. T. Chanrai, and C. Zard as well as numerous family concerns owned by Lebanese and Syrians. Usually the large trading companies distributed their goods through local agents, who in turn supplied a large number of petty traders. The range of goods handled by these companies was large and most of them had a technical division dealing with hardware goods, farming equipment as well as a motor division dealing with cars, lorries and agricultural machinery. The Lebanese and Syrians dealt mainly in textiles and provisions (groceries).

Before 1960, most of these big trading companies also traded in agricultural exports. Many of the Syrian and Lebanese traders started as agents of these companies and their role consisted of distributing the manufactured goods stocked by the companies, as well as purchasing agricultural produce for them. The establishment of produce marketing boards in Anglophone countries resulted in considerable loss of profit in the agricultural export trade, since all agricultural exports except rubber had to be purchased at prices fixed by the marketing boards, which also took over the sale of produce in the world market from the big European trading firms. The result was the gradual withdrawal of these companies from the produce trade and a complete take-over by African trading agents by about 1965. The retail trade has also been taken over by Africans in Ghana, following the Ghana Enterprises Promotion Law of 1969 which restricted retail trade to indigenes of Ghana. In Nigeria, a decree was promulgated in 1970 restricting retail trade and some other businesses to Nigerians as from 1974. But in the French-speaking countries the situation remains unchanged—in Senegal, the Ivory Coast and Togo for example, the retail trade is still controlled by French commercial houses as well as by Syrians and Lebanese. One of the immediate effects of the trade restrictions imposed in the English-speaking countries was the transfer by European and later some Syrian-Lebanese merchants of their capital from trading into manufacturing.

The African petty trader has always been an important arm of the distributive trade in manufactured goods. The large number of these traders and the ease with which one can set up as a trader are the most conspicuous features of the merchandise trade in West Africa. The great demand for the services of this large number of intermediaries in the retail trade has been attributed to the low purchasing power of the vast majority of the people. As a rule, those in the low-income group, that is more than 90 per cent of the population, buy manufactured goods in very small units. Sugar for example is retailed at about six cubes for one kobo, matches at one box for four kobo and cigarettes at one stick for one kobo. The number of petty traders is so large that one often wonders who the buyers are! In the towns, retail traders are to be found in market places, at street corners as well as in the frontage of houses facing major streets. Both women and men take part in petty trading but in Yorubaland the trade is dominated by women.

Often, local petty traders combine their business with the purchase of agricultural produce in much the same way as the big European companies and the Syrian-Lebanese family concerns did in the past. Manufactured goods are supplied on credit to cocoa and palm oil producers who, in return, trade their produce through these petty traders. Some traders move around the countryside from one rural market

PLATE 48—*Fulani milk sellers*

to another so as to get a large enough number of patrons. The bigger traders who deal in high-order goods such as radios, bicycles and refrigerators establish themselves in the major towns and cities. Many of these big traders still obtain their goods from the European wholesale firms or direct from the local manufacturing companies. An increasing number of West African traders from Aba, Onitsha and Lagos, however, order goods straight from Britain, France, West Germany, Japan, India and America.

TRADE IN AGRICULTURAL EXPORTS

The involvement of traders of manufactured goods with the trade in export produce was discussed in the last section. In this section, we touch on the role of the large number of middlemen in the export trade in agricultural produce. West African export crops, which include cocoa, palm oil, palm kernel, rubber, groundnut and cotton, are produced by tens of thousands of small-scale African farmers who own very small farms. Large-scale plantation agriculture is very restricted and products from such plantations account for less than 10 per cent of the total agricultural exports.

In the English-speaking countries, export produce, excepting rubber in Nigeria, is exported through marketing boards which have been set up by the governments to control prices paid to producers of agricultural exports. In almost all cases, the price paid to the producer is less than what the marketing boards receive in the world market. The reserves thus accumulated were meant to be used in topping up produce prices when there was a slump in the world market, but in practice, the large sums of money accumulated by the marketing boards has been used in financing industrial and other development projects in the cities. The Nigerian marketing boards sell their produce to the world market through the Nigerian Produce Marketing Company. It is the price control policy of the marketing boards that has forced out the large expatriate firms from the export produce trade. This policy has also resulted in the refusal of expatriate planters to invest in crops like cocoa and the oil palm, which must be marketed through the boards. Indeed some planters such as the United Africa Company (UAC) have already cut off oil palm trees in some of their estates, which have since been replanted with rubber.

The situation in the French-speaking countries, whereby the large European firms control the trade in export produce and imported general merchandise, has remained virtually unchanged. Producers of the various crops still accept low prices for their output and buy consumer goods from the traders. The Syrians and Lebanese continue as middlemen, although an increasing number of Africans now participate as middlemen in the produce trade.

THE TRADERS

We conclude this chapter by looking briefly at the people who organize the trade in export produce, general merchandize and staple foodstuffs. These traders fall into four groups, namely: 1) the big trading companies, 2) the Syrian-Lebanese, 3) the big African traders and licensed buying agents and 4) the numerous African petty traders of general merchandize and staple foodstuffs. (See plate 49.)

The big trading companies in the French-speaking countries have their headquarters mostly in Bordeaux and Marseilles although a few are based in Paris and Lyons. Some of the largest firms such as SCOA and CFAO operate in the English-speaking countries just as some big British firms have branches in the French-speaking countries. These firms are heavily capitalized and in the French-speaking countries they still control the wholesale and retail trade in general merchandise as well as the export trade in agricultural produce. In the English-speaking countries, the firms now restrict their activities to wholesale trade, supermarkets and manufacturing. The trade in motor vehicles and agricultural machinery is everywhere controlled by these firms, each of which has a monopoly in the distribution of particular types of vehicles in each country. In the French-speaking countries, the managerial and skilled

PLATE 49—Petty traders at Port Harcourt, Nigeria

personnel of these firms are still predominantly French, but in Ghana, Nigeria and Sierra Leone, most of the managerial staff and technicians are Africans.

Syrian and Lebanese merchants work with little capital and tend to use family labour in running their businesses which are usually on a small scale as compared with the big firms. They are found in all the countries but are particularly numerous in Senegal, the Ivory Coast, Sierra Leone and Nigeria. Most of them have since left Ghana following the enforcement of that country's Enterprises Promotion Law of 1969 which prevented aliens from engaging in certain economic activities, including retail trade and the transport business. A similar law in Nigeria came into effect in 1974, when most Lebanese and Syrians had to leave the country. Syrians and Lebanese usually started as agents of the big firms whose goods they distributed and for whom they purchased African produce. They are usually characterized as being very clannish and have become unpopular in many countries because of their role as smugglers and evaders of foreign-exchange regulations. They are also often accused of paying very low wages to African employees and refusing to comply with minimum wage rates or salary increases approved by governments.

On the basis of their scale of operation, employment policy and indulgence in smuggling, the big African traders can be compared with the Syrians and Lebanese. They operate as importers of general merchandize or as agents of the big firms in the export produce and merchandize trade. Wealthy African traders are few in the French-speaking countries, where the retail trade is still largely in the hands of the Syrians and Lebanese. In the English-speaking countries, the big African traders and licensed buying agents have since displaced the Syrians and Lebanese.

Finally we have the petty trader who is the final link in the chain of distribution of general merchandise and staple foodstuffs. The small capital required to set up as a petty trader (often less than ₦200 (£100) and the lack of other employment opportunities are largely responsible for the large number of people in retail trade. Many of these traders combine trading with farming while civil servants, teachers and other professionals often supply capital with which their wives set up as petty traders.

The market-women or market-mammys feature prominently as petty traders all over West Africa. They deal in a wide range of merchandize or foodstuffs and usually rent a market stall, although many of them trade in the open market place. Their wares have no price tags and they have to haggle with their customer over the price to be paid for each ware. Most of them do not keep records of their sales and rarely make a profit of more than ₦200 in one year. But there are also some very wealthy market-women who have become very influential in politics and other spheres of public life. Some of them have been responsible for educating their children up to university level, while others make substantial financial contributions to community development projects.

Chapter 10—Mineral Resources

West Africa has rich deposits of a large variety of minerals including iron ore, diamond, gold, bauxite and crude oil. Some minerals such as gold, iron ore, tin and salt were produced by the local people during the pre-colonial period. Gold from Mali and southern Ghana featured in trans-Saharan caravan trade via Timbuktu, and the former British colony of the Gold Coast (now the state of Ghana) derived its name from the rich gold deposits of south-western Ghana. Iron ore was mined and smelted in various parts of the savanna lands of West Africa and the search for tin in Nigeria started after British merchants had seen crude tin implements on display for sale by Hausa traders at Ibi Town (on the Benue River). In all cases, mining was on a small scale until the late nineteenth century and the early twentieth century, when large-scale mining started under the supervision of European engineers and technicians.

Compared with the situation in central and southern Africa, mining activities started rather late in West Africa and never played a dominant part in the region's economy until after 1960 when the production of crude oil, bauxite, diamond and iron ore was stepped up. Mining is better developed in the English-speaking countries of Sierra Leone, Liberia, Ghana and Nigeria which together accounted for about 70 per cent of all mineral exports from West Africa in the early 1960s. In the French-speaking countries, mining was neglected because of the widespread but groundless belief that there were no rich mineral deposits comparable to those of Ghana, Sierra Leone and Nigeria. Difficult terrain and poor communications also made prospecting expensive and sometimes risky.

Since about 1960, minerals have become very important in the export trade of Sierra Leone, Guinea and Liberia. In each of these countries, minerals have provided more than half of the exports by value since 1961. In the case of Nigeria, the dominant position of mineral oil in the export trade began after the civil war which ended in 1970. In Ghana, Mauritania, Sierra Leone and Liberia, minerals play a very important part in providing revenue to sustain the railways and port installation.

Prospecting for minerals continues in the various countries. The position in each country is discussed in the relevant section of the chapter dealing with the country. In this chapter, which gives a broad view of mining in West Africa, we shall consider only the most important minerals which are diamonds, iron-ore, bauxite, petroleum, tin, manganese and gold. The areas of production of these minerals are shown in Fig. 10.1 (p. 82).

DIAMONDS

Diamond is a mineral composed of pure carbon and as a precious stone of great beauty and value, it is used extensively in making jewellery. As the hardest naturally-occurring known mineral, diamond has been put to a variety of uses in industry. West African diamonds consist of a very small proportion of gemstones, the bulk of the mineral being suitable for use as industrial diamonds. In industry, diamond is used largely for the manufacture of grinding wheels for sharpening metal-cutting tools and in polishing operations. Diamond is also used for diamond drills in several operations, including dental and oil-well drills. The great demand for industrial diamonds encouraged expensive research to make synthetic diamonds—this was finally accomplished in 1955, when the General Electric Company produced industrial diamonds in its laboratory in New York.

Ghana is the leading producer of diamonds in West Africa and the second largest world producer (after Zaïre Republic) of industrial diamonds. The annual output is about 3 million carats while that of Sierra Leone, another leading producer, is 2 million carats. There is a higher proportion of gemstones from Sierra Leone, the diamond export of which is worth more than that of Ghana. In 1968, for example, Sierra Leone exported 1,522,000 carats worth ₦25,434,000 (£12,717,000) as compared with Ghana's export of 2,447,000 carats worth only ₦14,230,000 (£7,115,000). Other producers of diamonds are Liberia in the districts bordering on Sierra Leone (1 million carats), the Ivory Coast (500,000 carats) and

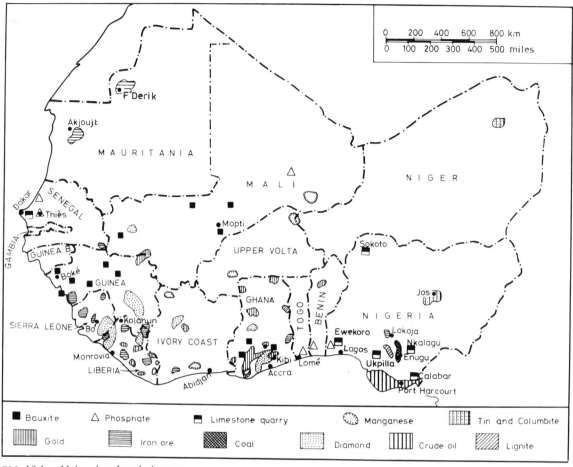

FIG. 10.1—Main mineral-producing areas

Guinea. The stones which occur mostly as alluvial deposits along river basins are produced by large mining companies as well as by individual African diggers who produce about 35 per cent of Ghana's diamonds and about 40 per cent of the annual output from Ivory Coast. Illegal mining and sales are widespread in Sierra Leone and Ghana, and have resulted in great financial losses to the governments. (See also Table 13, p. 83.)

IRON ORE

Iron ore deposits are widespread throughout West Africa and have been smelted for several centuries in primitive furnaces for use in making weapons and agricultural implements. Many of the ores have a high iron content, but often occur in small quantities which are not economical to work. All the ores are still exported to Europe and North America and so far, only large deposits located close to sea ports have been worked. Sierra Leone, Liberia, Guinea and

Mauritania are the main producers of iron ore. Production started in Sierra Leone as early as 1933 when the Marampa mines were opened. Liberian ores were first tapped in 1951 when the Bomi Hills mines were opened, followed by the Bong Hills, and the Mount Nimba mines. Today Liberia is one of the largest world exporters of iron ores. The great ore deposits in the Fort Gourand district of Mauritania have been worked only since 1963 and are much more extensive and of a higher quality than those of Guinea Republic where mining started much earlier (about 1950). Iron ore deposits have been discovered in the Agbaja Plateau and Enugu area of Nigeria but mining may not start until the proposed iron and steel complex in the country becomes a reality. (See plate 50.)

Commercially, the most important ores of iron are haematite (Fe_2O_3), magnetite (Fe_3O_4), limonite (hydrated iron oxide) and the carbonate siderite ($FeCO_3$). In West Africa, the largest and richest iron ore deposits under exploitation are haematite, the major mines of which include Mount Nimba (Liberia), Marampa, Tonkoli River and the Sula Mountains in

Sierra Leone and Fort Gourand in Mauritania. The Bomi Hills iron ore deposits in Liberia are the richest known magnetite ore (65 per cent iron content) in West Africa while the main locations of limonite are at Mount Patti, near Lokoja in Nigeria and in the vicinity of Conakry in Guinea. (See Table 14 below.)

Iron is certainly the most-used metal in industry and the manufacture and use of iron implements dates to the dawn of civilization. The demand for iron and steel products in West Africa has increased tremendously since independence in 1960 and so far almost all the iron and steel used in local manufacturing, including the construction industry are imported from Europe and America. An integrated iron and steel factory making use of local iron ore is considered to be overdue in West Africa. The Nigerian government set aside ₦60 million during the 1962–8 Plan for an iron and steel mill but the project did not get off the ground. A more elaborate iron and steel complex estimated to cost ₦240 million was again proposed during the 1970–4 Plan and since the site of the factory at Ajaokuta near Lokoja was selected only in May 1974 it appears that work will start on the project during the 1975–8 Plan. As of 1976 the project had not started, but it is likely that it will begin in 1977/8.

BAUXITE

Bauxite is the principal ore of aluminium and is a mixture of hydrous aluminium oxides formed through weathering of different types of rocks. A large amount of household equipment is now made from aluminium which has the property of being

PLATE 50—Train being loaded with haematite iron ore at Mt Nimba, north-eastern Liberia

very strong but light in weight. It is this property that makes aluminium very suitable for aircraft manufacture. The metal is also easily rolled into thin sheets and because of its high resistance to corrosion by

Table 13—Diamond exports from West Africa (thousand carats)

Country	1965	1966	1967	1968	1969	1970	1971	1972
Sierra Leone	1,525	1,319	1,160	1,683	2,020	1,955	1,934	1,846
Ghana	2,273	2,819	2,538	2,447	2,391	2,872	2,367	3,193
Liberia	300	300	600	793	836	826	739	880
Ivory Coast	199	181	191	181	204	215	276	352
Guinea	72	72	51	70	72	74	74	n.a.

Source: *United Nations: Economic Commission for Africa, Statistical Yearbook, 1973, Part 2, West Africa.*

Table 14—Iron ore exports from West Africa (thousand tonnes)

Country	1964	1965	1966	1967	1968	1969	1970	1971	1972
Mauritania	4,904	5,961	7,135	7,455	7,702	8,501	9,220	8,601	8,628
Guinea	427	755	610	701	829	2,032	2,000	—	—
Sierra Leone	2,041	2,334	2,218	2,158	2,535	2,427	2,427	2,569	2,283
Liberia	11,300	15,340	16,560	17,475	19,200	20,600	23,570	21,234	22,977

Source: *United Nations Economic Commission for Africa, Statistical Yearbook, 1973, Part 2, West Africa.*

PLATE 51—*Cutting out bauxite at Fria, Near Conakry, Guinea*

Table 15—Bauxite and alumina exports from West Africa (thousand tons)

Country	1965	1966	1967	1968	1969	1970	1971	1972
Guinea: Bauxite (produced)	1,870	1,609	1,644	2,112	2,460	2,460	2,635	2,650
Bauxite (exported)	241	251	250	1,000	1,000	n.a.	n.a.	n..a.
Alumina (exported)	522	525	530	531	572	6,610	665	700
Ghana: Bauxite (produced)	287	311	300	241	245	215	354	316
Sierra Leone: Bauxite (produced)	176	244	335	470	470	395	552	682

Source: *United Nations: Economic Commission for Africa, Statistical Yearbook,* 1973, Part 2, West Africa.

water, it is widely used for making water pipes and cooking utensils.

Guinea is the largest producer of bauxite in West Africa and may one day become a leading world producer, since one of the world's most extensive bauxite deposits occurs at the Guinean village of Sangaridi near Boke. Mining started in 1952 with the exploitation of the Kassa Island deposits (just off Conakry) which are expected to last till about 1980. There is another large reserve of about 300 million tons of bauxite in the Fria district, where an alumina plant was built in 1960. Table 15 shows the trend in the export of bauxite and alumina between 1965 and 1972. Ghana also has large reserves of bauxite (about 240 million tons), at Awaso, Mpreaso (near Nkawkaw)

and Yenahin. Existing bauxite mines are located at Mpreaso and Kibi and up till 1970 all the ore was exported, while the smelter at Tema depended on imported alumina. West African bauxite lies in thick beds on the surface and mining is essentially by open-cast methods. (See Table 15 above.) (See plate 51.)

PETROLEUM

West Africa became a major world producer of crude petroleum during the late 1960's, when Nigeria produced all the crude petroleum exported from West Africa. Production is centred around the Niger Delta and in offshore locations (Fig. 10.1). Small finds have

PLATE 52—Part of oil refinery at Lomé, Togo

been reported in Ghana and Senegal but production is still restricted to fields in Nigeria which is the second largest producer of crude petroleum in Africa (after Libya). Crude oil has become the most important export from Nigeria since 1969 when the crude petroleum export was valued at ₦272 million, increasing to ₦1,893.5 million in 1973. An oil refinery at Eleme, near Port Harcourt has supplied part of Nigeria's local petroleum-product needs since 1965 and the sites for two other refineries have since been selected at Warri and Kaduna. (See plate 52.)

TIN

Tin ore occurs as gravel deposits along the beds of ancient river valleys in the Jos Plateau area of Nigeria and in the Air Massif region of Niger Republic. Local mining by African metal workers started in the Jos Plateau many centuries before large-scale mining was undertaken in 1903. Open-cast methods are used in the plateau and although much of the mining opera-

tions have been mechanized, tin-panning or hand-working by Africans is still important. Formerly, the ore was exported in its raw form to Britain but since 1962, when a tin-smelting plant was built, the bulk of the metal is now exported in its pure form (tin ingots). (See Fig. 10.2.)

By-products of the Jos Plateau tin-mining industry include columbite, niobium, tantalite and zircon. These by-products are very rare minerals and are all exported to the United States of America.

The Air Massif deposits in Niger Republic were discovered in 1947 and mining started two years later. The first tin ore export of 130 tons was in 1950 and in 1952 when the world price for tin was very high (because of the Korean War), Niger exported 160 tons of tin ore valued at 60 million francs (CFA). Production dropped after the end of the Korean War in 1953 and mining has become rather uneconomic in this fairly arid, hot and sparsely settled region. Transport costs of taking tin ore to the coast and of taking supplies to the mines are very high and the cost of providing water and maintaining access roads

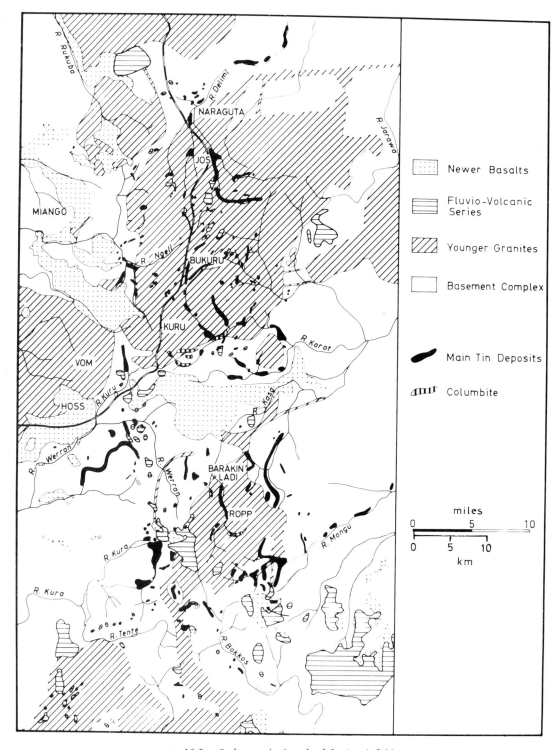

Legend:

- :::::: Newer Basalts
- ▤ Fluvio-Volcanic Series
- ▨ Younger Granites
- ☐ Basement Complex
- ● Main Tin Deposits
- ▥ Columbite

FIG. 10.2—Geology and minerals of the Jos tinfields

is prohibitive. The discovery of new deposits in 1955 is likely to encourage the mining companies to stay on especially since the government has reduced the tax on tin exports.

MANGANESE

Ghana is the third largest world producer of manganese (after the USSR and India) but the largest exporter of the mineral. The largest deposits occur at Nsuta (near Tarkwa), where mining started in 1917. The Ghanaian ore lies in deposits about 30m (100ft) thick on the crest of low hills and is mined by opencast methods. Manganese is also mined at Grand Lahou in the Ivory Coast where production started in 1960. Exports from the Ivory Coast average about 100,000 tons a year as compared with 250,000 tons from Ghana.

GOLD

Gold has been mined in Ghana since the tenth century AD, but modern mining started in 1880 and today, Ghana (formerly the Gold Coast) is the main exporter of gold in West Africa. With an export value of over ₦22 million in 1965, Ghana ranks as the fifth largest producer of gold in the world. The mineral is found in many parts of Ghana although the main workings are found within a 96.5km (60-mile) radius of Dunkwa, where Obuasi, the world's richest gold mine, is located. The gold occurs in bankets similar to those in South Africa. Ghanaian gold is obtained both by deep mining and by alluvial workings along the beds of the Offin, Ankobra and Tano rivers. (Plate 53.)

Small quantities of gold are also produced in Mali, Benin, Guinea, Nigeria and Liberia, where the mineral is obtained by the use of traditional methods of panning river gravels.

OTHER MINERALS

Chrome ore, copper, phosphates, limestone, salts and coal are some of the other minerals exploited in West Africa. Chrome ore has been mined near Hangha in Sierra Leone since 1937. Other deposits have been discovered in Benin and Togo but these have not

PLATE 53 — Pouring molten gold at the Ashanti Goldfields Corporation at Obuasi, Ghana

yet been exploited. Large deposits of copper occur at Akjoujt in Mauritania, where mining started in 1953. The oldest copper mines in West Africa are however, to be found in Sierra Leone and the Ivory Coast where small deposits have been worked since the first decade of this century.

Phosphates have been quarried at Pallo, near Thies (Senegal) since 1950. The largest phosphate deposits are, however, located at Akoumape, between Lomé and Anecho in Togo where mining started in 1961. Phosphates are also worked at Taika, 110km (70 miles) from Dakar (Senegal). Other deposits which have not yet been worked occur in the Lama River Valley in Benin, in the dry Timlesi Valley near Goa in Mali and at Abeokuta (Nigeria). The development of phosphatic fertilizer industries based on these deposits will go a long way to remedy the marked phosphate deficiencies in many West African soils.

The last three minerals worth considering are salt, limestone and coal. Salt mining in the Saharan belt has been undertaken for centuries by local tribes who exchanged the salt for gold and kola nuts from the forest belt. The major ancient mines were at Idji and Tarza in Mauritania, Taouderni in Mali, and Bilma in Niger Republic. Sea salt was also obtained through the evaporation of sea water by the coastal inhabitants of Senegal, Ghana and Nigeria. Local salt deposits have suffered a considerable decline following the importation of cheaper and better quality salt from Europe.

Good quality limestone for manufacturing cement occurs in many parts of West Africa and the oldest cement factories include the Bargney cement works near Rufisque (Senegal) and the Nkalagu Cement Factory in the Anambra State of Nigeria. Cement is also manufactured at Sokoto, Ukpilla, Calabar and Abeokuta, all in Nigeria, Takoradi and Tema in Ghana, and Bobo Dioulasso in Upper Volta.

Coal has been mined at Enugu since 1912 when the only coalfield in West Africa started production. The coal is sub-bituminous and of rather low quality. It was used primarily for driving the steam engines of the Nigeria and Ghana railways as well as for producing electricity. The demand for coal has, however, fallen since the adoption of diesel engines on the railroads and the commissioning of the Kainji hydroelectric power station in Nigeria.

Lignite or brown coal, which is used for domestic and industrial heating as well as for generating power, occurs near Onitsha and Asaba (in Nigeria). Lignite has also been discovered near Freetown, Sierra Leone; in the Tahoua region of Niger Republic, and near Ouagadougou in Upper Volta.

Chapter 11—Power Resources and Industrial Growth

Although manufacturing is still not well developed, the relative importance of the industrial sector has increased considerably since about 1960, when most West African countries became independent. In Nigeria, for example, manufacturing represented the second fastest-growing sector in the early 1970s, that is after petroleum. Other countries, especially Ghana, Senegal and Ivory Coast, have also shown great interest and made much progress in manufacturing. This great desire to industrialize arises partly from a recognition of the fact that the most developed countries of the world are also the most industrialized. There are, however, many other reasons for the growing emphasis on manufacturing. These include:

i)   the desire to provide employment for a rapidly growing urban population;
ii)   the need to conserve foreign exchange by substituting locally manufactured goods for foreign goods;
iii) the need to raise the quality of local exports crops and mineral ores) by semi-processing primary products and exporting them in a form that will earn more money per unit weight;
iv)   the desire to modernize (and diversify) the economy since industrialization is generally seen as evidence of modernity.

A wide range of industrial products is now produced in West Africa. The state of industrial development in each country is discussed in the chapter dealing with that country. In this chapter we examine the growth of manufacturing in West Africa, the basis for industrial growth and the various types of industries.

THE GROWTH OF MANUFACTURING

The pre-colonial period

Traditional manufacturing industries, some of which have survived till today, played an important part in the economy of West Africa during the pre-colonial and colonial periods. At a time when contact with the outside world was very restricted, farm implements and weapons had to be manufactured locally. A large proportion of the non-farm population obtained a living from various forms of manufacturing. The most important traditional industries included the spinning and weaving of cotton and silk cloth, the dyeing of cloth and leather, the fabrication of agricultural implements and weapons from locally smelted pig-iron, the manufacture of salt from sea water and mangrove bark, bronze works and carving. Small iron-furnaces were still common all over the grassland areas of West Africa during the early years of the colonial period. The products of the local charcoal and iron industries provided the raw material for the celebrated brass and bronze figurines of Benin, Ife and Igbo-Uku (all in Nigeria). The importation of cheaper and better quality goods from Europe resulted in the decline of local manufacturing. Indeed, the complete decline of iron-smelting and salt-making, amongst other manufactures, provides a clear example of the negative influence of European civilization on African inventiveness and culture.

A few traditional industries survive and some have been revived. Small-scale traditional industries are therefore of more than historical interest, since they still provide employment (even if on a part-time basis) for a considerable number of people. In the old city of Kano, for example, traditional cottage industries like cloth-making, leather goods and the manufacture of perfumes continue side by side with large-scale factory production. These cottage industries are still carried out as family businesses in which workers are trained on the job.

The colonial period

The colonial economic policy was that each colony should be self-supporting and that the necessary funds for financing, administration and development should be raised from the sale of primary products (minerals and crops) to the imperial country, who in turn would supply manufactured goods to the colonies. The territories of French West Africa were forced to buy and sell in French markets and in Nigeria and Ghana, Japanese goods were prohibited because they were underselling British manufactures. Manufacturing of any sort was discouraged because it would compete with industries in France or Britain. Even the export in 1927 of groundnut oil from Senegal to France had to be restricted because French oil-millers complained of the competition.

A few industries were, however, developed during the colonial period. These consisted primarily of the processing of agricultural raw materials for export and the upgrading of mineral ores before export. Most of these industries were therefore located at or near the source of raw materials. Examples include the pioneer oil mills in the forest belt, the cotton gins in the savanna areas of Nigeria and Mali, the tin-smelting plants at Jos and the plywood mills at Sapele. In all cases there was a considerable loss in weight after processing, resulting in substantial savings in transport costs.

The Second World War provided a great stimulus to industrialization in West Africa since the supply of goods from Europe was irregular. A number of factories producing consumer goods such as beer, soft drinks, cotton cloth and cigarettes were built to supply the local markets. The rate of growth of these industries remained very slow after the war, while the amount of money spent on capital as well as consumer goods manufactured in Europe continued to increase every year. It was not until the first few years of independence that greater emphasis was given to manufacturing.

Post-independence period

The end of the colonial period and of colonial economic policy was followed by a rapid growth in manufacturing. In Nigeria for example, the share of manufacturing in the Gross Domestic Product rose from 0.6 per cent in 1950 to 5.6 per cent in 1963 and 8.4 per cent in 1967. The principle of import substitution pursued by the newly independent countries contributed very much to the rapid growth of industries. Essentially, import substitution was directed at conserving foreign exchange by manufacturing locally most of the comsumer goods formerly imported from abroad. The industries which were located mostly in the cities, also helped to reduce mounting urban unemployment caused by the drift of primary school and college graduates into the cities. Foreign investors were attracted by various incentives including tax relief, pioneer industry status and profit repatriation laws. High tariffs on foreign goods also created a guaranteed local market

for the products of local industries. In many countries, the result of this protection has been the inability of manufacturers to produce enough goods such as cement, beer, flour etc. for the expanding internal market. Some manufacturers have tended to take undue advantage of this protection by producing goods of relatively low quality, hence the tendency for people to pay higher prices for imported goods, some of which are smuggled into the country.

THE BASIS FOR WEST AFRICAN INDUSTRIALIZATION

The factors which have influenced the choice and location of industrial concerns in West Africa are considered in this section. Power is probably the most important of these factors, since manufacturing has always been concentrated in urban areas which are provided with electricity. We shall therefore consider first the potential and developed power resources of West Africa and then go on to consider other factors such as raw materials, transportation, labour markets and capital.

The power resources of West Africa

The main sources of industrial power in the world today are coal, hydro-electric power and petroleum (oil and natural gas). Coal is the oldest source of power for large-scale modern manufacturing industry but in West Africa coal occurs only in Nigeria, where mining started in 1915. The lack of coal in other countries and the great expense involved in harnessing water power has certainly contributed to the slow development of manufacturing between 1900 and 1960. The importance of power as a factor in industrial location in West Africa is obvious from the fact that all the industrial areas are in locations like the Jos Plateau, which generate power from local waterfalls, or towns which are served by the various national electric power lines. (Fig. 11.1, p. 91; plate 54).

Coal, the main source of industrial power in Europe and North America, is very scarce in West Africa, being restricted to parts of the Anambra and Kwara States of Nigeria. The estimated reserves of Nigerian coal are about 200 million tons, which are inadequate for sustaining industrial growth all over West Africa. It is also unfortunate that Nigerian coal has a low heating power and is non-coking, being of the soft-bituminous type. The cost of delivery of Enugu coal to such major consuming centres as Lagos, Accra, and Kano remains very high, hence the need for alternative sources of power. Before 1950, however, Nigerian coal as well as coal imported from Europe, was the

PLATE 54—Akosombo Dam, Ghana

main source of power for generating electricity for domestic and industrial use. Important thermo-electric stations of the pre-Independence period include the Ijora B.P. station (Lagos) and the Oji River power station, both in Nigeria, and the Abidjan thermo-electric plant in Ivory Coast. Thermo-electric power stations built during the colonial period were essentially market-oriented, being located in the cities or mining areas. Today the main sources of industrial power are hydro-electricity, diesel oil and natural gas.

Small-scale production of hydro-electric power started before 1920 in the Jos Plateau tinfields where there are three plants on the Kura River and one on the River Gyel. Outside Nigeria, many small hydro-electric plants have also been established to provide power to urban industrial centres and mining districts. These small-scale hydro-electric power stations include the Markala Dam (near Bamako) in Mali, the 18,000kW Grand Chutes power station on the Samou River (Guinea), the 7,500kW Mount Coffee station on the St Paul River in Liberia, and the

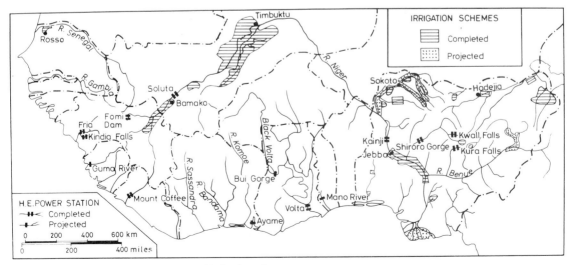

FIG. 11.1—Hydro-electric power stations and irrigation schemes

Ayame I and Ayame II plants on the Bia River in the Ivory Coast (Fig. 11.1). Two large-scale hydro-electric power stations have been completed as part of multi-purpose water development projects. These are the Volta River Dam at Akosombo (Ghana) and the Kainji dam on the Niger River near Bussa (Nigeria). The Volta power station has an initial capacity of 589,000kW and an eventual capacity of 883,000kW. The growing industrial complex of Accra-Tema depends on power supplied from this giant power station, which also sells electricity to Togo and Benin. The Kainji Dam power station, opened in 1969, has an initial installed capacity of 320,000kW which will eventually increase to 880,000kW, that is about the same ultimate capacity as at the Akosombo power station. The Kainji power station is, however, the first of three Niger Basin dams; the other two are to be built at Jebba on the Niger River and at the Shiroro Gorge on River Kaduna. Both power stations will have a joint capacity of 980,000kW but work on these is not likely to start till the middle 1980s when the demand for power is likely to exceed the total ultimate capacity of existing installations.

Diesel oil is used all over West Africa for generating power for small industrial establishments which are located outside the major industrial zones. Nigeria produces a lot of natural gas along with crude oil. Much of this gas is burnt off at present although some gas has been used to generate electricity at the 80,000kW Afam and the 60,000kW Ughelli power stations, both located at the source of natural gas in the Niger Delta.

Raw materials

West Africa is rich in agricultural and mineral raw materials both of which formed the basis of the early processing factories of the colonial period. About 75 per cent of the world's cocoa comes from West Africa but since large quantities of milk are also required in the manufacture of chocolate, West Africa produces only a small proportion of its chocolate demand. Several companies have, however, made use of local rubber to manufacture motor tyres and tubes. Local vegetable oils have also provided raw materials for many margarine, soap and detergent factories. The local tobacco and numerous textile factories also depend on tobacco leaves and raw cotton produced in West Africa.

The iron ore resources of all West Africa are vast (pp. 82–3) and can form the basis of several iron and steel manufacturing plants. However, no such plants have yet been established, although Nigeria hopes to establish one before 1978. Iron ore in West Africa is produced, therefore, for the export market. There are also vast deposits of bauxite for making aluminium but so far the only aluminium plant, which is located at Tema (Ghana), does not use local ore, but imported alumina, while Ghanaian bauxite is exported to Europe and North America.

A large number of the import-substitution industries in West Africa, however, depend very much on imported raw materials which cannot be obtained locally. Hops for making beer, steel rods for light engineering and construction industries, and chemicals for textile manufacture are amongst the raw materials that are imported from abroad.

Transportation

Goods' transportation by road, rail and water is vital both for assembling industrial raw materials and for distributing the final products to consumers. Fortunately, the transport situation in West Africa has been improving following the opening up and surfacing (with coal tar) of major roads since independence. The importance of transport as a factor in the location of industries, is obvious from the fact that the most important industrial towns are almost all located along railway lines. The desire to minimize transport cost, has also contributed to the location of industries making use of imported materials at the major ports of the various West African countries.

Labour

The increasing influx of primary and secondary school graduates into the towns ensures an abundant supply of unskilled and some categories of semi-skilled labour. Unskilled labour in West Africa is, however, characterized by extremely low productivity, and this has contributed to the high production costs in spite of low wages. The supply of skilled labour, including technicians, engineers and managers is still inadequate even in Nigeria, which has twelve universities and about ten institutes of technology. Many manufacturers have therefore had to employ expatriate skilled labour from Europe, America and Asia. Indeed, the French-speaking countries, notably Ivory Coast and Senegal, depend almost exclusively on skilled labour from France. The high cost of maintaining expatriate staff has been a major factor in the high cost of production of goods locally. Many industrial establishments therefore find it difficult to produce goods at prices competitive with imported goods, and have been able to survive only because of protective tariffs imposed by the governments.

Many of the large firms and government corporations operate in-service training programmes for local labour, and there is an increasing number of trade schools, especially in Nigeria. The salary structure, which favours arts and science graduates as compared with technicians, has tended to discourage young people from taking technical courses, which would supply the right type of manpower for large-scale industrialization.

Markets

The small size of national markets is one of the main reasons given for the slow rate of industrialization in the smaller countries. Existing customs barriers between the various countries have meant that manufactured goods in any West African country have had to depend mostly on the internal market of that country. The result is that many factories have had to operate below the optimum capacity, and therefore find it difficult to break even.

Large-scale industries have not received support from many foreign investors, who consider the market situation to be inadequate. It has been estimated, for example, that steel consumption for all West Africa in 1980 will be about two million tons per annum. Yet the economic size of a multi-product integrated steel works is an output of about three million tons per annum! In the case of an ammonia plant for nitrogen fertilizers, the minimum scale is estimated to be 50,000 tons per annum. At the present rate of fertilizer consumption, it is thought that West Africa will require about three of these plants. Since there are fourteen countries, and since most of them have small internal markets, the question that arises is the location of such an industry. Nigeria has the largest market in West Africa but other countries are also pursuing the road to industrialization. There is therefore a need for integrated planning of large-scale industries if West Africa is to become less dependent on the factories of Europe, Japan and North America. The case for such co-operation is discussed in Chapter 15.

Capital

Every country in West Africa still depends very much on foreign private capital for industrial growth. However, the situation is changing rapidly in Nigeria, where there are many indigenous manufacturing establishments financed from local private capital, as well as from public funds made available to industrial development corporations.

Almost all the factories established before independence were financed by foreign private trading companies, which had been doing business in West Africa since the early days of the colonial period.

Following the establishment of produce marketing boards in Nigeria and Ghana, commercial firms like the United Africa Company and John Holts diverted some of their capital from produce trade to manufacturing. This trend has been reinforced as a result of legislation restricting retail trade in consumer goods to nationals of Nigeria and Ghana. In the French-speaking countries almost all the capital invested in manufacturing is still provided by foreign multinational corporations.

The need for private domestic capital cannot be over-emphasized, particularly since manufacturing establishments run by public corporations tend to operate at a loss, while privately owned industries usually break even. Unfortunately, the vast majority of the people are poor and do not save enough to invest in manufacturing. The richer élite also have little or no savings since they use up much of their income in buying luxury goods and other expensive items.

TYPES OF INDUSTRIES

There are six main types of manufacturing in West Africa, namely: 1) processing of raw materials for export, 2) food and drink, 3) textiles and footwear, 4) the chemical and pharmaceutical industries, 5) building and construction materials, 6) metals and light engineering.

Processing of raw materials for export

Industries in this category include the extraction of palm oil and groundnut oil by peasants as well as in factories, the manufacture of rubber sheets and the manufacture of tin ingots for export. These are amongst the oldest and most widespread industries in West Africa. In Senegal, for example, about 40 per cent of the value of industrial production is accounted for by factories producing groundnut oil. Pioneer oil mills are found all over the palm belt of southern Nigeria, although well over 85 per cent of the palm oil produced still comes from peasant sources.

Generally, raw materials are processed before export so as to reduce the bulk of the product and thus save transport costs, as well as to make the export product less perishable. Examples include the production of sawn timber, plywood and veneers, the canning of fruits such as pineapple, the ginning of cotton and the manufacture of tin ingots. The factories are usually located at the source of the raw materials.

PLATE 55—Cotton mill in Ghana

Food and drink

Factories producing food and drink products are largely market-oriented, and are located almost exclusively in the capital cities of Dakar, Abidjan, Lagos, Accra, Conakry and the larger inland towns of Kano, Ibadan, Kumasi, Kaduna and Aba. Food industries include biscuit-making, the manufacture of bread, and corned beef, while the main types of drink produced include beer, stout and a large variety of mineral waters. Spirits, including gin, brandy and whisky, are now bottled in Lagos, Accra, Abidjan and Dakar. The spirits are all imported in barrels .except in Accra, where gin is manufactured locally. There are also large flour-milling factories, using imported grain, at the port-towns of Dakar, Lagos, Tema, Abidjan and Freetown. Chocolates and other cocoa products are also manufactured in the major port-towns. Coffee is processed and tinned in Abidjan, which also has one of the largest fruit canning factories in West Africa.

Textiles and footwear

Textile manufacture is one of the oldest and most widespread traditional industries in West Africa.

Cotton cloth made from locally grown cotton as well as silk cloth from local silk has featured prominently in West African trade for many centuries. Dyeing of cotton cloth using indigo dyes dates back to the founding of Kano City about AD 1080 and is still practised today in various parts of West Africa including Nigeria and Sierra Leone. Locally woven high-quality textiles such as the Kente cloth of Ghana, the famous Akwete cloth and the silk cloth of Iseyin and Okene are still in great demand. The production of these cloths is still carried out in cottages or on the verandas of the entrepreneurs' houses, in contrast to the large-scale factories which produce millions of square metres of cloth every year. In Nigeria, there are over a dozen textile mills located at Ikeja, Ilupeju, Kano, Kaduna, Aba, Onitsha, Ekiti and Asaba. Tema has the largest textile factory in Ghana, while the leading textile manufacturing centres in French-speaking West Africa are Dakar and Rufisque in Senegal, Bouake and Abidjan in the Ivory Coast and Segu in Mali.

There are many reasons why developing countries, including those of West Africa, tend to adopt the textile industry very readily. Amongst other things, the textile mill is relatively inexpensive as compared, for instance, with an iron and steel mill, which is so expensive that most developing countries cannot afford

94

the capital cost. Secondly, the textile factory is labour-intensive and is therefore well-adapted to providing employment to the increasing number of unemployed immigrants in the cities of West Africa. Finally, the large amount of foreign exchange expended in importing textiles is saved when the cloth is produced in local factories (see plates 55, 56).

Like cotton cloth, leather goods, including sandals and poufs, have been manufactured in West Africa for many centuries. Today, the shoe-making industry has moved from the cottage to the factory in places like Kano and Dakar. Large modern shoe factories also exist at Abidjan, Accra, Lagos and Port Harcourt. Leather for the shoes and rubber, including crepe rubber, for the soles, are all obtained in West Africa. Plastic shoes are also manufactured to meet the demand of those in the low income group who cannot afford to pay for the more expensive leather shoes. Raffia shoes on rubber soles are made at Ikot Ekpene

and have proved a great attraction to tourists from Europe and America.

The chemical and pharmaceutical industries

The chemical industry is one of the major import-substitution industries which uses imported raw materials. The main centres are therefore the port-towns of Lagos, Port Harcourt, Dakar, Abidjan and Accra-Tema. Its products include semi-finished ones such as dyes and industrial gases, which are used as inputs for other manufactures. The finished products include perfumes, paints, varnishes, insecticides, matches, pharmaceuticals and storage batteries. Although there are no plastics plants, a large variety of plastic goods such as household utensils, toys and combs, bowls and pipes are produced from imported polythene and polystyrene. Cheap and

PLATE 56—Printing cloth in Nigeria

colourful plastic shoes are also made from imported plastics materials. The lower income group, including the nomadic cattle Fulani, prefer plastic shoes to canvas or leather shoes, since plastic shoes are not only cheaper but can be readily dried after a rain-storm.

Petro-chemical industries have been planned for Nigeria, Senegal, Ivory Coast and Ghana. The main product of these plants will be nitrogenous fertilizers. At present much of the fertilizer used in West Africa is imported since the capacity of the fertilizer factory at Thies (Senegal), based on local phosphate deposits, is rather small.

Building and construction materials

Building and construction materials including cement, tiles, bricks, asbestos and corrugated iron roofing sheets, and metal frames for windows and doors are manufactured in most West African countries. Factories producing building and construction materials are usually located near the major urban centres, which provide the necessary market for the products. The only exceptions are factories manufacturing cement and bricks, which have to be located at or near to limestone and clay deposits, some of which are far from the main urban centres.

Cement factories are the most widespread. In 1976, for example, there were about six cement factories in Nigeria, located at Nkalagu (near Enugu), Ewekoro (near Abeokuta), Shagamu, Sokoto, Ukpilla in Mid-west State and Calabar. Yet the shortage of cement has continued to be a major factor limiting the execution of building projects; hence the continued importation of cement from abroad. Outside Nigeria, major cement works are located at Rufisque (Senegal), Takoradi, Bobo Dioulasso, Abidjan and Nauli in Brong Ahafo (Ghana). The major clinker-grinding plants which are market-oriented are located at Takoradi, Port Harcourt, Wellington (Sierra Leone), Tema, Abidjan, Cotonou and Lagos.

Four modern brick-and-tile factories exist in Mali at Bamako, Markala, Macina and Segou; there are also two in Guinea at Conakry and Kankan while Ivory Coast and Benin have four and two small factories respectively. There are also many other locations where bricks are produced by obsolete methods.

Metals and light engineering

In addition to steel doors, window frames and steel rods for house construction, there are many other factories manufacturing metal goods. Like textiles

PLATE 57—Building the Kainji Dam in Nigeria

and leather work, metal products were formerly produced in small units in the veranda of the workers' houses. Early products of this industry included metal drums and cans which served as containers, metal boxes and buckets. Since about 1955, many more metal products including large storage tanks, metal pipes, corrugated iron and aluminium sheets, truck bodies, nails and wire products have been manufactured in the major industrial areas of Accra, Dakar, Abidjan, Lagos and Port Harcourt.

Light engineering industries are located near the market and consist, amongst other things, of radio and car assembly plants. There are car assembly plants at Abidjan, Tema, Apapa, Cotonou, Lagos and Kaduna. Bicycle assembly plants are located in all the major ports as well as in Zaria. Radio and television assembly plants are more widespread, the larger plants being located in Abidjan, Tema, Bamako, Kano, Port Harcourt and Lagos.

LOCATION OF INDUSTRIES

In general the main factors which influence the location of industries in West Africa are accessibility to raw materials and markets. Power can now be transported readily and is not a localizing factor as it was during the early colonial period or in Europe during the industrial revolution. Labour, too, is very mobile since people are often willing to travel to work in industries which guarantee tham a good and regular income. The place of the port-towns as industrial centres deserves special attention. Most of these ports, particularly the capital cities, have a large market and a pool of skilled and semi-skilled labour to support large industrial establishments. In addition, port sites have proved very suitable for those import-substitution industries which depend on imported raw materials, since such raw materials can be transferred straight from the boat into the factory. Finally, government policy or political considerations have often featured in the decision to locate some industries in particular areas.

MARKET-ORIENTED INDUSTRIES

The most important market-oriented industries are: 1) food and drink, 2) tobacco products, 3) shoes, 4) textiles and clothing, 5) chemical products.
In the case of beer and soft drinks, the finished product is much heavier (bulkier) than the raw materials. It is therefore more economical to locate the factory at or near to the market for the finished

products. In addition, water, which is the principal content of beer and soft drinks, is often found in areas of population concentration which also provide adequate markets for these products. Industries like flour milling, which depend on imported grain, are located at the port-towns which are major break-of-bulk points, as well as major centres of population concentration (i.e. important market centres). The purchasing power of the average West African is very low, but the situation is better in the cities and industrial port-towns, where there is a concentration of wage-earners. Such centres therefore attract industrial establishments.

RAW-MATERIALS-ORIENTED INDUSTRIES

In order to reduce the bulk of products and thus save transport costs, processing meat, plywood and vegetable oil and up-grading mineral ores are usually carried out at the source of the raw materials. Important raw-materials-oriented industries in West Africa include the pioneer oil mills, groundnut oil mills, soap and margarine factories, rice mills and mineral concentration plants such as the iron ore beneficiation plants at Bomi Hills (Liberia) and Marampa (Sierra Leone) and the tin-smelting plants on the Jos Plateau.

Finally, government policy has often played a decisive role in the location of some industries. In many countries, the government has established industrial estates in selected towns so as to minimize the difficulties in acquiring land for factory sites. Often, as in Lagos and Port Harcourt, land has had to be reclaimed at great cost by government, which also provides basic facilities like piped water, tarred roads and electricity to industrial estates.

Some industries have been located in certain towns for political reasons, often in the capital city of a region which gives massive support at the polls to the government party. The need to provide employment opportunities in some areas has sometimes tended to over-ride other considerations. The textile mills at Asaba and Ado-Ekiti are neither market-oriented nor raw-materials-oriented, and can be considered to be among the many industries which have had to be built in a town from which the head of government originates. Another industry with a questionable location is the Calabar cement factory. The limestone for this factory is quarried at a point about 30km (20 miles) from Calabar while the bulk of the cement is transported by ferry to Oron to be marketed in the densely populated districts of Uyo, Eket, Abak and Ikot Ekpene.

PLATE 58 —Indigo dye pits at Kano, Nigeria. The rush cones are placed over the pits to prevent rain diluting dye.

The great concentration of modern industries in the port-towns has contributed to the extreme congestion of cities like Lagos, Accra-Tema, and Dakar, all of which attract a large number of job seekers. There is a great need to re-locate some industries so as to ease the housing, transport and water shortage problems of these centres. The palm kernel crushing mill at Lagos is one such factory. The traffic hold-ups, caused by lorries delivering palm kernels to the mill at Ikorodu Road, could have been prevented if the factory were located in a small town in the palm belt.

Chapter 12—Transportation

Before the beginning of the twentieth century, West Africa was more easily approached by way of the Sahara Desert, which has never been a complete barrier to communication between the Sudan and the Mediterranean. At this time, the Sudan had strong cultural and economic contacts with North Africa, and was relatively more developed than the forest belt. This was particularly true in respect of transportation. The Sudan had such beasts of burden as the horse, the camel, the donkey and even cattle, which are still used today for transportation. Contact and trade between towns and villages was better developed than in the forest belt where the main means of travelling was on foot. There was no form of wheel transport anywhere, and roads, which consisted of footpaths and tracks, were very poor and often interrupted by rivers which had no bridges. The only ferries at this time consisted of canoes which are still used in the more remote parts of West Africa.

Travelling was particularly difficult during the rainy season, when some tracks were completely submerged by water after a heavy rainstorm, and when the larger rivers with extensive floodplains overflowed their banks. Trade declined considerably during the rainy season, so much so that the trading populations of large commercial centres like Kano were reduced by more than half. Distances covered per day were necessarily short even in the Sudan which had animal transport, since the beasts had to rest and feed from time to time. For long journeys, travellers were faced with the problem of loading their beasts in the morning and unloading them at night to give them rest; and of course there was the problem of the scorching heat from the sun as well as the difficulty of obtaining water and grazing during the dry season.

With the establishment of colonial administrations at the beginning of this century, the centres of economic and political activity shifted to the coastal areas which became the main outlets for produce from the forest belt as well as from the Sudan. The development of modern transportation started at this time and consisted primarily of the construction of railways and roads to link the coast with those parts of the interior which produced crops or minerals required in the metropolitan markets of Europe. It is these transportation routes that were to lead to the development of agriculture and mining in parts of West Africa and today the most developed areas of this region are those areas which have a good network of roads (and in some cases are also served by railways). But vast areas did not benefit from these colonial transportation routes, which were restricted to those areas that were of economic interest to the colonial powers. Hence the fact that today there are still extensive parts of the countries which are not served by roads suitable for motorized transport.

With a few exceptions, transport developments in West African countries have followed similar patterns, in which the first phase was characterized by the dominance of river and inland waterway transport, and a multiplicity of small ports. The second phase was one of railway and road construction to link the coastal ports with hinterland market centres, while the third phase consisted of the building of feeder roads, running in an east-west direction. The final phase of connecting major centres with the nation's capital is still in progress in most countries (Fig. 12.1, p. 100).

RIVER TRANSPORT

Although the rivers of West Africa are not very suitable for navigation and have since been overshadowed by roads and railways, the creeks and rivers were the first means of penetration from the coast into the interior. In Nigeria, the Niger-Benue system and the Cross River provided important highways, just as the Senegal and Gambia rivers did in Senegal and Gambia respectively. Unfortunately, there are a number of physical handicaps which have restricted the use of rivers for transportation. One of such handicaps is the occurrence of rapids and falls, which restrict navigation to only a few stretches. Along the Niger, which is the most important river,

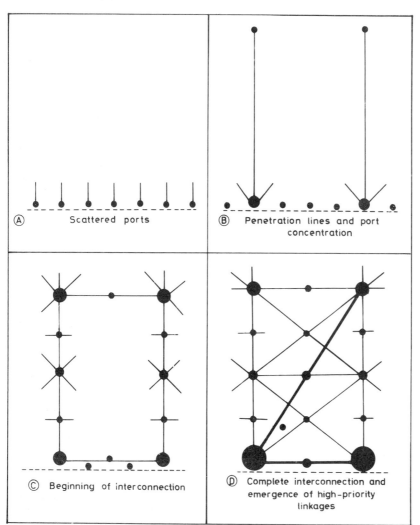

A — Scattered ports

B — Penetration lines and port concentration

C — Beginning of interconnection

D — Complete interconnection and emergence of high-priority linkages

FIG. 12.1—Taaffe model of road development in West Africa (The Taaffe model is a four-phase model of the sequence of transport network development in an underdeveloped country.)

PLATE 59—Navigating West Mahin Creek, Nigeria, by canoe

for example, navigation is only possible from Kouroussa to Bamako, Kulikoro to Ansongo, Niamey to Yelwa and Jebba to the sea. Only the Gambia and the Benue in Nigeria are not interrupted by waterfalls and rapids. But even these two rivers, as well as navigable sections of other rivers, suffer from extreme fluctuations in water level, which becomes very low during the dry season. The result is that navigation is limited to only a few months in the year.

Often, navigable sections of West African rivers flow through districts which produce very little for export or for internal exchange, largely because such areas are very sparsely populated. The result is that traffic on West African rivers is extremely small and, in some cases, the waterways can only be used by canoes and small boats, which are still important for local traffic. For long-distance traffic, the river has lost considerably to the road and railway.

The Gambia River is navigable for most of its length, and enters the sea through one of the few good natural harbours in West Africa. There are 58 river stations within Gambia Republic, and the river serves as a major transport route in that country. Unfortunately, much of its drainage basin lies in Senegal, which prefers to evacuate the produce of the upper Gambia Basin by road to Senegalese ports. The Gambia River is therefore deprived of much of the traffic of its natural hinterland. The people of Cameroon, however, make use of the Benue River which enters the sea in Nigeria. The Benue River-port of Garua in Cameroon handles a considerable traffic passing through Nigeria.

Along the coast, the lagoons and creeks still provide sheltered channels for coastal traffic, which was very important in the past. These creeks are still widely used for local traffic including the movements of staple foods, firewood and passengers from the nearby coastal areas to the cities of Lagos, Freetown and Porto Novo. Before the development of the Benin ports, there was a sizeable transhipment traffic in timber and palm oil along the creeks linking Lagos to the western delta ports of Sapele, Warri, Koko and Burutu. The creeks also provide good shelter for smugglers. The rapid silting-up of the shallow channels of these creeks and lagoons has made them unusable by large coastal vessels. (See plate 59.)

Two important man-made lakes, Lake Volta in Ghana and Lake Kainji in Nigeria, now permit low-cost water transport between settlements along the shores of these lakes. By regulating the water volume below Kainji, the dam at Kainji has also helped to improve the navigability of the Lower Niger below Bussa, while the canals and locks at Kainji allow cargo boats to get past the dam, to and from the riverine port of Yelwa.

RAILWAYS

In most countries of West Africa, the railway came before the road and in the early days, that is, before the First World War, railways were built to aid general economic development and to help establish effective political control. Construction was delayed by difficult terrain, particularly along the coast and by shortage of engineers. In the French-speaking territories, which were administered as a federation by France, there was an overall plan to link all the territories to the sea. The plan consisted of constructing four main-line railways to tap various navigable reaches of the Niger, which enters the sea in Nigeria even though most of its course is in French-speaking West Africa. The four main-line routes were 1) the Dakar-Niger, 2) the Conakry-Niger, 3) the Abidjan-Niger, and 4) the Benin-Niger railways. Not all the lines reached their hinterland termini (see Fig. 12.2).

The British colonial administrations of Sierra Leone, Ghana and Nigeria also aimed at linking the productive hinterland with the Atlantic ports. In Sierra Leone the railway was built to tap the iron ore and diamond mines and in Ghana the railway was restricted to the rich cocoa belt and highly mineralized districts of the south. The extension of the railway in Nigeria to the far north was prompted by the existence of rich groundnut and cotton fields in the Kano and Katsina Emirates and the discovery and mining of tin in the Jos Plateau.

West African railways, which cover a total distance of about 8,160km (5,100 miles), consist of rather narrow single tracks which are capable of carrying only light loads and at very slow speeds. There was neither money nor adequately skilled manpower to build a more modern railroad and, in any case, the volume of available traffic was not sufficient to justify greater investments. But some of the railways proved very successful in stimulating economic growth and regional specialization. Amongst such lines were the Dakar-Niger and St Louis-Dakar railroads in Senegal, both of which stimulated groundnut production as farmers moved to settle along the railways in areas which were formerly uninhabited wastelands. In Nigeria, the extension of the railroad to Kano in 1912 resulted in a phenomenal increase in groundnut exports from 2,000 tons in 1911 to 19,290 tons in 1913.

The main line railways include:

1) The 1,280km (800 mile) Dakar-Niger line from Dakar to Bamako, via Kayes, which stimulated groundnut production in Senegal and resulted in the westward movement of population to the groundnut belt.

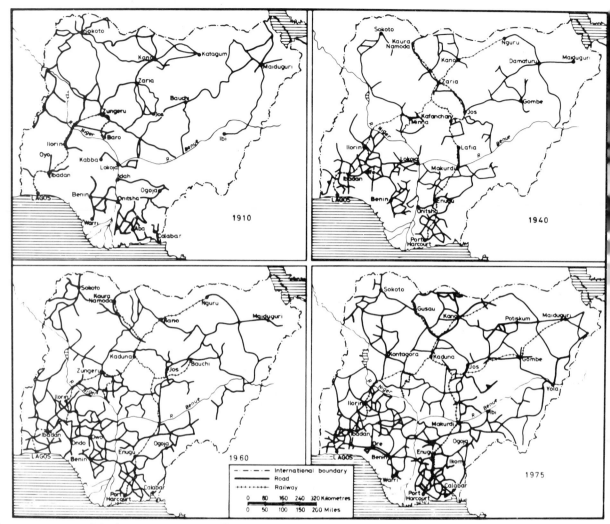

FIG. 12.2 — Road development in Nigeria (Taaffe model)

2) The 660km (410 mile) Conakry-Niger line from Conakry to Kankan. This line which was started in 1900 passes through very hilly country and was built at great cost of lives, materials and money. Steep gradients and sharp curves are common.

3) The 350km (227 mile) Freetown to Pendembu line with a branch line to the Marampa iron mines. The Sierra Leone government decided in 1972 to close down the main line to Pendembu which had been operating at a deficit for many years.

4) The 1,140km (710 mile) Abidjan-Niger line from Abidjan in Ivory Coast to Ouagadougou in Upper Volta. This line links Abidjan to the densely settled and labour-surplus Mossi country which exports a large amount of agricultural labour to the Ivory Coast.

5) The railways of southern Ghana which serve the gold mines of Obuasi and Prestea, the diamond mines of Oda and Kade and the bauxite mines of Awaso as well as the rich timber forests and cocoa belt of south-western Ghana. Although the Ghana railways serve the southern third of the country they handle more tonnage than all the lines in the French-speaking countries of West Africa.

6) The 3,200km (2,000 mile) Nigeria railway which consists of a western main line from Lagos to Kano and an eastern main line from Port Harcourt to Maiduguri. The 2′ 6″ (75cm) gauge Bauchi light railway, built 1912—14 was closed down in 1957 while the new 645km (400 mile) line from Kuru, near Jos, to Maiduguri was opened in 1964.

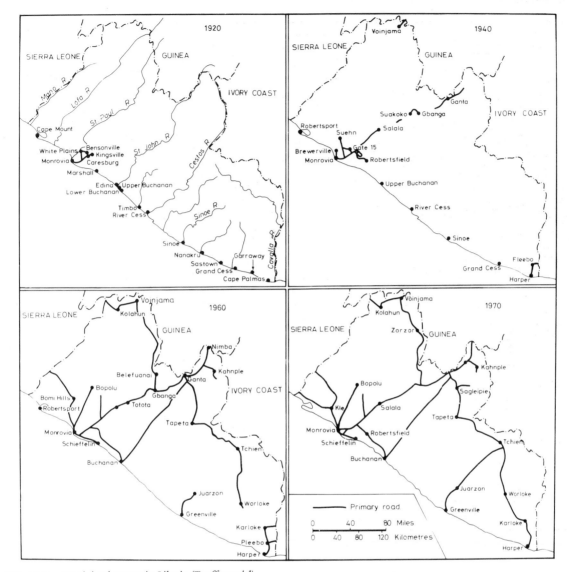

FIG. 12.3—Road development in Liberia (Taaffe model)

ROAD TRANSPORT

The development of road transport started after the main rail lines had been completed and it was not until after the Second World War that serious road development programmes were undertaken. The decade beginning from 1960 when most West African countries obtained independence from colonial rule was a period of rapid road development featuring the building of new earth roads and the tarring of some of the major trunk roads (for example, see Figs. 12.2 and 12.3 above).

In the period before 1945, there was a deliberate effort to ensure that roads served as feeder lines and not as competitors to the railways. In French West Africa for example, the road system was developed as a prolongation of each rail line or to connect various sections of the rail network. In Nigeria and Ghana, the road distance between towns was generally longer than the distance by rail and while the railway ran from south to north, the roads followed an east-west direction. This subordination of roads to rail transport has since disappeared in Nigeria where the road has emerged as the most important means of transporting cargo and passengers. Until 1960 long-distance traffic was controlled by the railways, but since 1961 long-distance road haulage has increased,

103

PLATE 60—*Working on the Adomi Bridge, Ghana*

resulting in greater losses for the slower and less flexible railway.

Most of the roads are surfaced with laterite and many of them become impassable after a heavy rainstorm. Tarred roads are sometimes not well maintained and may degenerate to a state which is worse than laterite roads. The poor surface of roads and the characteristic narrow bridges have contributed considerably to the high accident rate on these roads.

Road transport is largely organized on a small scale by individuals or a group of blood relations. Returns on investments are quick although the risks are high in view of the high accident rate. As a rule, passenger services run by these small-scale operators are generally unsatisfactory and never keep to any scheduled departure or arrival times. A few companies, including Midwest Lines (Nigeria) Ltd, The Oriental Lines (Nigeria) Ltd and Ekene Dili Chukwu Ltd (formerly Greyhound (Nigeria) Ltd) now provide an efficient and reliable service to some of the major cities of Nigeria. (Plates 60, 62, 63, 64).

PORTS AND SHIPPING

West Africa has a rather straight coastline with very few shallow inlets and even fewer natural or hospitable harbours. The lagoons which occur along many parts of the coastline are often completely shut off from the high seas by sand bars and where inlets occur as at Lagos and Porto Novo, rapid silting has necessitated the building of expensive breakwaters to keep the inlets open. The inlets of riverine ports in the Niger Delta have also suffered from rapid silting, resulting in the death of ports like Forcados and Brass or in the construction of expensive moles, as at Escravos, to keep the inlet open to shipping. Indeed, the late penetration of West Africa from the coast has been largely attributed to the character of the coastline, and for many decades, European traders anchored their vessels in the seas, and made use of surf boats to unload and load cargo.

Physical handicaps notwithstanding, many ports (mostly artificial) have been built, often at great cost, since the beginning of this century; and today, all the coastal states have at least one sea port. The great increase of foreign trade since 1960 has resulted in extreme congestion in ports like Lagos, Dakar and Abidjan; hence the construction or projected construction of a few more modern ports (plate 61).

One of the largest sea ports in West Africa is Dakar in Senegal which can admit ships drawing up to 10m (33ft) at any tide. Other important ports include Freetown, Abidjan, Tema (Ghana), Cotonou, Conakry, Lagos, Sapele and Port Harcourt. The Gambian port of Banjul (Bathurst) is served by a good natural waterway but has remained largely undeveloped despite its 300-year history of shipping. The small size of cargo handled at Banjul, whose natural hinterland lies in another country, Senegal, and the meagre resources of the Gambian government have prevented the development of this port. Sierra Leone's major port of Freetown has the best natural harbour, but like Banjul, it has not been highly developed due to lack of capital and the small size of its trade. On the other hand, large sums of money have been spent on building the modern artificial ports of Abidjan, Tema, Lagos and Port Harcourt, which serve much more extensive and richer hinterlands.

Most West African ports are linked up with their hinterlands by roads or railway or both, and with the possible exception of Banjul, ports whose access to their hinterland is restricted to river transport have suffered considerable decline as in the case of Burutu, Abonnema and Bonny or have been completely abandoned as in the case of Brass, Forcados and Buguma. For the larger ports, the demands of modern shipping have necessitated the installation of modern equipment for handling cargo and in almost every case, the ports have become major centres of industrial activity and population concentration.

Most of the ships using West African ports belong to foreign shipping lines, largely of British, French, American and Japanese origin. Indeed, until 1960 when most West African countries became independent, only Liberia had a sizeable merchant fleet, although even that consisted of foreign-owned vessels flying the Liberian flag. The number of indigenous shipping companies, both government- and privately-owned has increased considerably since 1965, the major ones being the Nigerian National Shipping Line and the Black-Star Line of Ghana.

AIR TRANSPORT

In view of the poor state of land transportation in West Africa, the importance of air transport for mail,

PLATE 61 —View of Lagos harbour from the Marina

PLATE 62 — *Mammy wagons on the road near Ibadan, Nigeria*

PLATE 63 — *Crossing a locally made bridge at Afikpo, Nigeria*

passenger and high-value cargo cannot be over emphasized. In Nigeria, for example, a rail journey from Lagos to Port Harcourt takes three days as compared with twelve hours by road and less than two hours by air. It is to save time, which is money to the businessman, and to avoid the high incidence of ghastly motor accidents on the country's poor roads that an increasing number of people now travel by air, in spite of the high fares charged by the country's only airline—Nigeria Airways. Unfortunately the flight schedules are not always reliable owing to the small number of available aircraft.

With the exception of the smaller countries like Gambia and Benin which can hardly balance their budget, each country operates a national airline which has a monopoly over internal flights. In practice, however, it is mainly Ghana and Nigeria that can afford to purchase outright a few aircraft while most of the French-speaking countries hire the craft that constitute the 'national' fleet. Most of these government-owned airlines operate at a loss and have virtually become service establishments rather than economic ventures. In addition to government-owned aircraft, the bigger commercial firms, such as petroleum exploration and production companies, use private planes or charter flights for their businesses.

The number of airports, almost all of which are owned and maintained by government corporations, has increased considerably since 1950. Most of the larger urban centres and all Nigerian state capitals have an airport each, but international airports are mostly restricted to the national capital of each country except that Nigeria has six international airports, the two commonly used ones being Lagos and Kano. There is also a large number of airstrips useable by light aircraft in an emergency.

INTERNATIONAL HIGHWAYS

If the River Niger were navigable throughout its length, it would have provided a major natural highway linking the countries through which it flows (Guinea, Mali, Niger and Nigeria). Unfortunately, this great river is interrupted at many places by rapids and waterfalls which constitute impediments to navigation. The failure of French-speaking Senegal to utilize the River Gambia waterway, which enters

the sea in another country, suggests, however, that the Niger would not have been fully exploited during the colonial period, even if its course were not interrupted by rapids and falls. This observation leads on to the fact that there are few man-made West African highways (roads and railways) which cross international boundaries.

The situation in East Africa in which the former British colonial territories of Kenya, Uganda and Tanganyika were linked together by road and Kenya and Uganda by rail suggests that a similar development would have occurred in West Africa if Nigeria, Ghana, Sierra Leone and Gambia shared a common border. Since these countries are separated by French-speaking countries, each tended to develop as if it existed in space, with the result that there were no transportation links with neighbouring countries. French-speaking West Africa, which covers a continuous area of land, benefited by the development of cross-frontier roads, particularly in the days of the Federation of French West Africa. There were, however, no railway links between the territories except for that linking the Ivory Coast to Upper Volta, which was formerly administered as a part of Ivory Coast. The Dakar-Koulikoro railway which links Senegal with Mali was also built when both countries were colonial territories of France.

In 1970, that is, ten years after independence, cross-

PLATE 64—Transporting hardwood logs on the Kumasi-Takoradi road, Ghana

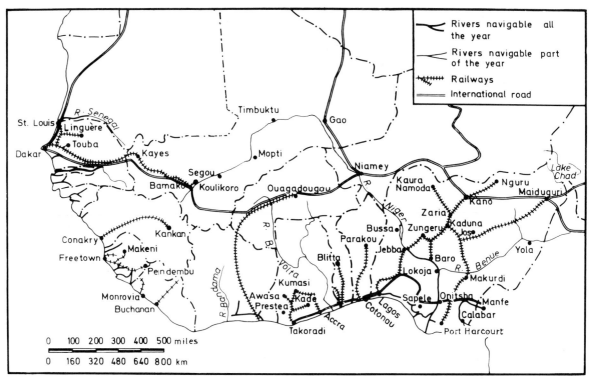

FIG. 12.4—Roads and railways of West Africa

frontier transportation remained poorly developed (Fig. 12.4, p. 106). There is, however, daily air traffic between most countries, but since only a few people can afford the air fares, people crossing the frontiers are obliged to do so through dirt roads or by sea. This is an unhealthy situation in so far as inter-state trade is concerned. Yet greater trade contact between the countries of West Africa is necessary for the successful establishment of a West African economic community and the transformation of the present colonial-type economy which is still largely based on exports of primary products.

Direct routes must replace the present circuitous routes which seek to bypass the territory of neighbouring countries, particularly those which are not in the same language or monetary zone. The Fort Derik to Nouadhibou railway in Mauritania is an example of a circuitous route which could have been avoided if the Mauritanian government had arranged with the government of Rio de Oro to follow a shorter and direct route. It is an example of the economic cost of the political fragmentation of West Africa. Circuitous routes also abound in French-speaking countries which seek to use ports in other French-speaking countries, thereby failing to develop or use more direct routes leading to ports in English-speaking countries. Today the eastern parts of Guinea Republic still evacuate their products through Conakry, instead of through the nearer ports of Freetown and Monrovia, which are located in different monetary zones.

SECTION D: REGIONAL CONTRASTS

Chapter 13—North and South in West Africa

Some of the more obvious contrasts between north and south in West Africa have been indicated in the preceding chapters of this book. In this chapter we shall attempt to explain the basis of these contrasts, as well as the similarities. The cultural and trade contacts which existed between the north and south in the past are discussed along with the changes which have taken place since the beginning of this century.

Amongst other things, we have observed (Chapters 2 and 3) that the climate and vegetation of the southern or coastal belt of West Africa differ considerably from those of the northern or interior parts of the region. These environmental differences arise from the fact that the south is nearer the sea and therefore comes under the full influence of the south-west rain-bearing winds, while the north lies closer to the Sahara Desert and therefore comes under the influence of the dry and dusty north-east winds for most of the year. Several other differences also exist between north and south, and some of these differences, including farming practices and field crops are directly influenced by climatic conditions. Differences in pre-colonial history, as well as in the predominant religions of the far north and the south, are also largely explained by the location of these areas relative to the sea and the Sahara Desert. Even the clothes worn by the people, their house types and the building materials that they use differ between north and south; but since the end of the Second World War, some of the cultural contrasts have become less marked, largely because of improved transportation and the expansion of education, both of which have helped to facilitate inter-regional trade and social contacts.

PATTERNS OF AGRICULTURAL PRODUCTION

One of the basic differences between north and south is the kind of crops grown. Root crops such as yams, cassava and cocoyams form the staple food of the south, except that rice is the dominant staple food in

the area west of the Bandama River (Ivory Coast), while grains such as guinea corn (or sorghum), millet and acha (hungry rice) are the staple food crops of the drier north. In pre-colonial times, an indigenous variety of rice was cultivated in riverine floodplains of the inland Niger Delta (Mali) and the Sokoto River Valley (Nigeria) but today this has largely been replaced by imported varieties of paddy rice which is cultivated along the Sudanese riverine floodplains, along the mangrove swamps of the coastlands west of the Bandama River and in the rain-fed swamps of Abakaliki and Afikpo areas of Nigeria. Cassava, which is a rather hardy crop, is grown as far north as Sokoto, while groundnut which does best in the drier sandy soils of Senegal and the far north of Nigeria is also grown on a small scale in parts of the coastal areas, including the Niger Delta.

Turning to export crops, we find that the rainy south produces mainly tree crops like cocoa, rubber and oil palm while the drier north, with a short rainy season (growing period) produces cotton and groundnuts (peanuts). Tree crops are perennial crops as distinct from the export crops from the north which are annual crops well suited to the shorter growing season of the north. The kolanut which has been an important item of internal trade in West Africa for many centuries is a tree crop produced in the south, although the major consuming centres are in the north.

Farming practices and field sizes also differ. Largely because of the open nature of the grassland landscape, the preparation of farmland in the north is easier than in the forested south, where the farmer expends much time and labour cutting the bush before firing it. This is one reason why northern farmers cultivate larger fields than their southern counterparts. Seed grains are also cheaper than seed yams for example, and northern farmers with a small capital outlay can afford to plant much larger areas as compared with southern farmers.* Thus while farm sizes in the south rarely exceed 1 hectare ($2\frac{1}{2}$

---

*In Abakaliki district, the cost of seed yam for a 0.4 hectare (i acre) farm in 1960 was put at ₦60.00 as compared with ₦1.50 for seed rice.

PLATE 65—Cattle on a dairy farm in Plateau province, Nigeria

acres) many farmers in the north cultivate 2 hectares (5 acres) or more. It is also striking that northern farmers plant their crops on ridges while those in the south plant on mounds. The transitional character of the Middle Belt is obvious from the fact that the farmers cultivate both root crops (on mounds) and grains (on ridges). Ox-drawn ploughs are used along with the hoe in the north, but not in the south where the universal hoe and matchet are still the main farm implements. The use of modern agricultural machinery is restricted to government demonstration farms and the new farm settlement schemes, although a number of tractor hire services have been established in many areas.

Cattle rearing is almost restricted to the far north because the presence of the tsetse fly which carries a deadly cattle disease called trypanosomiasis prevents the keeping of cattle in the south and Middle Belt, except on the fly-free highlands of the Futa Jallon, the Jos Plateau, the Biu Plateau and the Adamawa Highlands. A resistant breed of dwarf cattle is, however, reared in parts of the forest belt, but the supply of fresh milk which is an important item of food is largely restricted to the far north. Large numbers of cattle brought down from the north on hoof or by lorry and railway are, however, commonly seen grazing in the south while waiting to be sold for slaughter (plate 65).

It is important to realize that the Cattle Fulanis and the Tuaregs who own and keep most of the cattle in

West Africa are nomads. They do not normally farm the land, just as the Hausa, Wolof or Bambara farmers do not keep cattle; although some of these settled cultivators own a few cattle which they place under the care of nomadic Cattle Fulani and Tuareg herdsmen. Mixed farming as it is known in Europe or North America is therefore not practised in West Africa, although a number of government schemes have been started with the view to settling the nomadic cattle rearers and encouraging them to practise mixed farming. Currently, there exists in many areas an arrangement whereby nomadic cattle rearers graze their herds on fallow bush in return for some payment in kind, in the form of millet or guinea corn. Cattle dung produced while the herds are grazing is often the only manure applied on such farmlands. But on heavily deforested areas such as the Jos Plateau, where there is an acute shortage of cooking fuel, the cattle dung thus accumulated is dried and used as fuel.

The nomadic life led by the Cattle Fulani and the Tuareg is caused by the fact that during the dry season, water and grazing for animals is hard to find in the far north. These cattle rearers therefore migrate south towards the Niger and Benue valleys or in the direction of the Sokoto River or Lake Chad where both water and grazing are available at this time of the year. Fulani cattlemen also migrate downhill from the Futa Jallon, the Jos Plateau and the Adamawa

Highlands during the dry season, their movements being directed towards the riverine floodplains. During the rainy season, when the riverine areas become heavily infested with tsetse flies, the cattle rearers return to graze their cattle near their homes in the far north or on the fly-free uplands named above.

EARLY CULTURAL CONTACTS AND THE RELIGIOUS FACTOR

Some of the fundamental differences between north and south arise from the fact that during the pre-colonial period, the north had greater trade and cultural contacts with the Mediterranean world than with the south. It is true that there was a sizeable trade in kola, natron, gold and iron tools between north and south, but the main arena of trade for the northern peoples was the shores of the Mediterranean sea. Timbuktu, Kano (formerly Katsina) and Kukawa were the termini of the three trans-Saharan caravan routes linking the western Sudan to the coast of North Africa. These cities served as distributing points for salt from the Sahara Desert and manufactured goods from Europe and the Middle East, as well as collecting points for cotton-cloth, slaves, animal skins and leatherwork from the western Sudan. At this period some of the coastal people traded directly with European merchantmen anchored off the coast, exchanging slaves, ivory and, later, palm oil for guns, alcoholic drinks and various types of manufactured goods.

These early trade contacts were followed by the introduction and eventual adoption of two foreign religions, Islam and Christianity, both of which have had far-reaching effects on the culture, political systems and educational advancement of the people. Islam, the predominant religion of the far north was introduced from the Arab world through the influence of trans-Saharan traders to cities like Goa and Timbuktu, and later spread eastwards through conquest to the far eastern parts of the northern states of Nigeria. By the middle of the nineteenth century, Islam had become the state religion of those areas of the north which had come under the Fulani and Bornu empires. Christianity, on the other hand, was introduced by European missionaries to the coastal areas of the south and spread gradually inland after the formal establishment of colonial rule in various parts of West Africa. Before the beginning of the Second World War the sphere of effective Christian influence was restricted to the south just as that of Muslim missionaries was restricted to the north,

except that the Muslims were penetrating southwards into Yorubaland. The Middle Belt remained essentially a zone of traditional religions in which Islam and Christianity competed for converts.

The importance of the missionaries to the study of modern West Africa lies largely in their role in the spread of western education and technology. During the colonial period, almost all the schools in West Africa were established and run by Christian missions, who received financial aid in the form of grants from the colonial administrations. Since the Muslim rulers of the north resented and sometimes prevented the intrusion of Christian missions, most of the schools established as of 1960 were located in the south. In consequence, most West Africans who are able to read and write English or French come from the south. In Nigeria, the educational gap between north and south was so great that up till 1966 government departments (state and federal) as well as foreign private businesses in the former Northern Nigeria were staffed predominantly by Nigerians from the south. Unfortunately many southerners interpreted this situation to mean that they were intellectually superior to the northerners. Naturally the northern peoples, who have a rich cultural heritage and a much longer period of formal education in Arabic and of recorded history, resented this attitude and became very apprehensive of a situation in which the civil service and almost every sector of the economy was dominated by Nigerians from the south. It happened that the vast north formed one political unit while the south consisted of three states. The situation whereby, given the pattern of political support and the level of political immaturity of local politicians, the north was in a position to dominate political power for many years, was also strongly resented by Nigerians from the south. Many of the political misunderstandings between north and south, culminating in the massacre of eastern Nigerians in the north in 1966 and in the Nigerian civil war (1967–70) can be traced back to these fears. Hence the great need to bridge the educational gap between north and south, now that the country has been broken up into smaller states.

TRANSPORTATION AND TRADITIONAL POLITICAL SYSTEMS

Before the colonial period when roads and railways were built, there was greater contact between the villages and ethnic groups in the north than was the case in the south. Two factors were responsible for this, namely: 1) the use of animal transport (camels, horses, oxen, donkeys) for transporting people and goods as compared with trekking and head porterage in the south, and 2) the open character of the grassland landscape, which was easier to cross than the forest in the south. The greater ease of movement in the north was an important factor which made it possible for rulers to police vast territories which formed parts of their empires. West Africa's ancient empires, including Old Oyo, were therefore restricted to grassland areas, with the exception of the forest kingdoms of Benin and Ashanti. The most prominent of these grassland states included Mali, Songhai, Bornu, the Hausa states, Mossi and more recently the Fulani empires of Macina and Sokoto-Gwandu—see Fig. (iii). The Fulani empire in Nigeria was one of the most extensive of the Sudanese states but in spite of various attempts, the Fulani soldiers, who operated largely on horseback, were unable to penetrate and police the forested south.

In the south where transportation was either on foot or by dug-out canoes, there were no large political units except in Benin and Ashanti. Even the large ethnic groups such as the Ibos, Ibibios, Ewes and Ijaws could not exploit the fact of a common language to form large political units. Rather, Ibo and Ibibio political organization remained essentially fragmentary with the village group constituting the largest independent political entity.

Since the end of the First World War, the transportation situation has changed completely following the construction of roads and railways, which are concentrated in the south, where the sea ports are also located. Settlements in the south have become more accessible, particularly since the large-scale expansion of tree-crop farming, which is restricted to the south. Generally the south is much richer and better developed, and today the outlook of the north has largely been reversed since the primary products are exported through sea ports located in the south, through which imported goods also get to the north.

Important developments have also taken place in the north. Kano is, for example, a growing industrial and commercial centre. Export crop production has expanded while trade and cultural contacts between north and south have increased, thanks to improved means of transportation and free movement of population, at least within each country. Northern peoples migrate in large numbers to work in the tree-crop farms and cities of the south, while many southern traders and technicians settle to work in northern cities. The food demands of these migrants have contributed to the increasing flow of foodstuffs between north and south. The kola nut trade has increased, and so has the cattle trade between north and south.

Yet the visitor or traveller through West Africa will not fail to notice the marked differences that still exist between north and south. Differences due to the climate and culture appear to be quite obvious, but not so those associated with the widening gap in education, except as between rural and urban areas. There is a great need to narrow this gap by making primary education compulsory in the north so as to ensure a more balanced economic growth between north and south.

Chapter 14—English-speaking and French-speaking West Africa: Some Contrasts

The regional contrasts between north and south (or between the interior and the coastal belt) considered in the last chapter, have been caused largely by geographical factors of location and climate. The contrasts considered in this chapter, on the other hand, have been caused largely by the types of colonial policies adopted by France and Britain, the two dominant colonial powers which ruled West Africa up till independence in 1960. The effects of their divergent policies on the organization and growth of the economy as well as on the culture of the people of the different countries are discussed at length, because the cultural and economic barriers created by these colonial powers have so far proved more difficult to overcome than the physical barriers of relief and climate. Thus while the Yorubas of south-western Nigeria trade freely with the Hausas of the far north of Nigeria, there is a considerable restriction on trade between the Yorubas of Nigeria and the Yorubas of neighbouring Benin. It is these man-made barriers of the colonial period that must be removed before some form of economic and political union can be achieved.

With the exception of Liberia, the English-speaking countries were formerly colonial territories of Britain, while all the French-speaking countries were formerly under France. Only Guinea Bissau and the Equatorial Guinea island of Fernando Po, whose official languages are Portuguese and Spanish respectively, are neither French-speaking nor English-speaking. Since the inhabitants of these two territories constitute less than one per cent of the population of West Africa. West Africa consists essentially of English- and French-speaking countries.

AREA, TERRITORIAL CONTIGUITY, AND SIZE OF POPULATION

The first striking fact about the two West Africas is the vast area 4,744,301 sq. km (1,831,300 sq. miles) and contiguity of French-speaking West Africa as compared with English-speaking West Africa, which is not only much smaller in area (1,295,337 sq.km or 500,000 sq. miles), but consists of enclaves which penetrate inland from the coast. Every English-speaking country is separated from the other by one or more French-speaking countries. The physical distance separating the English-speaking countries of Gambia, Sierra Leone, Ghana and Nigeria has been partly responsible for the non-existence of some form of economic union similar to that existing between the contiguous English-speaking East African countries of Uganda, Kenya and Tanzania. Rather, since independence from Britain, the former British-ruled territories have tended to become more independent of one another following the voluntary withdrawal of each country from such colonial-period joint services as the West African Currency Board, the West African Airways Corporation and the West African Institute for Oil Palm Research. The French-speaking countries, with their advantage of contiguity have fared only a little better. Most of them participate in a joint air service and in most countries, the CFA franc is still the official currency. Each country, however, tends to deal directly with France on most matters and there is in consequence not much economic and cultural association.

It is also striking that although English-speaking West Africa covers an area of just about one-quarter that of French-speaking West Africa, it supports as much as three-quarters of the total population of West Africa. The population of Nigeria in 1963 was 56 million or twice as much as that of the whole of French-speaking West Africa. Vast areas of the French-speaking countries are therefore very sparsely populated and with the exception of the Mossi territory of Upper Volta and parts of Guinea, the population problem of French-speaking West Africa is one of inadequate manpower to develop its agricultural, timber and mineral resources.

LEGACIES OF THE COLONIAL PERIOD

Both in theory and practice, there have been marked differences in the colonial techniques of France and Britain, and in this section we review the impact of these differences on the character and pace of development of both the material and human resources of the two West Africas.

Arthur Creech-Jones, a former Secretary of State for the colonies gives the basic outline of British colonial policy in West Africa as 'to guide the colonial territories to responsible self-government within the Commonwealth in conditions that ensure to the people both a fair standard of living and freedom from oppression from any quarter'. Thus, right from the beginning Britain administered each territory as a distinct political entity and tried to make each colony pay its way and balance its annual budgets. Local people were encouraged to develop export agriculture, while the plantation system was completely rejected on the grounds that it would deprive the people of their land. In Nigeria the plantation system was also rejected on the grounds that it could induce a large-scale movement of labour from one area to another, and that such migrations would disrupt local societies.

France, on the other hand, considered her territories in West Africa to be a part of Greater France. All land was state land, except that which an individual African registered with the French authorities and, unlike the English-speaking countries, large concessions were given to foreign investors to establish tree-crop plantations. Each territory so depended economically on France that almost twenty years after independence most French-speaking countries still depend on 'aid' from Paris in order to balance their annual budgets. As provinces of overseas France, Senegal, Ivory Coast and other territories elected deputies to sit at the French Legislature in Paris. Each British territory, on the other hand, had its own legislature and its own governor, but no direct representation in the British Parliament.

British rule in West Africa was carried out largely through the agency of local chiefs, while the French assumed direct control of local affairs, making use of administrative officers from France. The British policy of indirect rule and the French policy of direct rule, as well as the colonial land policies of both metropolitan powers, have resulted in marked differences in the development of the economy and manpower resources of the two West Africas. Thus, although African peasant farmers produce the bulk of the export crops from both groups of countries, the

African contribution to export agriculture in French-speaking West Africa is much less than in the English-speaking countries, where almost all the export crops come from small farms cultivated by African farmers. In the Ivory Coast, Togo and formerly in Guinea, much of the coffee, cocoa and banana exports originate from European-owned plantations worked by African labour. A few plantations also exist in English-speaking countries, but most of these date from the period when African politicians had taken over control of agricultural policy, since the British colonial government was opposed to the principle of alienating land to non-African planters.

The British policy of encouraging Africans to produce for the export market was very successful in Ghana and Nigeria, where many farmers responded very well to price incentives. In the Ivory Coast, on the other hand, the situation was quite different, at least in respect of the production of cocoa, which was introduced from Ghana in 1912. Largely as a result of the desire to meet the domestic demands of France for cocoa, the administration of Governor Angoulvant introduced a forced agricultural policy whereby farmers were compelled to cultivate a stated minimum area of cocoa. The most important export crop from Ivory Coast has, however, always been coffee (40 per cent by value in 1965); although its future is now uncertain since the present high price paid to Ivory Coast coffee farmers is made possible by a system of price support instituted by France. In 1959, for example, Ivory Coast farmers obtained about twice the world market price for their coffee, a situation which has tended to increase the dependence of the local economy on France.

It is important to stress at this point that the colonial period brought no revolution to African agriculture, and that any improvements in the processing of crops were restricted to areas producing crops for export to the metropolitan markets. The result is that most West African farmers in the 1970s continue to farm on a small scale, using cutlasses and hoes, the same implements which they used before the colonial period. Roads and railways were built to open up those areas producing crops or minerals for export, with the result that at independence in 1960, as much as 80 per cent of the people remained unaffected by most of the changes that occurred during the colonial period. Export agriculture induced considerable rural-rural migrations and brought wealth to many farmers, especially in the cocoa-growing areas. In many other areas, on the other hand, agriculture yielded little more than enough to pay taxes and buy some cheaper types of imported manufactured goods, including cotton cloth, hurricane lanterns, three-legged pots, salt and farm implements.

It is probably in the organization of the commercial sector of the economy that the greatest contrasts exist between the two West Africas. Wholesale as well as retail trade in manufactured goods is run almost exclusively by Frenchmen and Syrians or Lebanese in all French-speaking countries, where even shop attendants, hair-dressers, petty traders and night-club owners are also Frenchmen, Arabs or Asians. The situation in the English-speaking countries is completely different. Here, expatriates have been obliged to quit the wholesale and retail trade in manufactured merchandize, especially in Nigeria and Ghana where laws have been passed restricting a number of enterprises to indigenes of each country. The prosperous market-women in Nigeria and Ghana, who dominate the retail trade in manufactured goods and constitute a significant force in local politics, rarely exist in the French-speaking countries. Rather a 'poor white' class of Frenchmen and women as well as Asians control the small commercial businesses which are owned by Africans in the English-speaking countries. The continuing domination of the entire economy not only by French capital but also by French personnel is striking. In the Ivory Coast, the situation is one in which French control of the economy has increased so much that in 1972, the number of French citizens in the country was reported to have almost doubled since Independence in 1960. Indeed, Dakar and Abidjan are more like French cities, and unlike Lagos and Accra, where Africans own all the houses, Frenchmen own most of the good houses and hotels. Indeed, many of them are landlords who rent rooms to African migrant workers in these cities.

The manpower situation in the French-speaking countries reveals quite clearly the failure of the French policy of assimilation, which aimed at making Frenchmen out of a restricted number of educated Africans. The smaller proportion of trained manpower in French-speaking countries, has been attributed to this deliberate policy of producing just enough educated Africans to fill the jobs that the French were prepared to make available to them. It has also been attributed to the rejection by Africans of French attempts at assimilation. In Senegal for example, the rejection of European-type education by the people was essentially a rejection of an attempt to convert them from Islam to Christianity. The British approach of allowing missionaries a free hand to run schools, produced many more educated people compared with the situation in French-speaking countries, where most children who went to school studied in government schools.

In consequence, unlike the English-speaking countries where the civil service is manned exclusively by indigenous people and where school teachers,

university staff, both academic and administrative, as well as the armed forces have been almost completely indigenised, the situation in French-speaking countries, excepting Guinea, is very different. In Senegal and Ivory Coast in particular, civil service departments and schools are still predominantly staffed by Frenchmen who also dominate the officer group in the armed forces. In 1972, the University of Dakar had a teaching staff of over 90 per cent French citizens and depended almost entirely on funds from France while Nigerian universities, like those of Ghana, were staffed largely by indigenous people, excepting perhaps Ahmadu Bello University at Zaria, which still had a large expatriate teaching body.

It is not surprising therefore, that during the colonial period and after, there have always been more Frenchmen resident in French-speaking West Africa than Englishmen resident in English-speaking West Africa. On the whole the number of British people in West Africa has declined greatly since 1960, while that of Frenchmen has shown a significant increase. One of the consequences of this situation is the great dependence of countries like Senegal, Ivory Coast, Togo and Dahomey on food imports to meet the demands of the expatriate population as well as of the increasing African élite, some of whom tend to be more French than the French. This constitutes a drain on the meagre foreign exchange earnings of these countries, and is largely responsible for the chronic trade deficit situation and the inability of some of these countries to balance their budgets. Since these expatriates and local élites are concentrated in a few cities and since they own the bulk of the development capital, the economy of these countries has revolved around satisfying their needs, rather than those of the vast majority of the African population. Thus, in spite of impressive figures of growth in the national economy of Ivory Coast, for example, the rural areas remain as backward and undeveloped as ever—a good example of 'growth without development'.

The facts presented above, show clearly that economically and educationally, the French-speaking countries are less developed. It would be misleading, however, to attribute the undeveloped state of the economy entirely to French colonial policy, since the French-speaking countries are generally poorer in primary resources than the English-speaking countries. Even Ivory Coast which is very rich in agricultural and forest resources is greatly handicapped by her small population to the extent that the country recruits as many as 60 per cent of its unskilled workers from other countries, notably Upper Volta. The small size of the population of French-speaking countries has also set a limit to the types and size of manufacturing plants, in view of the restricted size of the home market. This observation is of course also applicable to Gambia and Sierra Leone, but Nigeria and Ghana, each of which has a larger home market, have been able to support larger industrial plants.

The land-locked French-speaking countries of Niger, Upper Volta and Mali are extremely poor in mineral resources, while their climate is generally too dry to permit agriculture without irrigation. No country of English-speaking West Africa suffers from such dry conditions, since the drier parts of northern Nigeria are still better watered than Niger Republic or Mali. Indeed the only growing area of the interior of West Africa where export agriculture is well-established is the Nigerian Sudan, where cotton and groundnuts feature as prominent cash crops in the Kano and Sokoto Emirates. Attempts to develop export agriculture in the interior of French-speaking West Africa, including the area of the inland delta have so far failed.

There is a greater concentration of industrial development in the coastal cities of French-speaking West Africa. Large interior cities like Kumasi, Jos, Kaduna, Oshogbo, Kano and Zaria rarely exist in French-speaking West Africa. In consequence, internal road network and air transport is less developed than in English-speaking West Africa. Labour migration from rural to rural as well as from rural to urban centres is predominantly from the interior towards the coastal lands in French-speaking West Africa. In Nigeria, on the other hand, there is a considerable movement of educated people from the coastal areas to the cities of the interior where there are openings in teaching, the railways, mining fields and private businesses.

In West Africa the 'colonial economic pact' required that the colonies must provide export crops for the imperial countries who in turn would provide manufactured goods to their dependencies. The French enforced this theory so firmly that they refused to allow such French-speaking territories as Guinea, Niger or Mali to use natural outlets which passed through English-speaking countries. Rather, the French insisted that all land-locked French-speaking countries should use ports located in other French territories! This is the main reason why the Gambia waterway has not been used by Senegal. It is also in pursuance of this policy that no attempt was made to develop road transportation between Guinea and Sierra Leone or Liberia, for the evacuation of exports from eastern Guinea, the natural outlet of which lay through these two non-French-speaking countries.

The search for and mining of minerals started much earlier in the English-speaking countries of Nigeria, Ghana and Sierra Leone. Often it was mining which provided the main reason for building some

roads and railways, which helped to open up parts of these countries. In French-speaking West Africa, the known mineral deposits did not attract early attention from French investors and when, later, the iron ore and bauxite deposits of Guinea were mined, the capital invested came largely from non-French sources. Mineral deposits in Ivory Coast remained undeveloped until after the Second World War, unlike in neighbouring Ghana, where large-scale mining of gold, diamond and manganese started during the early years of the colonial period.

On the eve of independence, France gave active support to those territories who opted to stay out of the Federation of French West Africa, a colonial-period arrangement which could have been retained to the mutual benefit of the component political units. The result has been the emergence of independent countries, most of which are not economically viable and are militarily very weak. This situation has made it possible for France to continue to control the economy and influence political trends in these countries. In a rather patronizing way, for example, France pays higher prices for cocoa and coffee from her former dependencies than is payable in the world market and gives 'aids' to these countries, which in return buy almost exclusively from French markets. Hence the curious situation in which Dahomey imposed (until 1972) a 98 per cent duty on Nigerian and Ghanaian-made cigarettes as compared with 23 per cent duty on cigarettes from France and other countries of the European Economic Community.

During the negotiations for independence, both Britain and France tried to ensure that after independence, their former colonial territories would remain in the sterling and franc monetary zones respectively. France made membership of the franc zone a necessary factor for continued supply of credit to the newly independent countries. The greater control by France of the franc zone is obvious from the fact that about eighteen years after independence, all the French-speaking countries, with the exception of Guinea and Mali still use the CFA franc as the only legal currency. British control over the sterling area has been much looser and has since ceased in Ghana (1965), Sierra Leone (1972), and Nigeria (1973), following the adoption of new and separate currencies by these countries. As a rule, banking facilities are much poorer in the French-speaking countries, which depend on the branches of the larger French banks for this service. Indigenous banking houses comparable to the Ghana Commercial Bank, or in Nigeria the African Continental Bank, the National Bank and the Mercantile Bank, do not exist in the French-speaking countries.

The efforts made by Britain and France to retain

their former colonial territories within their respective monetary zones, were prompted by the desire to promote and maintain existing trade links between themselves and their erstwhile colonies. As may be expected, the French-speaking countries, with the exception of Guinea, still trade mostly with France. The situation is very different in the English-speaking countries. Nigeria's trade with Britain, for example, has declined very much since independence while her trade with Japan, West Germany, France and Russia has increased remarkably. French and Japanese cars have since replaced British-made cars as the dominant brands in Nigeria. A similar trade trend is observed in Ghana and Sierra Leone.

Chapter 15—The Economic Community of West African States

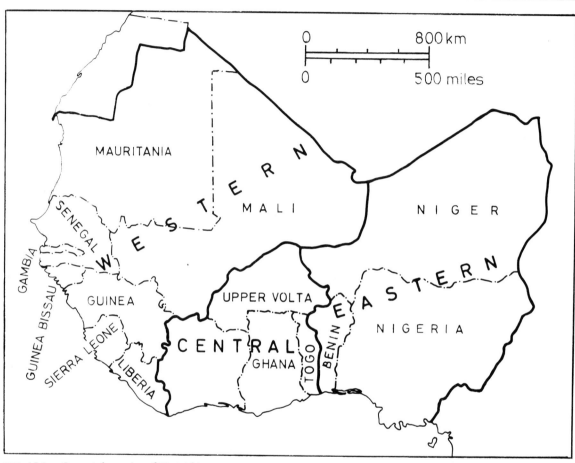

FIG. 15.1—Suggested grouping of West African states
(M. Barbour)

The break-up, at independence in 1960, of the colonial-period Federation of French West Africa was a major set-back to the economic integration and possible political unification of West Africa. The dissolution in 1957 of the West African Currency Board, the West African Frontier Force and the West African Institute of Economic and Social Research, all at Ghana's demand, was also another major backward step which was caused, surprisingly, by the late President Nkrumah, who is well known for his support for an African continental government. However, since 1961 there have been several unsuccessful attempts to form supra-national economic and political associations. Efforts at establishing the Economic Community of West African States (ECOWAS) have been intensified since 1970, and on 28 May 1975, the Community was born when the heads of state of the fifteen member countries signed in Lagos the treaty of establishment. In this chapter we review the case for supra-national associations, inter-national co-operation and the West African Economic Community or Common Market. The problems facing these proposals as well as the prospects are also discussed.

THE CASE FOR A WEST AFRICAN ECONOMIC COMMUNITY

Even before the end of the colonial period, many West African leaders were aware of the fact that political independence was meaningless without economic independence. They recognized the fact that the sure way to achieve economic independence was through co-operation between the independent states, some of which are so small and poor that they cannot afford to maintain a permanent mission at the United Nations. At present most West African countries still depend very much on 'foreign aid' for financing capital projects, and in some cases for balancing their budgets. It is also a well-known fact that the United States of America and the Soviet Union, each of which has one vote in the United Nations, play a more decisive and influential role in that world body than the combined forces of the existing fourteen West African countries. It is not difficult to see that political independence is a necessary, but not a sufficient condition for autonomous and effective participation in international politics. A united West Africa would be a force to reckon with both politically and economically. Fortunately many West African leaders are now more conscious of the need for some form of political and economic integration, particularly since the formation of the European Economic Community (EEC), of which many of them have become associate members. The case for a West African Economic Community is indeed a strong one and is considered by many people to be overdue (Fig. 15.1).

The small size of the domestic markets is considered to be one of the main obstacles to industrial development in many West African countries. The domestic markets of countries like Benin, Togo, Niger and Upper Volta are considered to be comparable to that of a medium-sized American or European city! Many industries established in these countries have therefore had to operate at sub-optimum levels and therefore hardly make any profits.

At present, trade barriers set up by the fourteen countries which depend heavily on import and excise duties for revenue have tended to restrict inter-state trade, thereby limiting the market for goods manufactured within each country. The sure way to tackle the market problem is to form a free trade area, a customs union or better still a common market. This will make it possible for Nigerian manufactures, for example, to earn free entry into Benin and vice versa. The situation whereby Benin still imposes a higher duty on Nigerian-made cigarettes as compared with cigarettes made in France will thereby cease. It is a sad reflection on the West African economic scene that a situation such as this should exist fifteen years after independence. It is even sadder that as a result of such restrictions the amount of tobacco produced by the Nigerian farmer has had to be restricted so as to prevent over-production. The income of the tobacco farmer is therefore also restricted, a situation which would not exist if Nigerian-made cigarettes could compete on the same terms for customers in other West African countries.

The continued over-dependence of the economy of West African countries on the export of primary products has made them rather vulnerable to the fluctuations of world prices in these commodities. The need to utilize these primary products in local factories has been recognized, and is a major factor in the desire to expand the industrial sector of the economy. The increasing use of synthetic raw materials suggests that the future of primary products is uncertain, and West African countries would do well to expand the internal markets for their raw materials if they are to avert serious economic crises. At present, some countries like Ivory Coast and Benin have inadequate generated power to support large-scale manufacturing. But fortunately, neighbouring countries like Ghana and Nigeria have power installations which are not fully utilized because of inadequate demand. An economic union or co-operation would make for better planning and a more effective use of West African power resources for the overall benefit of West African peoples.

The case of the iron and steel industry demonstrates clearly the need for economic union or even some form of political union. At present, no country except Nigeria has the market or capital to support a modern integrated iron and steel works. Yet West Africa has large deposits of high-grade iron ore in Mauritania, Sierra Leone, Guinea and Liberia as well as smaller deposits elsewhere. A combined market of all the states would be more than adequate in view of the growing demand for iron and steel products for industrialization. A large steel mill is required and this could be jointly sponsored by the states. At present, Ghana has built a steel mill to produce 40,000 tons per year from scrap and eventually from local iron ore, and Nigeria has a small steel mill at Enugu which uses scrap and operates at a loss! Nigeria has a plan to build a ₦ 240 million steel complex by 1978, while Niger has planned a small iron factory based on local iron ore near Say to produce 20,000 tons of reinforcing rods and cast iron every year. Joint production of iron and steel, making use of low-cost but high-grade ore from Mauritania, Liberia and Sierra Leone would be more beneficial to all and would create more employment and more opportunities to train local technologists and would conserve considerable foreign exchange. Such a joint plan has so far

119

been prevented by the present independent approach to development by the small states which cannot afford the capital or market, and have therefore fallen prey to large monopolies from European countries and the United States of America.

West Africa also has the resources to sustain a large chemical industry to produce fertilizers to make possible the much-talked-about revolution in agricultural production. Togo has over 50 million tons of high-grade phosphate deposits, which is now shipped in crude form to be manufactured in other countries. But Togo does not produce enough power to support a local fertilizer factory. At the same time, the neighbouring countries of Ghana and Nigeria have modern hydro-electric power stations with an installed capacity which is far in excess of the national consumption. Ghana has in fact been selling electricity to Togo since 1972 but an economic union could provide better terms for the sale of electricity produced from Kainji and for natural gas to states like Benin, Togo, Niger and Chad.

Political fragmentation, the attachment to different monetary zones, and existing discriminatory duties, have contributed considerably to the small volume of inter-state trade between West African countries and the continued economic domination of these countries by their former colonial rulers. This situation has made it possible for foreign multi-national firms, some of which have an annual budget which is much greater than that of some West African countries, to continue to exploit these countries. By extracting minerals in one country and processing them in another, some foreign firms have been able to play one state against another to obtain more favourable tax and royalty rates from the economically weak and small West African countries, thus reducing the share of revenue due to such countries from their mineral wealth. Bauxite mined in Guinea for example is processed in Cameroon and as a result, neither Guinea nor Cameroon is in a position to bargain effectively with the company concerned, since neither of these countries can afford the capital to mine or smelt the ore. It is also thought that the main reason why France supported the Biafran secession was to ensure more generous terms for exploiting crude oil in a smaller political unit than it could hope to get from a larger and economically powerful united Nigeria. Some form of economic or political union would certainly be of great advantage to West African countries and would, amongst other things, lessen the great dependence of these countries on Europe and North America.

Currently, West Africa loses considerable revenue by exporting her timber mostly in the form of logs rather than in the processed forms of sawn timber and plywood. It is also wasteful to export shelled groundnuts instead of groundnut oil and cakes. An economically united West Africa with a large enough internal market to support large-scale manufacturing would go a long way towards eliminating these and other wastages.

EARLY ATTEMPTS AT POLITICAL INTEGRATION

The first three years after the Second World War saw the formation of two political parties which cut across territorial boundaries to embrace almost all the French-speaking countries of Africa. These parties were the Rassemblement Democratique Africain (RDA) in 1946 and the Independents d'Outre Mer (IOM) in 1948. It was at the IOM congress in 1953, held at Bobo Dioulasso, that a federal republic of French West Africa was proposed. But shortly after the meeting, Senghor of Senegal favoured the division of French-speaking West Africa into two states, each with a premier and a parliament to be located at Dakar and Abidjan. This general enthusiasm for political integration continued after the first few months of independence, after which the various countries started to drift apart, while each country became more concerned with its internal security and economic growth, particularly after the collapse in 1960 of the Mali Federation.

In 1958, shortly after Guinea had achieved independence from France, the country entered into a political union with Ghana, which had achieved her independence a year earlier. This union was the first attempt at some form of collaboration between an English-speaking and a French-speaking West African country.

Another attempt to form a political union was made in January 1959 when Senegal, Dahomey, Sudan (Mali) and Upper Volta drew up a plan to form a federation with headquarters at Dakar. When, however, the federation was formally inaugurated on 25 March 1959, both Dahomey and Upper Volta had withdrawn. The union, which assumed the name of the Mali Federation, soon ran into difficulties because Senegal, the richer and more developed country wanted a loose federation while Sudan (Mali) insisted on a unitary state. The union came to an end in August 1960 when Senegal seceded while the Sudanese Republic adopted the name of Republic of Mali.

Two years later the Republic of Mali joined the Ghana-Guinea-Mali union, a few months after the collapse of the Mali Federation. This three-nation union was named the Union of African States (UAS)

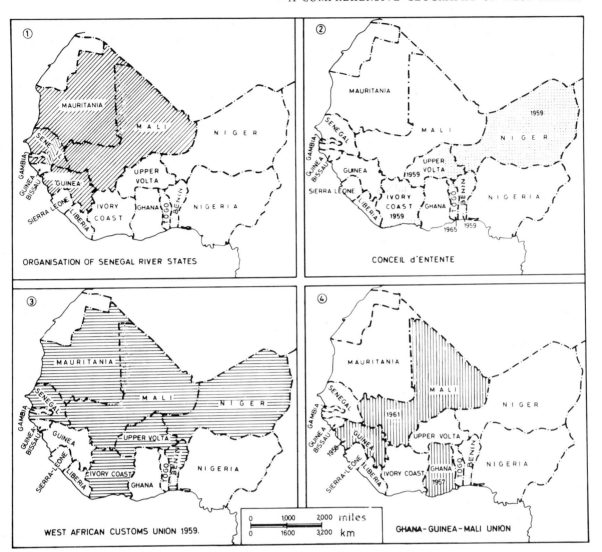

FIG. 15.2—*Member states of existing supra-national bodies*

and was seen by its founders as the nucleus of the United States of Africa.

At the time of the fall of Nkrumah in 1966, the union had not achieved much and may be considered to have been discontinued in 1966 when Nkrumah sought and obtained political asylum in Guinea.

ALTERNATIVES TO POLITICAL UNION

The break up of the Mali Federation, the death of the Union of African States involving Ghana, Guinea and Mali and the abortive attempt by Biafra to secede from Nigeria all serve to emphasize the difficulties inherent in altering the existing political boundaries of West African countries. It appears that although most countries have accepted in principle and made public pronouncements about the urgency for political union, many of the governments are still not ready to make the sacrifices that such a union will entail. Economic integration is therefore seen to offer the best hope for some form of inter-state co-operation. Indeed, during the early years of independence when Ghana was the leading spokesman for political union, the Nigerian government considered some form of economic, cultural and educational co-operation to be a necessary starting point towards eventual political union.

Economic integration can take any of the following forms depending on the degree of co-operation required:

1) A free trade area which involves abolition of tariff restrictions among the participating countries, but leaves each country to establish independent tariffs against other countries.
2) A customs union involving the abolition of internal barriers to trade and a common tariff against third countries.
3) A common market where restrictions on both trade and factor movements are abolished.
4) An economic union which combines the abolition of restrictions on commodity and factor movements with harmonization of national economic policies.
5) Total economic integration in which monetary, fiscal, social and other policies are unified and in which a supra-national authority takes decisions binding on all member states.

Fifteen years after the independence of most West African countries in 1960 the whole region has still not been constituted into a free trade area. Yet the free trade area is considered to be the simplest form of economic integration to negotiate. There have, however, been attempts to form customs unions and common markets embracing a group of countries.

In 1962, a West African Customs Union (see Fig. 15.2) of almost all the French-speaking states was formed by Dahomey, Ivory Coast, Mauritania, Niger, Mali, Senegal and Upper Volta. Later that year, Mali withdrew from the Union which despite considerable internal stresses, managed to maintain a monetary union and a common franc zone currency.

The United Nations Economic Commission for Africa (ECA) has also been interested in forging some form of economic integration so as to foster greater economic development in West Africa. After a series of meetings and consultations arranged by ECA, the representatives of twelve countries met at Accra in May 1967 to sign the articles of association for a West African Economic Community. Four English-speaking countries, Nigeria, Ghana, Sierra Leone and Liberia, signed the agreement while the remaining eight signatories were French-speaking countries. It is unfortunate that nothing was done after signing the agreement, with the result that this admirable effort by the ECA to bring about economic integration in West Africa ended in failure.

Other attempts at economic integration have since been made, including the bilateral agreements between Nigeria and Togo in 1970 and the widely publicized attempt in 1973 by Nigeria, Ghana and Togo to form a nucleus of a West African Community. In April 1972, another West African Economic Community called CEAO was launched in Abidjan. The founding members were Ivory Coast, Upper Volta, Mali, Mauritania, Niger and Senegal, but other West African countries were called upon to join it. The position in 1976 was that all the fifteen member countries had ratified the treaty establishing the Economic Community of West African States. Under the treaty, members may not increase customs and similar duties, with agreed exceptions, between 1976 and 1978, and it is planned that by 1990 a customs union will be established. All citizens of member countries are to be regarded as 'Community citizens' who will be free to move and reside anywhere within the Community.

BARRIERS TO ECONOMIC INTEGRATION

The failure of various attempts at political and economic union suggests that there are some factors which tend to work against any form of integration. One such factor is the colonial economic chains which bind many countries to the economic apron strings of their former colonial rulers. A good example of these economic chains is the existence of separate monetary zones, namely the franc, dollar and sterling zones. The problems of obtaining foreign exchange have contributed to the small volume of trade that is carried on between many neighbouring countries like Nigeria and Benin, Ghana and Togo or Sierra Leone and Guinea. Rather, many countries still continue to maintain a trade pattern which is not very different from what it was during the colonial period, when most primary products went to France or Britain, who in turn supplied manufactured goods to the various countries.

On the whole, the economic chains binding the French-speaking countries to France have been much greater compared with the position in the English-speaking countries. Indeed it is widely believed that it was the desire of France to ensure her continued dominance of the economy of her former West African territories that made her support, and even encourage, the break up at independence, of the colonial-period Federation of French West Africa. Presently most French-speaking countries still depend on 'aid' from Paris to subsidize their budgets. And although many of these countries have since realized that the profits that accrue to France, as a result of existing trade arrangements, are far greater than what is given as 'aid', they appear to be helpless in breaking the chains that France has put around their necks. It is surprising, for instance, that many French-manufactured goods, including Peugeot cars, cost less in Nigeria than in French-speaking Benin or Togo, and yet these countries continue to buy almost exclusively from French markets. France in turn gives preferential treatment to primary exports from French-speaking West African countries. But what these countries need is trade on fair terms rather than aid and their present economic dependence on France. The resulting feeling of security, which is essentially false, must be replaced by one of self-reliance. This would be best achieved through belonging to a West African Common Market, not through being an associate member of the European Economic Community.

It is, however, often argued that the basis for trade does not exist between countries like Nigeria, Ivory Coast and Benin, since these countries produce similar crops for the domestic as well as the export market. This argument is no longer tenable today, since some countries like Nigeria now consume almost all their palm oil and kernel as well as cotton and a large proportion of rubber in local factories. Indeed, Nigeria may soon begin to import palm oil and raw cotton because some textile factories have been forced to close down temporarily owing to a shortage of cotton. A basis therefore exists even for trade in primary products, but particularly in manufactured goods from such industrial areas as Abidjan, Dakar, Accra-Tema and Greater Lagos.

The poor state of transport and communications between states is a major problem. This factor should, however, not be over-emphasized, in view of the fact that Nigeria now survives as one political unit, even though some areas are hardly accessible to motorized transport and postal services and telecommunications are still very unsatisfactory. Most of the existing roads and railways were built to serve an essentially colonial export-oriented economy, dominated by the movement of primary products from the interior to the ports of export at the coast. There are no international railroads apart from that linking Ivory Coast to Upper Volta and that linking Senegal to Mali. These two international lines were, however, built when these countries were administered by France as territories of French West Africa. No English-speaking country is linked by railway to any French-speaking country, and roads linking one country to another are often very poor towards the borders, and often circuitous (see Chapter 12). Air services between different countries are few and expensive. A crash programme to develop inter-state transport is essential for the expansion of trade between West African countries.

Probably the most serious barrier to economic integration and eventual political union is the growing national consciousness of states which have only recently become independent, and the fear of economic and political domination by the larger and richer states. Smaller countries like Togo, Gambia and Benin are afraid to forego their colonial-based national identity, while the French-speaking states fear the dominant role which the wealthier and more influential English-speaking countries of Nigeria and Ghana would exercise in an economically integrated or politically United West Africa. In addition, the relatively wealthier countries like Ivory Coast are hesitant to enter into a union in which their potential wealth may be tapped to develop countries which are less endowed with natural resources. Fears of economic domination and political subservience have been largely responsible for the mass expulsion of non-nationals by Sierra Leone, Ivory Coast and Ghana between 1963 and 1970, an action which has only succeeded in worsening the labour deficit situation in Ghana and Ivory Coast.

EXISTING SUPRA-NATIONAL ORGANIZATIONS

We end this chapter by discussing briefly three existing supra-national organizations: the Chad Basin Commission, the Niger River Commission and the Organization of Senegal River States (see Fig. 15.2). These organizations emphasize the fact that most West African countries appreciate the need for some form of economic and political association.

The Chad Basin Commission was formed in 1964 to co-ordinate projects aimed at the social and economic development of the member countries of Cameroon, Chad, Niger and Nigeria, and thereby prevent conflict among bordering countries in their efforts to exploit the water resources of the Lake Chad Basin. Amongst other considerations are the proposals to extend the Nigerian railways to Fort Lamy in land-locked Chad and the trans-Cameroon railway to southern Chad. A scientific survey of the water resources of the Basin has since been carried out with the help of UNESCO, while some irrigation projects have already been started in Nigeria and Chad.

Cameroon, Guinea, Benin, Ivory Coast, Mali, Niger and Upper Volta are the present members of the Niger River Commission which was formed in 1963. The absence of Nigeria in this list is curious in view of the fact that about one-third of the Niger and almost the entire length of its main tributary, the Benue, flow through Nigerian territory. The job of the Commission so far has consisted of a survey aimed at improving navigation and general economic development along the Niger River.

The last of the existing supra-national organizations is the Organization of Senegal River States which was founded in 1968 to replace the Senegal River States Committee of 1963. The council of this organization is charged with initiating, executing and controlling projects aimed at developing the Senegal River Basin. The organization intends to co-ordinate land and river transport in the Basin and has also considered the construction of a dam at Mantali in Mali for the purpose of providing a steady supply of water for irrigation.

Part II

The Countries of West Africa

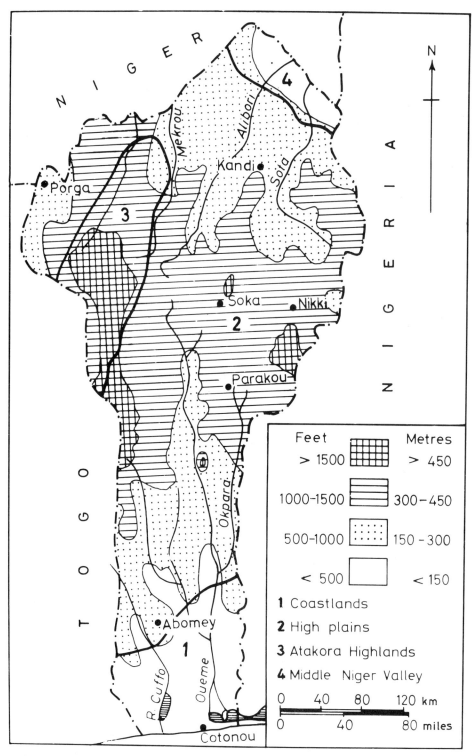

FIG. 16.1—Benin: physical regions

Chapter 16—The Republic of Benin

Like other French-speaking West African countries, with the exception of Guinea, Benin became independent of French rule in 1960. It is a small country with an area of 113,000 sq. km (43,480 sq. miles) and a population of 2.9 million (1974). Like Togo, Benin is a narrow country, with a width of 122km (75 miles) in the south and a north-south length of 672km (420 miles). As a result of its northward extension the three major geographical regions of West Africa, the coastland of Guinea, the Middle Belt and the Sudan are represented in Benin, except that in this country, savanna vegetation extends as far as the coast. (See Plate 66.)

RELIEF AND DRAINAGE

Apart from two small areas of low relief, the coastal plain in the south and the lowland of the Middle Niger Valley, Benin consists of high plains developed primarily on old hard rocks of the Basement Complex. The Atakora Highlands in the west, and the Nikki Hills in the east are the two prominent highland areas in the country. In the region of latitude 10°N., there is a low watershed separating the headwaters of rivers draining south into the Bight of Benin from those which flow northwards to join the Middle Niger. Important south-draining rivers include the Oueme, Okpara and Cuffo, while the main rivers draining into the Niger are the Mekrou, the Alibori and the Sota.

In terms of its land relief, Benin may be divided into four physical regions (Fig. 16.1). These are: 1) the coastlands, 2) the high plains, 3) the Atakora Highlands, 4) the Middle Niger Valley.

1. The coastlands

A narrow belt of sand ridges separates the open sea from the string of narrow lagoons and marshland, which start from Benin and continue eastwards to join the creeks of the Niger Delta. The only channels linking the lagoons to the open sea cut through the coastal sand ridges at Cotonou and Grand Popo.

Immediately north of the coastal depression of lagoon and swamps, the ground rises to form a low, flat plateau of clayey soils called the Terre de Barre (from the Portuguese word *barro* meaning clay). This plateau is about 150m (500ft) high and is cut into three parts by the valleys of the Cuffo and Oueme Rivers which flow through it in a north-south direction. Lake Aheme which lies along the course of River Cuffo is the largest lake on the plateau. It is 24km (15 miles) long and has an average width of 3km (2 miles).

North of the line joining Pobé to Athieme through Toffa, the land drops suddenly to form another west-east depression called the Lama Marsh. This is a region of black fertile soil whose usefulness as farmland is restricted by the fact that the drainage is poor and that vast areas are either permanent marshland or are completely inundated during the rainy season. The extreme north of the coastal lowlands, that is the area north of the Lama Marsh, consists of low plateaux of sandstone with very few perennial streams. Water supply presents a serious problem in this area of dry valleys and low water tables, which reminds one of the sandstone plateau of the Udi-Nsukka Uplands in Nigeria.

2. The high plains

The high plains which rise in a series of steps as one approaches the interior are developed on old hard rocks. Granite which weathers into clayey soil is the most common rock and is usually exposed as bare rock surfaces on higher ground. On lowland areas, the soil is clayey and often thin. Some of the most fertile soils in this region occur along the valleys of the Oueme and Okpara Rivers, but cultivation along these valleys is often hampered by flooding.

Lateritic soils are particularly common along the interfluves. Indeed, many flat-topped low hills found in this region of high plains have survived as a result of the protection against erosion provided by the capping of lateritic crust. Many other inselbergs, usually dome-shaped and in various stages of disintegration, also occur in this region of Basement Complex rocks.

127

PLATE 66—Oil palm estate, Pobé, Benin

In addition to the inselbergs, the surface of the plains is sometimes broken by small hilly areas such as the Ouari-Maro Hills and the Delcesse Hills which rise more than 210m (700ft) above the general level of the surrounding area. Occasionally, as in the area east of Paraku, the surface of the land is so flat as to give rise to extensive swamps.

3. The Atakora Highlands

These highlands constitute the most prominent relief feature of Benin and are a north-east continuation of the Togo ranges. The highlands are formed by resistant metamorphic rocks and consist of a series of discontinuous ridges which formerly combined to form a high plateau surface. Some of the highlands have peaks exceeding 600m (2,000ft) above sea level and are bounded by escarpments of about 300m (1,000ft) high.

Much of this region drains northwards towards the Middle Niger Valley. Rivers such as the Mekrou and Pendiari have cut deep and narrow valleys through the highlands. Road construction is rendered rather difficult by the relief, and contact between the inhabitants is still very restricted.

4. The Middle Niger Valley

Only a small portion of the Niger Valley, less than 160km (100 miles) out of a total length of 4,160km (2,600 miles) lies in Benin. Several rapids occur in areas where old hard rocks outcrop along the river bed.

CLIMATE AND VEGETATION

Climate

The climate of Benin is similar in many ways to that of the neighbouring country of Togo. The annual total rainfall (Fig. 16.2) increases inland from about 1,270mm (50in.) along the coast to about 1,370mm (54in.) in the region of the low watershed along latitude 10°N., and then decreases to about 1,000mm (40in.) in the Niger Valley. A double-maxima regime which is characteristic of the coastlands east of Cape Three Points features along the coast. At Porto Novo and Cotonou, the maximum rainfall occurs in June and October, both peaks being separated by the short

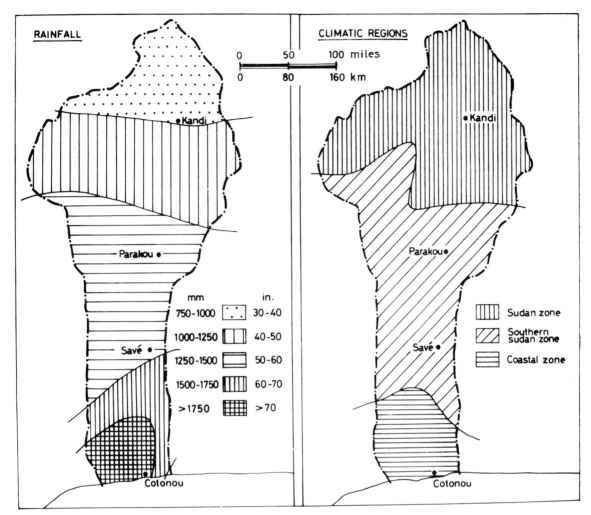

FIG. 16.2—Benin: rainfall and climatic regions

dry season which occurs in August. There are therefore four seasons along the coast; but in the central and northern parts of the country only two distinct seasons are recognized–the dry season (November to April) and the rainy season (May to October).

Other characteristics of the rainfall are the fact that it comes in sharp thunderstorms and that it is related to the wind system of West Africa. The rainstorms are particularly violent in April and May but in the months of June and July, the rain is more persistent and may last from morning till evening. The rainy season decreases from eight months along the coast to five months in the far north.

March is the hottest month but there is a marked decrease in temperature everywhere with the onset of the rains, the coolest month being August, the month with the greatest cloud cover. Temperature variations in the south are very small, the mean daily maxima being between 27°C and 32°C (80°F—90°F),

while the mean minima are between 21°C and 24°C (70°F and 75°F). There are greater variations which are recorded in the north, especially during the dry season.

Vegetation

The sandspit fronting the sea is covered by a relatively open vegetation of scrub or cultivated coconut palm groves. North of the coastal lagoons, marshland vegetation of grass predominates. This coastal marshland is separated from the interior and more extensive Lama Marsh by the clay district of the Terre de Barre, which has a mixed deciduous forest vegetation.

North of the Lama Marsh, the vegetation consists of grass-woodland with isolated patches of dense forest in the south. These forest islands are particularly numerous west of the Oueme River. In areas which have been largely deforested, elephant grass, growing

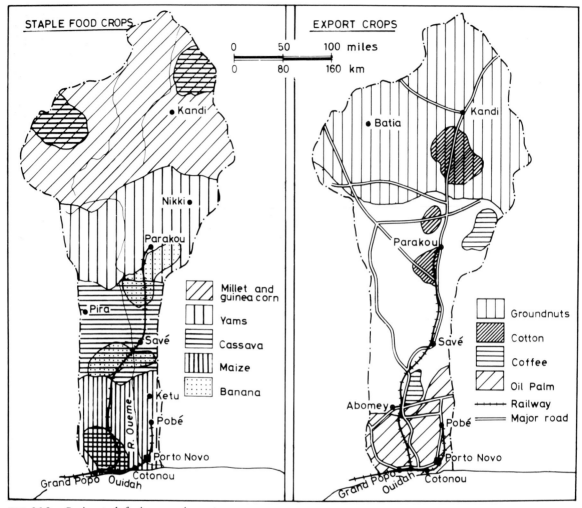

FIG. 16.3—Benin: staple food crops and export crops

to a height of 3.5m (12ft), is the dominant vegetation. Further north, in the sudan subzone which extends to the Benin-Niger frontier, the grass becomes shorter. The shea-butter tree which is carefully preserved when the bush is fired for farming or hunting is numerous in this northern grassland area in which there also grow silk cotton trees and small groves of acacias.

OCCUPATIONS

In 1973, 75 per cent of the people were farmers, while about 8 per cent lived on fishing. A further 4 per cent of the people were classified as herders while the remaining people were engaged in various other occupations such as hunting and petty trading. There were only 35,000 wage-earners in that year, about 24,500 working in the public sector. The central government is the largest employer of labour (18,000 in 1973).

Farming

The Fons and other people of the south are energetic farmers, who carry out intensive cultivation of food crops including yams, cassava, maize and sweet potatoes. Rice, beans and millet are the main crops of the north while cassava and groundnuts grow almost everywhere (Fig. 16.3).

Crops grown both for export and for local consumption include the oil palm, coconuts, cotton and groundnuts. Large oil palm plantations were common in Southern Benin long before the period of French rule. These plantations, owned largely by the kings of Dahomey and Porto Novo, were planted by slave-labour. Today many peasants own small plantations planted with selected seedlings supplied by the Ministry of Agriculture.

Coconuts are grown both by Africans and French companies along the sandbar and near the coastal lagoons.

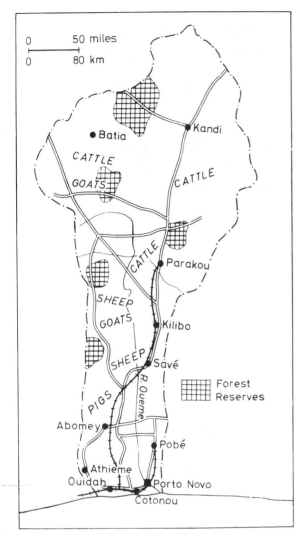

FIG. 16.4—Benin: forest reserves and livestock

PLATE 67—Smoking and drying fish at Ouidah, Benin

Livestock farming (Fig. 16.4) is common in the north where there are about 500,000 cattle and 1,100,000 sheep and goats. The pig population of 350,000 is concentrated in the south. Benin imports cattle from Niger to supplement her local meat supply.

Hunting

Hunting is an important occupation, particularly in the south. The hunters, who use various traps and dane guns, usually go out in groups, each of which is headed by a leader. Since domestic animals, such as goats, chickens and the small-breed lagoon cattle are killed only on special occasions, bush meat, which hunters bring home, provides an important source of protein. Some of the meat is dried over fires and sold in the main rural periodic markets.

Fishing

Fishing is the main occupation of the people living along the coast where about 10,000 tons of smoked fish are produced every year. Some fishermen specialize in sea-fishing, but the great majority fish both in the sea and in the lagoons and lakes behind the coastal sandbars. Smoked fish from Benin is commonly found in Lagos markets in Nigeria (plate 67).

Cottage industry

Wrought iron, formerly made from local ores smelted in primitive furnaces, is still used for making farm implements and hunting weapons. Cloth-making (weaving and dyeing) is widespread. Other important crafts industries include wood-carving and pot-making. As in other parts of West Africa, these crafts are mostly carried on as part-time occupations by people who also farm or fish. Usually the crafts season starts during the slack period in the farming calendar.

Manufacturing industries

Manufacturing is still an insignificant sector of the country's economy even though the country has a higher proportion of local skilled manpower than most French-speaking West African countries. The first factories consisted of palm oil mills and a groundnut oil mill of 10,000 tons capacity. The soap factories at Cotonou, Porto Novo and Ouidah make use of local vegetable oils. Other industries include

131

a brewery, a soft drinks factory, transistor assembly workshops and factories for assembling Citroën vehicles and bicycles. In 1968, the greatest industrial project in the country, a factory for manufacturing jute sacks, was launched by a joint Italian-Dahomeyan company called SODAK. The growing industrial district of Cotonou also has factories producing paints, plastic sandals and textiles. Until 1970, the production of electrical energy (24.5 million kW in 1969) was inadequate for developing large industries and it appears that the agreement signed in 1968 with Ghana and Togo for the supply of electricity from Akosombo will boost industrialization. The small internal market remains a serious limiting factor to industrial development.

MINERALS

There was no systematic prospecting for minerals in the country before independence and although a few minerals have been discovered, mining is still not fully developed. The iron ore of the Atakoras Highlands was formerly worked by local Africans and is still awaiting exploitation. Low quality iron ore (30–40 per cent grade) has been discovered near Kandi in the north but the deposits have not yet been worked because of the great distance from the coast. The titanium-bearing alluviums found in the centre and north of the country have also not been mined because of transport costs. Other minerals include chrome ore in the Natintingou district of the northwest and limestone, which supplies a local 300,000-ton cement factory. Production has not yet strated on the crude oil discovered offshore in 1968 by Union Oil of California.

POPULATION AND TOWNS

The most numerous ethnic group in the country is the Fon (850,000) who like the people of Ashanti and Benin in Nigeria were organized into a powerful state during the nineteenth century. Fon kings were usually warlike and their armies were known mainly because they included several thousand amazons (women soldiers). Another prominent group in Benin is the Yorubas (200,000), who live in the south-east of the country. Other ethnic groups include the Adja who number 300,000 and the Bariba whose population in 1962 was 210,000.

Most of Benin's 2.6 million inhabitants live in the southern provinces of Atlantique, Zou, and Oueme. The main areas of low density in the south include the Lama Depression and the central part of

the Terre de Barre, along which passed the old slave road from Ouidah to Abomey. In the far north, the region of the Niger Valley is also sparsely settled.

Since the more developed part of the country is in the south, where the ports and tree-crop plantations are located, many people migrate from the north to find jobs in the south. There is also some movement of people from Benin into Togo and Nigeria for the same purpose of seeking employment. Benin Yorubas are also found as traders in many other West African countries. (See Fig. 16.5.)

Porto Novo is the capital of Benin. It is located on the north side of the Oueme Lagoon, which links up with Lagos and along which foreign imports formerly reached Porto Novo. The market importance of the town has declined considerably since the opening in 1959 of the new port of Cotonou. Road connections with the interior and with Nigeria are very poor and its population was about 79,000 in 1969.

Cotonou, unlike the old town of Porto Novo, is a French creation which has grown up to become the commercial capital of Benin. The best buildings, streets and fashionable shops are in Cotonou rather than Porto Novo. Also, it is in Cotonou that Benin's international airport is located. Cotonou is also served by rail and has good road connections with Lome and Porto Novo. There is also a growing industrial estate located near to the new port. Its population in 1972 was 175,000, of which over one thousand were Frenchmen, who still man most of the industrial and commercial establishments.

EXTERNAL TRADE AND BALANCE OF PAYMENTS PROBLEMS

In 1965, the export trade of Benin, consisting primarily of palm produce (40 per cent by value), cotton (11 per cent) and groundnuts (19 per cent), was valued at 3,367 million francs CFA (₦ 10 million) while the country imported goods, mainly textiles (21 per cent), machinery (18 per cent) and food items (16 per cent), to the value of 8,491 million francs CFA (₦ 24 million). Unfortunately, this highly unfavourable balance of trade is a regular feature of the Benin economy. It started in 1924, owing to limited export possibilities and increasing demand for manufactured goods. It is strange that in view of the continued trade deficit situation, the country still imports large quantities of foodstuffs (over 850 million francs CFA per annum since 1965) rather than expand production at home. In 1965 for example, one-quarter

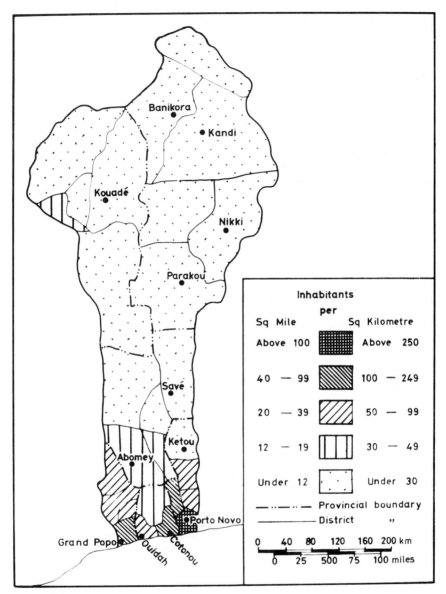

FIG. 16.5—Benin: population

of the imports by value were foodstuffs. This situation has been attributed largely to the neglect of food-crop farming by farmers who tend to pay more attention to export-crop production.

Amongst other things, the balance of payments situation has meant a steady increase every year of the national debt, which rose to about 10,100 million francs CFA (₦25million) in 1967. It is this chronic inability to balance its budget that has forced Benin to depend heavily on foreign aid both for buying capital goods and for financing current public expenditure (including payment of salaries). The economic situation is also the main cause and not the result of political instability in the country.

The bulk of the foreign exchange earnings comes from the south, with palm produce accounting for 40 per cent by value of export earnings. Cocoa is not an important crop in Benin but the tonnage exported from Cotonou has been increasing in recent years. This is caused by high prices offered in Benin, and the relative ease with which cocoa traders in the western States of Nigeria smuggle cocoa crops into Dahomey. There is also extensive smuggling involving consumer goods including alcoholic drinks, motor car tyres and textile goods. Smuggled diamonds from Zaïre Republic and Ghana are also an important but unreliable export which earned ₦1.2 million in 1967.

133

Chapter 17—Fernando Po

PLATE 68—Spanish-style architecture in Malabo (St Isabel), Fernando Po

Equatorial Guinea, which is made up of the island of Fernando Po and the mainland enclave of Rio Muni is the youngest of the newly independent African countries. It became independent of Spanish rule in 1968. In this chapter we shall consider only the island territory of Fernando Po, since the mainland territory lies outside West Africa. Fernando Po is by far the richer, and more developed section of the country. The capital of Equatorial Guinea, Santa Isabel, is also located on the island of Fernando Po.

The island is named after the Portuguese explorer Fernao de Po who was probably the first European to visit the island, in 1471. It is the largest of the four volcanic islands which form a seaward extension of the Adamawa-Cameroon Mountains. Like the Adamawa ranges, the island has a marked north-east to south-west trend. It has an area of 2,030 sq.km (780 sq.miles), about half the size of the Lagos State of Nigeria, and is about 70km (44 miles) long and 35km (22 miles) wide. (See plate 68.)

RELIEF AND DRAINAGE

Fernando Po lies on a continental shelf which is nowhere more than 100m (330ft) deep throughout the 32km (20 miles) stretch that separates it from the mainland. It has a narrow coastal plain, particularly in the south, and a rather rugged interior consisting of volcanic hills. The highest parts of the territory are in the north where Santa Isabel peak rises to 2,960m (9,860ft) and in the far south, in the region of San Carlos peak 1,974m (6,480ft). Small short mountain streams rush down the hills, providing considerable heads for developing water power. The highland areas of the south are characterized by deep steep-sided valleys and numerous craters, several of which contain crater lakes. It is the beauty of its natural scenery that gave the island its original name of 'Formoso' (meaning 'beautiful'). (See Fig. 17.1.)

CLIMATE, VEGETATION AND SOILS

Fernando Po has an equatorial climate, which in the central parts has been considerably modified by altitude. Along the west and north coast, the rainfall averages about 2,410mm (95in.) per annum increasing to over 2,670mm (105in.) at higher elevations. As in southern Nigeria, the rainy season lasts from March to October, but there is no short dry season in August which is in fact the rainiest month in Fernando Po. The precipitous south coast which lies in the direct path of the rain-bearing monsoon receives as much as 10,160mm (400in.) of rain per annum, about the same amount as Debunscha, at the foothills of the Cameroon Mountains.

The natural vegetation of the coastal lowlands and hills is high forest and it is in these lower areas that the tree-crop plantations are located. Except in the south and in the more inaccessible areas, plantation crops have largely replaced the forest vegetation. Above 1,200m (4,000ft), much of the forest has been destroyed to create pastureland, although relics of the forest may still be found along the valleys of mountain streams. (See plate 69.)

Fernando Po has very rich soils which are formed from volcanic rocks. The soils here are reported to be much richer than similar soils on the mainland. As in other equatorial areas, the soils are heavily leached as a result of the heavy rainfall which together with the steep slopes of the land provides conditions for the development of gully erosion.

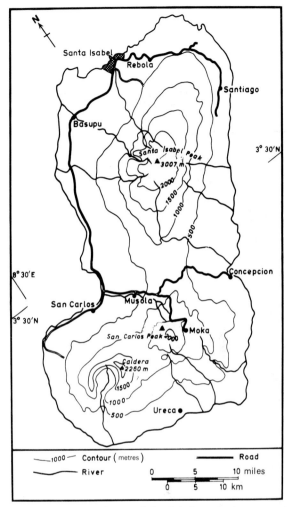

FIG. 17.1—Fernando Po: relief and drainage

ECONOMIC ACTIVITIES

Food-crop production

Although Fernando Po has fertile soils and sufficient rain for crop production without the use of irrigation, the island does not produce enough food for its growing labour force. One main reason for this food deficit situation is that much of the land (80 per cent of the cultivated area) and available labour is used for cul-

Table 16—Trade balance of Benin in million francs CFA

	1962	1963	1964	1965	1966	1967	1968	1969	1970	1971
Import	6,627	8,249	7,762	8,491	8,270	10,806	12,211	14,129	17,660	21,202
Export	2,699	3,155	3,254	3,367	2,585	3,750	5,505	6,937	9,062	11,648
Balance	−3,928	−5,094	−4,508	−5,124	−5,685	−7,056	−6,706	−7,192	−8,578	−9,554

Note: 668 francs CFA = £1.00 = ₦2.00.

135

tivating export crops, of which cocoa is by far the most important. Most indigenous families cultivate export crops since land can always be obtained under the provisions of the 1944 Land Act which entitles each family to not less than 4 hectares (10 acres) of land for cultivating export crops. As a result of the emphasis on export-crop production, Fernando Po imports a considerable amount of yams, garri and palm oil from Nigeria, and the inhabitants were hard hit by food shortages during the 1966–70 political crises in Nigeria when the Nigerian government prohibited the export of foodstuffs from the country.

Cassava and yams are the main food crops cultivated by the indigenous Bubi people who also live on plantain, banana and palm oil. Maize, cocoyams and beans are also cultivated in holdings which rarely exceed one-tenth of a hectare in area. Other crops grown for internal exchange as well as for export include tobacco, sisal, groundnuts and sugarcane.

Another feature of the food-crop economy is the production of food crops by most of the migrant labourers from Nigeria. Crops like yams, cassava, maize and cocoyam are cultivated on small plots of land allocated to plantation workers, who are also given some free rations of food as part payment of their wages. Temperate vegetables such as potatoes, lettuce, cabbages and carrots are cultivated with great success in the interior uplands as well as in the suburbs of the main towns of Santa Isabel, Moka and San Carlos. (See Fig. 17.2.)

Plantation agriculture

The export trade of Fernando Po is based almost entirely on cocoa, most of which is produced from small plantations. Most of these plantations (about 800) are owned by African farmers while Spanish planters own about 200 cocoa plantations. Generally, Spanish-owned plantations are much larger in size, averaging 56 hectares (140 acres), as compared with 4.8 hectares (12 acres) for African-owned plantations. These plantations are concentrated along the northern and western parts of the coastal plain (Fig. 17.3).

Labour is a critical factor in the cocoa economy and the expansion of plantation agriculture depends largely on the availability of labour. At present cocoa exports fluctuate with the labour situation. In 1962 for instance the cocoa output was 23,600 tons as compared with 38,000 tons in 1966/7, decreasing to 33,000 tons in 1968. Unfortunately the island is very sparsely populated, and has therefore had to depend largely on migrant labour which comes mainly from the congested districts of the Imo and Cross River States of Nigeria.

Unlike cocoa, coffee is grown almost exclusively

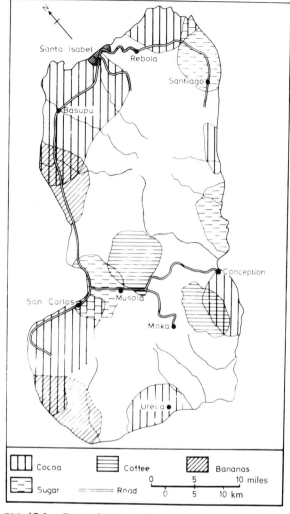

FIG. 17.2—Fernando Po: export crops

on Spanish-owned plantations. About 20 per cent of the total area of 61,000 hectares (152,500 acres) of coffee farmed in Equatorial Guinea in 1968 was located in Fernando Po (and 80 per cent in the mainland territory of Rio Muni) as compared with 90 per cent of the cocoa area. The total coffee tonnage produced in the island in 1968 was only 1,400 tons (cf. 38,000 for cocoa).

Livestock rearing

Cattle do well on the grassy highlands lying between 1,200 and 1,605m (4,000 and 5,350ft) above sea level. The main ranching area is the Moka district where the cattle population is owned by Spanish settlers. The animals which were introduced from Switzerland and the Canary Islands have done so well that

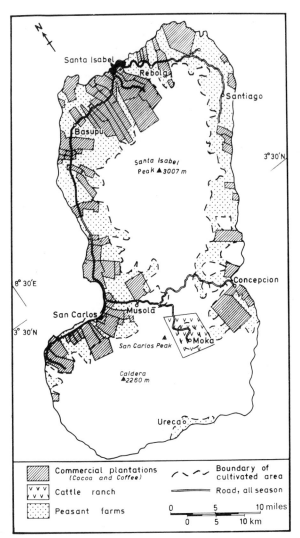

FIG. 17.3—Fernando Po: agricultural land use

Fernando Po is now self-sufficient in dairy products, although some meat is still imported from Cameroon Republic. In 1967 the cattle population was 2,300, of which 2,080 were in the Moka district.

Goats, sheep and poultry are kept in the villages. In 1967, there were 17,570 goats, 15,280 sheep, 8,730 pigs and 91,000 chickens. Modern poultry keeping is largely restricted to European farms.

Forestry

Extensive areas of high forest occur in areas lying between the coastal plantations and the highland pastures. Steep slopes and valley sides also support dense forests which provide timber for domestic use as well as for export. In the country as a whole,

forestry products come third in the export trade (by value), after cocoa and coffee.

Mining

A few limestone deposits are worked to feed the only cement factory in the country. Quarrying of stones for building is also important. Mineral oil and gas are suspected to occur in large quantities in the continental shelf and the results of offshore drillings, which started in 1967, have been encouraging.

Manufacturing industry

There is as yet very little industrial development in Fernando Po, and almost all the existing industries are concerned with the processing of local agricultural and forest products. At independence in 1968, there was one cement factory, two fish-canning factories and three soap works. There are also factories for processing cocoa and coffee, paper processing and leather work. Small-scale industries include saw milling, mechanical workshops and corn milling. Power for industry and domestic use comes from thermal power stations, using coal and diesel.

POPULATION AND SETTLEMENT

In 1962, the population of Fernando Po was about 71,000 of which 22,550 were migrants, predominantly of eastern Nigerian origin. The number of migrants to the island increased to over 45,000 in 1969 as a result of the influx of refugees from the short-lived Republic of Biafra (formerly Eastern Nigeria). The indigenous inhabitants are called Bubis (from the Bantu stock) and numbered 33,500 in 1962. The Bubi population was on the decline during the early decades of this century, but since about 1950, there has been a slight increase in their numbers.

Over 90 per cent of the 7,500 whites in 1962 were Spaniards (government officials, missionaries and plantation managers), but the number of Spaniards declined to no more than 600 after the disturbances of March 1969, which broke out barely one year after Spain granted independence to the territory. There is also a small but economically very active mulatto group called the Fernandinos, a mixture of Bubi and Portuguese or Spanish blood. In 1962, this group numbered only 2,500.

The migrant population is employed almost exclusively on the plantations and in 1962, 80 per cent of the migrants were men. The African population of the island is therefore predominantly male

137

PLATE 69 — Extinct volcanoes and montane cathedral on Fernando Po

and in 1962, there were about two men to one woman! Apart from the Protestants and a few Muslims amongst the migrant population, most of the inhabitants (about 80 per cent) are Roman Catholics.

The Bubis, who are found mainly in the coastal areas, live in small villages. Their huts are rectangular and generally larger than most African huts. In the cooler highland areas, the huts usually have up to three fireplaces as well as a thick layer of thatch on the outer walls.

Housing is provided free for plantation workers who live in barrack-like villages. A room of about 3.6 metres (12ft) square is allocated to each family or to at least two unmarried male labourers. Some of the larger plantation villages have small hospitals or maternity homes and shopping facilities.

The capital city of Santa Isabel

Santa Isabel is the capital and largest town in Equatorial Guinea. It was founded under the name of Port Clarence in 1827 by the British who leased the port from Spain so as to station their anti-slavery naval patrol there. About a half of the total population of Fernando Po and 60 per cent of the non-African population lived in Santa Isabel in 1962. The town is well planned and is noted for its spacious streets and stone buildings.

The port of Santa Isabel has a natural deep-water harbour which is semi-circular in shape. Most of the trade of Fernando Po and all passengers arriving by boat pass through this port which also has regular boat and canoe services with Calabar. There is also a regular boat traffic between Santa Isabel and Bata in the mainland territory of Rio Muni and with the Cameroon port of Douala.

Santa Isabel is more of a European than an African town and is more like Dakar or Nairobi, rather than Ibadan or Kano. Its layout, shopping facilities and catheral are more Spanish than African and even the generally less satisfactory African suburbs are much cleaner and healthier than the slums of Ibadan or Lagos.

Other towns

San Carlos, Conception and Moka are the other important urban centres. San Carlos is the second port and the centre of the banana trade. Moka derives its importance from the cattle industry while Conception is a prominent holiday resort.

138

TRANSPORTATION

The road network of Fernando Po (Fig. 17.2, p. 136) shows clearly that the primary purpose of road construction is to facilitate the transportation of cocoa and coffee from the plantations to the main ports of Santa Isabel, San Carlos and Conception. Roads suitable for motorized transport are therefore restricted to the plantation districts which are located in the lowland areas bordering the northern, eastern and western coasts. Along the southern coast where there are no plantations no road has been built. There are also no roads in the rugged uplands of the interior and the only trans-island highway which passes through these uplands is the main access road linking the cattle-rearing district of Moka to the port-towns of San Carlos and Conception. The total length of motor roads is about 800km (500 miles) of which just over 190km (120 miles) is tarred.

Santa Isabel has the only international airport which can take all types of jet aircraft. There are two other airstrips at San Carlos and Moka.

FOREIGN TRADE

Largely as a result of Spanish preferential duties for cocoa and coffee from Fernando Po, the island has always had a positive trade balance. It is the special price (above world market prices) paid by Spain for cocoa from Fernando Po that enables the island's cocoa economy to compete with Ghana and western Nigeria, where production costs are lower. And since Spain buys almost all the exports from Fernando Po (92 per cent by value in 1967), the removal of Spanish preferences will have an adverse effect on the island's economy. Spain is also the largest supplier of imports (66 per cent in 1967).

Chapter 18—Gambia

PLATE 70—Banjul, Gambia

Gambia obtained its independence from Britain in 1965 and is by far the smallest country in West Africa. It has a land area of only 11,000 sq.km (4,000 sq. miles) or three times the size of the Lagos State of Nigeria, and a population of less than 400,000, which is less than half of the population of metropolitan Lagos. The shape of the country is rather peculiar, stretching as it does from west to east for 480km (300 miles) with an average width of not more than 32km (20 miles). The Gambia River, after which the country is named, is the dominant relief feature and has always remained the most important means of transport in the country.

Attempts to get this mini-state amalgamated with Senegal which surrounds it on three sides have so far failed with the result that Gambia still survives as one of the 'freaks' of colonialism in West Africa. Its excellent waterway has never been fully utilized since much of its natural hinterland forms part of another country which has spent much money in building artificial ports rather than using the excellent natural harbour at Banjul. Like Senegal, Gambia is a poor country which probably does not see much economic advantage in a union with her big neighbour. Their two economies depend overwhelmingly on groundnuts and both cultures have much in common.

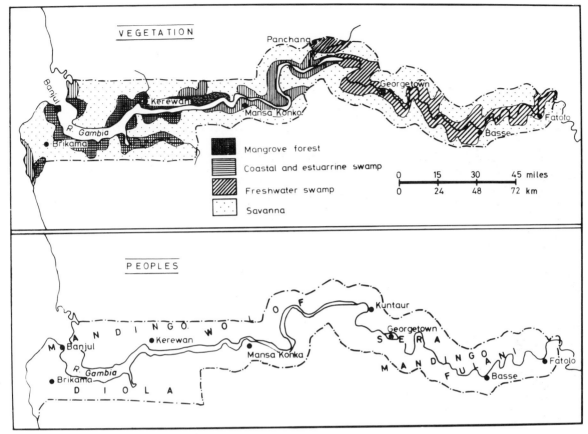

FIG. 18.1—Gambia: vegetation and peoples

RELIEF, DRAINAGE AND SOILS

This is a low-lying country in which no place has an elevation of more than 180m (600ft) above sea level. The coastal region in particular is a rather flat and monotonous area of marine and windborne sands but the relief of the country is best discussed under three regions, namely: 1) the Gambia floodplains, 2) the surrounding pleatux, 3) the Gambia River.

1. The Gambia floodplains (or *Bantos Faros*)

These are areas of grassland vegetation which are usually submerged during the flood season. Much of the area is populated by raffia palm and the soils, which consist of light alluvium, are very fertile. Above Kuntaur which is the upper limit of salt water and mangroves, the fertile floodplains provide the richest rice lands of the country. The area from Kuntaur to the sea is however useless for farming because of the regular invasion of sea water which has made the soils saline.

2. The surrounding plateaux

These areas consist of low hills of sandstone separated by shallow valleys. Much of the land is covered with lateritic soils and is relatively very infertile. Tall grass and baobab trees abound. Being above flood levels, the plateaux, despite their poor soils, have attracted many settlements and therefore support a relatively dense population. Fortunately the soils are light and suitable for groundnut cultivation.

3. The Gambia River

The river is about 20km (12 miles) wide at its mouth at Cape St. Mary but narrows to only 5km (3 miles) at Banjul. It has a bar at 8m (27ft) depth at the mouth but this can be crossed by ships at any state of the tide. It rises in the Futa Jallon Highlands and has a length of over 1,120km (700 miles). Ocean vessels drawing up to 4m (13ft) can go up to Kuntaur which is 240km (150 miles) from the sea, while smaller craft can go a further 225km (140 miles) at all seasons of the year. For the first 130km (80 miles) upstream from Banjul,

141

the river is fringed with mangroves but further inland the swamps give way to red ironstone cliffs. Hippopotamuses and crocodiles are very common in the upper reaches which are also dotted with many towns and villages, most of which have port facilities for the landing of river vessels. Like other West African rivers, the Gambia experiences considerable seasonal fluctuations in water levels. The penetration of salt water also varies with the seasons, being about 150km (93 miles) upstream of Banjul in the wet season and increasing to 225km (140 miles) during the dry season.

CLIMATE

Unlike other parts of West Africa, the rainy season starts from the interior (in April) and reaches the coast towards the end of June. The interior also has a longer rainy season (April–September) as compared with that of the coastal areas (June–October). August is the rainiest month everywhere. The annual total rainfall rarely exceeds, 1,140mm (45in.), but small as this amount may appear, it is sufficient to cause extensive floods along the *bantos faros* (*fadamas*).

The interior is much hotter than the coastal area which benefits from regular sea breezes. Temperatures are also more even in the coastal areas which do not experience severe harmattans as do the interior parts of the country. The hottest months are June to October which are also the wet-season months. During the dry season, which is characterized by clear skies and constant sunshine, the mean maximum temperature is about 27°C (81°F) and the mean minimum 20°C (68°F).

POPULATION AND SETTLEMENT

In 1963, the population of Gambia was 316,000 but according to the 1973 census there were 494,300 people in the country. More than 90 per cent of the people live in rural areas and apart from Banjul, which has a population of 28,000, no other settlement has more than 5,000 persons. The most densely settled areas are the interior plateaux which are free from floodwaters.

Although Gambia is a very small country, it is inhabited by people of different ethnic groups (see Fig. 18.1) of which the most numerous is the Mandinka or Mandingo (130,000) who are found settled all over the country. The Fulanis, who are found in most countries of West Africa, are also represented here. They number 70,000 and live mainly in the middle- and upper-river districts. Their main occupation is

cattle-rearing. The Wolofs or Jolofs (40,000) are found mainly in Banjul and the surrounding areas but the area south of Banjul is the home of the Jolas who are the most numerous people in the Casamance province of Senegal, and who live in scattered agricultural hamlets.

At Banjul, as in Freetown, Lagos and Accra, there is a large group of detribalized Africans who consist mainly of descendants of liberated slaves. This group is usually referred to as the Aku community of Banjul, and is rather influential in commerce and politics.

The large number of foreigners (aliens) in Gambia (35,000 in 1963) is striking. According to this census, as many as ten per cent of the population were born outside the country. Of this number 21,000 came from Senegal and consisted primarily of seasonal migrant farmers, although some were permanent immigrants. The rest of the migrant population came from Mali, Guinea and Portuguese Guinea and most of them worked as labourers or self-employed farmers on groundnut farms. The strange farmers, as the migrants are called, usually live in the villages of the local people from whom they rent farmland. Usually, the migrants work for three days on their own farms, and for two or three days on the farms of their landlords, who also provide them with accommodation.

Banjul (28,000)

The capital city of Banjul is a well-planned town built on a low-lying sandbank. It is the main commercial and administrative centre as well as the most important port of the country. Almost all the groundnut exports from the interior, including those smuggled in from Senegal are sent to Europe from Banjul whose deep-water wharf takes ships drawing up to 8m (27ft) of water. The airport at Yundum provides a direct link with London and many West African countries. (See plates 70, 71.)

Other settlements

The other important settlements in the country are either river-ports or district headquarters or both. One of these port-towns is Georgetown which is located on MacCarthy Island. It was originally settled by escaped slaves and later grew up to become an important interior port for evacuating groundnuts. Its decline followed the establishment of Kuntaur, at the highest point of navigation on the River Gambia for ocean vessels. Other up-river ports include Balingho, Kerewan, Basse and Bansang.

Farm villages in the lower Gambia Valley are usually sited along the boundary between the plateaux and the floodplains so as to avoid floodwaters. This arrangement is also beneficial since the villages are located near the swamps where the women grow rice and the uplands where the men cultivate groundnuts. Further upstream, the *bantos faros* stand much higher than the river level and are therefore less liable to flooding. This is why there is a number of settlements on the *bantos faros* of central and upper Gambia.

AGRICULTURE

Food-crop production

The economy of Gambia is based on agriculture, which is dominated by peasant production for home consumption and internal exchange as well as for export. Rice is the most important food crop and is grown mainly in swamps although a little amount of upland rice is also produced. The main producing areas are the *bantos faros* (floodplains) of the middle reaches of the Gambia River, the lower reaches being too salty for the crop. Rice seedlings are usually raised in small fields or nurseries before being transplanted in late July when the farms are flooded. On the nearby uplands, millet, maize and cassava replace rice as the main field crops. Guinea corn is also important. Most farmers practise mixed cropping but do not often produce enough to feed their family. And inspite of a determined effort by the government to increase local food production, Gambia is still not self-sufficient in food production and has continued to import rice every year. It is hoped that current attempts at reclaiming the saline mangrove swamps for rice cultivation will result in a considerable increase in the quantity of locally-produced rice (Fig. 18.2).

Farming along the floodplains can be considered to be permanent cultivation in that the fields are cultivated every year unlike in the uplands where the farmers adopt the rotation of bush fallow system. Permanent cultivation along the floodplains is made possible by the annual floods during which the soils are replenished by alluvium spread by floodwaters.

Export crops

The export trade of Gambia is based entirely on groundnuts which are exported through the Gambia Oilseeds Marketing Board. More than 84,000 hectares

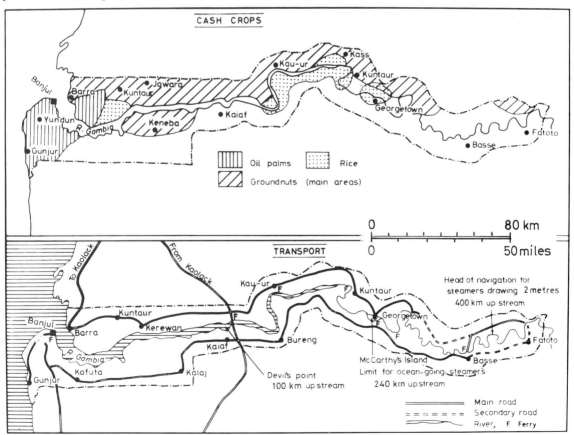

FIG. 18.2—Gambia: cash crops and transport

PLATE 71—Creole style houses and woman with stone pattern cloth in Banjul, Gambia.

(207,480 acres) are put under the crop every year and almost every farmer in the country cultivates ground-nuts. Groundnuts form the principal source of wealth in the country, accounting for about 98 per cent of the export earnings. The buying season, which lasts from December to April, is a period when money gets into the hands of most farmers and when dealers in consumer goods make maximum sales.

Groundnuts grow best on the light and rather infertile soils of the grass-covered plateaux. Fortunately the rainfall is everywhere above the minimum of 735mm (25in.) required for the crop to thrive under the hot and dry climate of the plateaux. In addition to local peasant farmers, a large number of migrant farmers from Mali and Guinea come in every year to grow groundnuts in Gambia. These migrants usually rent farmland from the local people and normally return to their country of origin after harvesting and selling their crops.

The first year that groundnuts were exported was in 1830 and since then the output has risen gradually, reaching a peak in 1968, when 150,000 tons were exported. A considerable proportion of the crop is consumed locally.

Other agricultural products from the country include palm kernels, hides and skins and beeswax. Palm kernel and beeswax formed the basis of the early export trade after the abolition of the slave trade, but today both account for about 3 per cent of the export by value. Cotton is grown for making local cloth.

Livestock

Although Gambia is infested by the tsetse fly, which is fatal to cattle, the cattle population of the country has increased considerably following the successful use of innoculation against trypanasomiasis. In 1970, there was an estimated 250,000 head of cattle in the country, largely under the control of the local Fulanis. Gambia also imports cattle for slaughter from Senegal and Mauritania.

Sheep (76,100) are also common and are in great demand during Muslim festivals. Poultry is kept in every village in the form of small local chickens which are left to wander around the homesteads in search of food. A major poultry scheme launched in 1948 by the then Colonial Development Corporation (now Commonwealth Development Corporation) was abandoned three years later resulting in a loss of about 3.2 million dalasi (₦1,600,000). The project, which was aimed at supplying the British market, was located at Yundum, where the only international airport is also located.

MANUFACTURING INDUSTRY

The establishment of light industries in Gambia has been greatly handicapped by the smallness of the home market and the fact that Gambia can hardly market her products in Senegal. The only industries of importance are groundnut milling and a ship-repair workshop at Banjul. There are, however, a number of small cottage industries making gold and silver ornaments, leather bags and sandals for sale in Banjul and other towns.

EXTERNAL TRADE

Almost all the exports of Gambia (90 per cent in 1962) went to the United Kingdom and Italy, the proportion to Italy being slightly higher than that to the United Kingdom. In the same year the United Kingdom accounted for 40 per cent of Gambia's total imports, the rest coming from Japan, India, West Germany and the Netherlands. Unlike neighbouring Senegal which sent 85 per cent of her exports in 1962 to France and obtained 70 per cent of her imports from that country, the trade policy of Gambia is less discriminatory. In 1968/9 Gambia imported goods to the value of 37.2 million dalasi (N 18.6 million) exceeding the previous year's value by 24 per cent. Total exports in the same year were valued at 29.6 million dalasi (N14.8 million) showing a 30 per cent increase over the previous year. The unfavourable balance of trade recorded for that year is unfortunately a regular feature of the Gambian economy which is far from healthy. Indeed for two years after independence, Gambia had to depend on grants and aid from the United Kingdom to balance her budget and it is only since 1967/8 that Gambia has been able to balance her budget.

In addition to groundnuts, which account for over 90 per cent by value of her exports, Gambia also exports a small quantity of palm kernels (valued at less than 400,000 dalasi (N200,000) per annum. Important items on the import list include textiles and clothing, rice, building materials and motor vehicles.

THE QUESTION OF INTEGRATION WITH SENEGAL

Gambia and Senegal were administered together for twenty years up till 1783 as the British colony of Senegambia. In the 1870s negotiations to exchange Gambia with some French West African territory were twice broken off because of opposition from the people of Gambia as well as from some British merchants and politicians. Thus the opportunity to re-unite the two territories of Gambia and Senegal was lost.

Today, it appears that the solution to Gambia's economic problems lies in union with Senegal, which is twenty times as large as Gambia. The population of Senegal in 1963 was ten times as large. A political union would make for an effective use of the Gambia waterway and natural harbour of Banjul, and Senegal would feel less concerned about subversion against her by refugees resident in Gambia. Large-scale smuggling from Gambia into Senegal would stop.

The problem today is that while Senegal wants Gambia to be fully integrated with her, the Gambians reject the idea of their country becoming a province of Senegal. Rather they want a federal arrangement with substantial autonomy for Gambia, but this is not acceptable to Senegal.

Table 17—Trade balance of Gambia in million dalasis

	1960	1965	1966	1967	1968	1969	1970	1971	1972
Imports	16.1	29.0	32.5	35.0	43.9	40.6	37.4	54.4	49.5
Exports	13.9	24.4	28.5	31.9	26.8	24.4	35.1	27.7	37.4
Balance	−2.2	−4.6	−4.0	−3.1	−17.1	−16.2	−2.3	−26.7	−12.1

Source: *United Nations E.C.A. Statistical Yearbook*, 1973, Part 2, West Africa, pp. 8–9.

Note: 100 dalasi = £25 = N50.00.

Chapter 19—The Republic of Ghana

PLATE 72—*Aerial view of Accra, Ghana*

Ghana became independent of British rule in 1957 when it adopted its present name in preference to the former name of the Gold Coast. Its present name is taken from the ancient Sudanese empire which existed about 1,000 years ago in the region of present-day southern Mali. It is believed that the present-day inhabitants of Ghana came from this ancient Sudanese kingdom.

The country has an area of 239,000 sq.km (92,100 sq. miles) and an estimated population of 9.1 million (1972). It is the most advanced, though by no means the largest or richest country in West Africa. Its present economic problems include an unfavourable trade balance, over-dependence on cocoa production, rising unemployment and lack of self-sufficiency in basic foodstuffs like cassava and yam, large quantities

of which are imported from Togo and Benin.

In other parts of the world, Ghana is best known for its place as the world's largest cocoa producer as well as for the dynamism of the late ex-President Kwame Nkrumah, the man who led the country to independence.

PHYSICAL REGIONS

Considering the geology and the relief of the land, Ghana may be divided into six physical regions. These are: 1) the coastal lowlands, 2) the Accra-Trans-Volta Plains, 3) the Togo-Akwapim Hills, 4) the Ashanti-Kwahu Uplands 5) the Volta Basin, 6) the northern and western high plains. (See Fig. 19.1.)

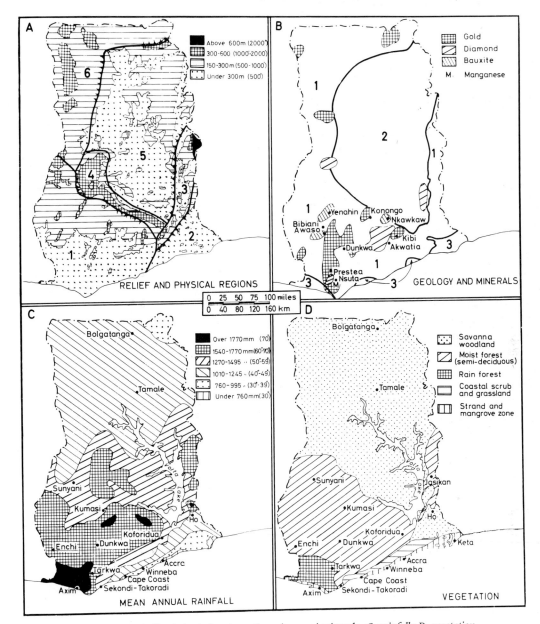

FIG. 19.1—Ghana: A. relief and physical regions: B. geology and minerals: C. rainfall: D. vegetation.

1. The coastal lowlands

The coastal lowlands consist of highly dissected plains underlaid by old hard rocks of the Basement Complex. Several hills and ridges which are separated by wide flat-bottomed valleys occur all over the plains. These hills and ridges are aligned in a north-east to south-west direction and several of them have a thick capping of lateritic soils.

All rivers in this region follow a north-south direction. Some of the more important rivers include the

Tano, which is by far the longest river in the region, the Ankobra and the Pra.

East of Cape Three Points, several lagoons occur behind the sandy beaches that fringe the coast. This part of the coast is also characterized by bays and headlands, unlike the rather smooth stretch west of the cape. Most of the trading forts and castles of Ghana including those of Princes Town, Cape Coast and Axim were built on the cliffs of these rocky headlands.

Lake Bosumtwi which is located 29km (18 miles)

147

south-east of Kumasi is a unique feature of the physical landscape of the region. It has a diameter of about 10km (6 miles) and a depth of over 72m (240 ft), and is thought to be a crater lake.

2. The Accra-Trans-Volta Plains

These plains are the westward extension of the clay plains or the Terre de Barre of the coastal areas of Togo and Benin. This region is commonly known as the Accra Plains, but since Accra lies at the western limit of the region, it is better to describe the area as the Accra-Trans-Volta Plains. The whole area is gently undulating and because of the open character of its poor grassland vegetation, it is possible to observe its vast extent as far as the eye can see. Low hills, numerous inselbergs and ridges occur here and there to break the monotony of the rural landscape.

The Accra-Trans-Volta Plains are characterized by broad and ill-defined valleys which carry seasonal streams. The lower Volta, which is the main river draining the region, enters the sea in a delta while the other important stream, the River Todzie flows into one of the numerous lagoons along or near the coast. The Keta Lagoon, which is the largest of the saline lagoons, is an important source of fish and salt.

3. The Togo-Akwapim Hills

The Akwapim range of hills begin a few kilometres north of Accra and continue north-eastwards beyond the Volta Gorge to become the Togo Hills. It is along the water gap created through the hills by the Volta River that the Volta Dam at Akosombo is built. The general height of the land in the region is between 300 and 450m (1,000–1,500ft), but there are several summits which rise above 600m (2,000ft). Unlike the Accra grass plains in the south, these hills are covered by dense forest vegetation owing to the heavy rains which are caused by the high local relief of the region. It was in the Akwapim Hills that the first cocoa trees in Ghana were cultivated.

In general the Togo Hills are much higher and more dissected than the Akwapim ranges. The valleys of the Togo Hills are also much wider while the slopes are more forested than those of the Akwapim Hills.

4. The Ashanti-Kwahu Uplands

Although these uplands are generally higher and more extensive than the Akwapim-Togo ranges, they are much less rugged. The western slope of the uplands consists of a scarp surface which overlooks the coastal lowlands. Like the Akwapim-Togo Hills, the uplands have a much higher rainfall of 1,400–1,520mm (55–60in.) and a much denser forest vegetation than the coastal areas of south-east Ghana.

These uplands constitute the main watershed of the country and separate rivers flowing into the Volta Basin from those which flow directly into the sea. The region, which is well watered, is a major cocoa-growing area.

5. The Volta Basin

This region consists of a great syncline filled with sandstone. With a total area of about 103,630 sq.km (40,000 sq. miles) or about 45 per cent of the area of the country, it is the largest physical region of Ghana and has an average elevation of not more than 180m (600ft). It is surrounded on all sides by highlands and is truly shaped like a basin. The entire basin is drained by the Volta River system, and lately by the great Volta Lake.

The Volta Basin is Ghana's problem region. It has shallow and infertile soils. Parts of it are flooded in the rainy season but suffer from lack of water during the dry season. The area is largely infested by diseases like sleeping sickness and river blindness. It is not surprising therefore that the region is sparsely settled and very poorly developed.

In the south, that is, in the region of the Afram Plains, the average height of the land is 90m (300ft). The Afram River, which drains that southern part, is one of the main tributaries of the Volta. Much of its valley has been drowned to form the Volta Lake.

Lake Volta is a large man-made lake impounded behind the 75m (250ft) high dam at Akosombo, built to provide hydro-electric power for the country. The lake covers an area of 8,485 sq.km (3,275 sq. miles) and is a major fishing ground in Ghana.

6. The northern and western highlands

This is a region of high plains developed on old hard rocks of the Basement Complex. Granite inselbergs and bare rock surfaces are common particularly in the northern parts of the region. The general elevation of the region is about 180–360m (600–1,200ft). It has very good soils and is an important farming region.

CLIMATE AND VEGETATION

Climate

Fig. 19.1C shows the mean annual rainfall of Ghana and should be compared with the relief map of Ghana

(Fig. 19.1A). You will find that the rainiest part of Ghana is the south-west, with an average annual rainfall of over 2,030mm (80in.) along the coast. East of Cape Three Points, the coast becomes very dry, particularly in the Accra-Trans-Volta region which is the driest part of Ghana. The rainfall of this coastal dry belt is less than 990mm (35in.) per annum, that of Accra being only 785mm (27in.).

You will also notice the effect of relief on the rainfall of Ghana. The Mampong scarp is an effective climatic divide separating the region of heavy annual rainfall in the south-west from the areas of lesser rainfall in the Volta Basin. The annual rainfall on the Togo Hills is considerably higher than that in the nearby Volta Plains.

The area approximately south of latitude 8°N. has four seasons, namely:
i)   the long dry season, when the harmattan blows (November–April)
ii) the first or long rainy season (May–July)
iii) the short dry season or monsoon drought (late July and early August)
iv) the second or short rainy season (September and October).

The rainiest month in this southern part is June.

By comparison, that part of Ghana lying north of latitude 8°N. has only two seasons. These are:
i)   the dry season (November–April)
ii) the rainy season (May–October).

The dry season is a period of high temperatures exceeding 32°C (90°F) in the day and is characterized by cool nights and low relative humidity. This is also the period when the harmattan blows.

Other aspects of the climate such as reliability of the rainfall, are similar to those for the rest of West Africa as outlined in Chapter 2.

Vegetation

The map of vegetation zones (Fig. 19.1D) resembles very closely that of the mean annual rainfall (Fig. 19.1C). Can you explain why this is so? If you have any difficulty, turn to the section on the climate and vegetation of West Africa (Chapters 2 and 3). More detailed information on the vegetation can also be obtained in this section.

The main vegetation zones are shown in the key to the map but it is sufficient to discuss the vegetation of Ghana under two heads. These are: i) the forest group, ii) the savanna group.

Forest vegetation is restricted to the south-west and the rainy uplands of eastern Ghana. Dense tropical rain-forest vegetation occupies a relatively small area in the rainiest part along the coastal lowlands of south-west Ghana. The rest of the south-west is covered by a less dense semi-deciduous forest, much of which has been cut down and planted with cocoa.

Deciduous forests also clothe the summits and slopes of the Togo Hills, which is another cocoa-farming area. There are also patches of true forest vegetation along the beds of rivers in the grassland areas of the far north.

Savanna or grassland vegetation covers about two-thirds the area of Ghana, including the coastal areas east of Cape Three Points. The coastal savanna is peculiar to Ghana, and is so dry that trees of the far north including the borassus palm and the baobab are found growing very near the coast. Immediately behind the coastline, the coastal savanna gives way to a largely man-made vegetation of dense groves of coconut palms.

You will notice from Fig. 19.1D that the coastal savanna covers a relatively small part of Ghana. Apart from another small area of sudan or acacia savanna in the extreme north-east, the rest of Ghana supports the Guinea savanna vegetation, which has a much higher tree density. The Guinea savanna zone supports a yam-grain economy as compared with the grain-pulse economy of the sudan savanna.

AGRICULTURE

Farming practices

Farming practices and farm implements in use are as outlined for corresponding belts (forest or grassland) in the chapter on agriculture in West Africa (Chapter 7). As in other parts of West Africa, shifting cultivation is common in sparsely settled areas, but in most parts of the south, this method of farming has since been replaced by fixed cultivation. Factors which have brought about fixed cultivation include the spread of individual land ownership in place of communal land ownership and the increase in rural population resulting in a shortage of farmland. These two factors are related in the sense that it is the shortage of farmland that has led to the failure of the traditional system of landholding in which authority over land was vested in the chief or village council. Today, people such as the Krobo farmers of Ghana can pay cash for land even outside their ethnic territory.

Other factors which have led to the spread of fixed cultivation are road building, the expansion of cocoa farming and the creation of forest reserves. Since cocoa takes a long time to bear fruit, it is necessary that the farmer lives in one place for a long time. By restricting the area of land available to some village groups, the creation of forest reserves caused a shortage of farmland and thus the fixation of settlement.

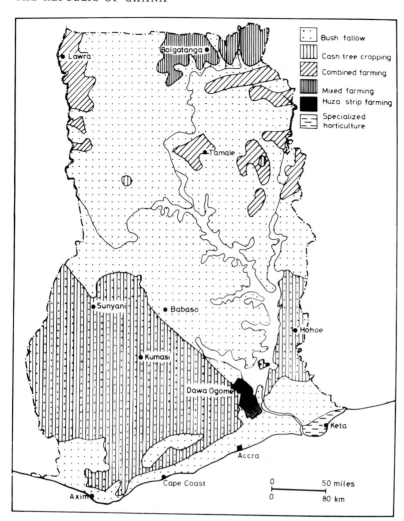

FIG. 19.2—Ghana: land use types

Legend:
- Bush fallow
- Cash tree cropping
- Combined farming
- Mixed farming
- Huza strip farming
- Specialized horticulture

0   50 miles
0   80 km

Although most Ghanaians are farmers, the country does not produce enough food to feed its people. The main food-deficit areas are the Accra plains and the coastal lowlands. Foodstuffs like palm oil, garri and yams are not produced in sufficient quantities, and have to be supplemented by imports from the neighbouring countries. It is usual to claim that the emphasis on cocoa cultivation is the cause of food shortage in parts of Ghana. There is no doubt that in the cocoa belt, land which could have been used for food crops is planted with cocoa, but it is important to realize that most of the food eaten in the cocoa belt is grown by the cocoa farmers themselves.

Farming regions

The main farming regions of Ghana correspond with the vegetation regions, namely the forest region, the region of coastal savannas and the northern savanna region. (See Fig. 19.2.)

The most important farming zone within the forest region is the cocoa belt which lies along the northern and eastern part of the forest region. Cocoa is the principal crop but plantain, maize, cocoyam and cassava are also cultivated. It is in the Krobo district and the south-eastern part of the forest that food production is carried out on a commercial scale, even if by African standards. In these districts, there are large farms in which maize, cocoyam and cassava are grown for sale in the neighbouring metropolitan district of Accra-Tema.

In the region of coastal savannas, food production is largely restricted to cassava which appears to be the only crop that can stand the dry climatic conditions and poor soils of this area. Maize is grown where conditions are wetter, while coconuts are planted along the coastal sands. Fishing is, however, the main occupation of this region, which is settled by some of the most skilled fishermen along the coast of West Africa. The Accra plains support numerous herds

150

of cattle, and can become a major cattle-producing area if the problems of poor grazing and water shortage during the dry season can be overcome.

Farming in the northern savanna region is primarily concerned with the production of food for the home, although there is a growing export trade in yams, poultry and livestock to other regions of Ghana. Cattle-rearing is important in the far north which is almost completely free of tsetse flies. The variable nature of the rainfall makes agriculture rather precarious in the far north, which is plagued by crop failures and food shortages during the so-called hungry season (March—May).

One of the main food-exporting zones in the region is the north Ashanti yam belt which supplies yams to Kumasi, Accra and other large towns. Farm sizes are larger here than in most parts of Ghana and most of the farmers employ hired labour. Swamp rice is important in the eastern districts which also produce yam and guinea corn.

Production and marketing of cocoa

As the largest source of revenue to the government and the main source of wealth to the people of the south, cocoa plays a very important part in the economy of Ghana. It accounts for about two-thirds of the value of exports from the country and provides employment for thousands of people including farm labourers, lorry drivers, dock workers, buying agents and their middlemen. The present high level of social and economic development in the country has been made possible by revenue from cocoa.

Cocoa was introduced into Ghana in the second half of the nineteenth century and by 1899 about 324 tons were exported from the country. In 1914 the export figure was 50,000 tons, rising to an all-time record of 311,000 tons in 1936. After 1936, production declined so much that from 1937 to 1959 it was higher prices, rather than increased production, that maintained the prosperity of the cocoa belt and the country. Annual production averaged 240,000 tons in the 1950s but rose sharply to 420,000 tons a year between 1960 and 1964 and to 520,000 tons in 1965. Since then production has averaged about 400,000 tons a year.

Today, Ghana is the world's largest producer of cocoa. The most remarkable fact about the Ghana cocoa industry is that production is controlled by peasant farmers, not by plantations. Cocoa farms vary in size from less than 0.5 hectares (1.25 acres) to over 20 hectares (50 acres), the average size being 1 hectare (2.5 acres).

Cocoa seedlings are usually inter-planted with food crops for the first four years. Seedlings are planted rather closely at about 1.5m (5ft) intervals and the first sizeable harvest comes when the trees are about six years old. Planting takes place in March and April, and the main harvesting season is from October to January followed by a light harvest season (April—June).

Most cocoa farmers employ paid labour at all stages of cocoa production. The labourers consist mainly of migrants from northern Ghana, Sokoto Province in Nigeria and the Mossi district of Upper Volta. There are also a number of Krobo labourers, but many Krobo migrants buy and own large cocoa farms. Many cocoa farms are owned by absentee landlords who are usually lawyers, teachers and civil servants living in far-away places. Such farms are usually looked after by caretakers who live close by.

The preparation of cocoa beans for export is a critical process in the cocoa industry since the quality of the crop, and therefore the price paid to the farmer, depends on how the beans are prepared. The pods are usually split in the farm and the beans are carried to the village where they are piled into heaps and covered with leaves and left to ferment. During fermentation, which takes about six days, the beans are thoroughly mixed every two days. The beans are then spread out on mats, corrugated iron sheets or concrete slabs to dry in the sun.

The dried beans are sold through various categories of middlemen to the Cocoa Marketing Board, which controls the sales and export of cocoa. The Marketing Board was set up during the Second World War so as to stabilize the price paid to the cocoa farmer, and thereby prevent the extreme fluctuations in prices and the consequent hardships which cocoa farmers suffered before the war. The Board announces a fixed producer price every year and appoints licensed buying agents, who in turn buy from small-scale middlemen. The cocoa is then sold in the world market by the Marketing Board, and in years when the price is high in the world market, the Board is expected to keep the difference between the price it receives and the price it pays to the farmer so that when the prices fall in the world market, the accumulated funds can be used to subsidize the price paid to the farmer. In practice the Board has usually paid less to the farmer than it receives in the world market with the result that by 1953, the Board had already accumulated £53 million sterling which was in 1976 approximately equivalent to 130 million cedis.

All licensed buying agents have depots where the cocoa is graded before it is packed for shipment. Grade I cocoa obtains a much better price than grade II cocoa and must have less than 5 per cent bad beans.

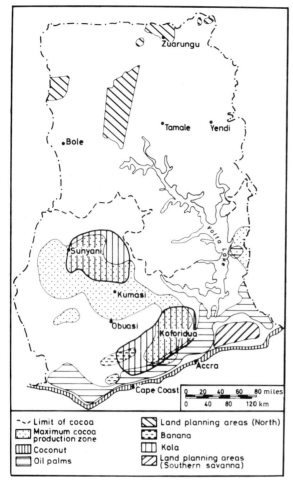

FIG. 19.3—Ghana: tree crops

Legend:
- ~·~ Limit of cocoa
- Maximum cocoa production zone
- Coconut
- Oil palms
- Land planning areas (North)
- Banana
- Kola
- Land planning areas (Southern savanna)

One of the problems facing cocoa production is the spread of Swollen Shoot disease which is carried from tree to tree by the mealy bug, a small insect which feeds on the sap of trees. The only effective way to combat the disease is by cutting out affected trees, a practice which is not very popular with farmers. Vast areas of cocoa farms have had to be abandoned because of the disease, which is also responsible for the fact that kola is replacing cocoa in some parts of the cocoa belt. Black Pod fungus is another serious disease which destroys many ripening cocoa pods.

Other cash crops

Kola is perhaps the oldest cash crop of the forest zone. It is in great demand all over the western Sudan where kola nut is eaten more as a stimulant (like tobacco or coffee) rather than as food. Up till 1930, Ghana was the leading supplier of kola nuts to Nigeria, but that country now produces enough for its Sudanese population.

Although kola trees grow throughout the forest belt, commercial production takes place in the area to the north and west of Kumasi and in the Oda-Koforidua area which is located in the south-eastern part of the forest belt. It is in this latter area that kola is replacing cocoa.

The oil palm was formerly important but has become very insignificant today largely as a result of emphasis on cocoa production. Apart from a few plantations such as the 400 hectare (1,000 acre) estate at Sese, near Takoradi, almost all the palm oil comes from palm trees growing wild on farmland or fallow bush.

Nearer the sea, the coconut palm becomes the most important economic crop. The dry nut is exported as copra although a considerable proportion is crushed locally to produce oil used in making soap and margarine. The husks are used as fuel while the fibre or coir is used in making ropes. Coffee is produced on a small scale in the Togo Hills at Amedzofe and along the Ivory Coast border in the Wenchi-Sunyani District.

Livestock

The livestock population has increased considerably in recent years, although a fair proportion of the animals slaughtered each year is still imported from Mali and Niger. The domestic cattle population is concentrated in the northern region and the Accra Plains where the shorthorn breed is common.

The dry and open grassland vegetation of the Accra Plains does not provide a good environment for the tsetse fly, and is therefore suitable for keeping cattle. Unfortunately the area is too dry and water, as well as grazing, is scarce. Since the local people do not breed their cattle primarily for sale, and since the shorthorn cattle are small and grow slowly, the Accra-Tema urban population have had to import much of their meat, although there are numerous local breeds in the Accra plains. (See Table 18 opposite.)

FORESTRY AND FOREST PRODUCTS

Forest products play an important part both in the subsistence economy and the export trade of the country. After cocoa and minerals, timber is the most valuable export (Table 19, p. 154), Ghana being one of the largest producers of hardwoods in the world. Although a proportion of the timber exports comes from the 14,508 sq.km (5,600 sq. miles) of forest reserves in the south-west, the main source of timber both for the home and the export markets is the

Table 18—Livestock in Ghana

	1966	1967	1968	1970	1972
Cattle	528,000	552,000	543,000	903,000	908,000
Sheep	486,000	509,000	640,000	1,339,900	1,332,000
Goats	412,000	550,000	566,000	1,412,400	1,700,000 *
Pigs	81,000	83,000	107,000	268,000	280,000
Poultry	941,000	2,326,000	2,517,000	8,874,000	12,000,000 *

*F.A.O. Estimates.

13,627 sq.km (5,260 sq. miles) of unreserved forest.

Several species of timber-producing trees are exploited, the most popular being mahogany, wawa, sapele and odum (iroko). Timber is exported mostly in the form of logs, although sawn timber and plywood now feature in the list of timber exports. Unlike the cocoa industry, timber extraction is largely controlled by foreign private capital.

Firewood, which is the main source of domestic fuel, is another important product of the forest. Other forest products include rubber-bearing plants such as the *Funtumia* and the *Landolphia*, kola, building poles and chewing sticks.

MINERALS AND MINING

Long before cocoa was introduced into Ghana, the country was famous for its gold output, and it was gold that gave Ghana its former name of Gold Coast. Other important minerals mined in Ghana are diamond, bauxite and manganese. These minerals are all to be found in the south-western part of the country, an area which is considered to be one of the most mineralized in the world.

Early mining activities were confined to gold production and were handicapped by poor transportation, labour shortage and technical problems. The first railway from Sekondi to Tarkwa was a mining line built to tap the local gold resources. Labour shortages arose from the reluctance of the local people to work in the mines and up till the 1960s, a large proportion of miners in Ghana came from outside the country. Early goldmining was also handicapped by the fact that the depth of mining pits was limited by the water table, since the local miners could not deal with water seepage. Today, mining is highly mechanized and the labour problem has largely been solved.

Gold is found either in the solid rock (lode gold) or in alluvial sands (alluvial gold). The gold-bearing alluvia are called placer deposits, while the most important gold-bearing rocks belong to the Birrimian formation.

Three methods of mining are employed and these are (i) deep mining, (ii) open-cast mining, and (iii) dredging or panning. Deep mining is the commonest method and accounts for 90 per cent of the gold produced. Explosives and expensive machinery are used in deep mining which is controlled by large companies. The famous Ashanti goldfield mine at Obuasi is one of the deeper mines, some of which exceed 600m (2,000ft) in depth. Other areas of deep mining operations are Tarkwa, Prestea, Konongo and Bibiani. In the Tarkwa district, where bands of gold outcrop along hillsides, the mines consist of adits (sloping tunnels) driven into the side of the hill.

Open-cast mining consists of removing the top soil first before digging up the gold ores, using mechanical excavators. It is the best method of mining in those areas where the gold deposits lie near to the surface, but is now of limited use since the surface deposits have largely been worked out. Panning or dredging is important along the valleys of the Rivers Ofin, Ankobra, and Tana, all of which flow over gold-bearing rocks. Large dredgers are used to bring up the sand from the river bed. The sand is then washed to obtain the little particles of gold contained in it.

Almost all the gold produced is exported in the form of gold bars (or bullion). Gold is still the most important mineral export and between 1964–8, it accounted for 47 per cent of the total value of mineral production compared with 29 per cent for diamonds, 21 per cent for manganese and 33 per cent for bauxite (see Table 19).

Diamonds were first discovered in the Birim River in 1919 and in the Borsa Valley (near Tarkwa) in 1922. In the Birim Valley production is controlled by large European companies who work the rich gravel deposits at Oda, Kade and Akwatia. About 90 per cent of the stones produced in the country come from the Oda-Kade area. In the Bonsa Valley, the deposits are worked by Africans who operate in small family groups or even individually. These groups of miners merely dig up the gravels which they wash in calabashes. A large number of these African diamond-diggers come from Nigeria and Benin.

Ghana is now the second largest world producer of

diamond by weight and the fifth by value. Most of the local stones are of comparatively low value and are used for industrial purposes. The total recorded production was in 1960 3,273,000 carats, but in 1969 the output had fallen to 2,391,000 carats following the introduction of stricter exchange controls in 1961 and the drop in production by African diggers.

Manganese is found in small deposits in Birrimian rocks in several parts of Ghana, but the main deposits which are being worked are located at Nsuta. The ores are extracted by open-cast methods in which mechanical shovels are employed to strip the overburden and dig up the ore which is then taken to washing and grading plants.

Ghana is now the third largest world producer of manganese, after the USSR and India and in recent years the value of manganese produced in the country has exceeded that of diamond. Since 1960, annual output has fluctuated between 400,000 and 600,000 tons. The mineral is used mainly in the production of steel but also in the making of dry batteries, paints and disinfectants.

Bauxite is likely to become the most important mineral in view of the recently commissioned Volta River Dam built to provide power for manufacturing aluminium at Tema. The main deposits are at Kanaiyerebo, near Awaso, but there are also substantial deposits at Yenahin and Ejuanema (Fig. 19.1B, p. 147).

Extraction of the ore is by open-cast methods, using mechanical excavators. All the ore is still exported although some of it will in future be processed and made into aluminium at the VALCO Tema factory which now uses imported alumina to manufacture aluminium bars.

THE VOLTA RIVER PROJECT

The Volta River Project, costing 400 million new cedis (about N 400 million at the 1966 exchange rate),

is by far the most ambitious development project undertaken in West Africa, and one for which the Nkrumah administration will long be remembered. Ghana, like other West African countries, except Nigeria, has no coal, which is a major source of industrial power. Fortunately, the country is rich in potential hydro-electric power which could be harnessed to produce the power needed to execute the industrial programme of the government. The Volta River Project was undertaken specifically to provide the power to develop the bauxite resources of the country and for industrialization generally. It was commissioned in 1966 and by 1968 it supplied 97.5 per cent of the national electricity consumption of 2,590 million kWh. Over 70 per cent of the power produced at the Volta power station in 1968 was sold to only one consumer, the American-owned VALCO alumina smelter at Tema.

The project involved the construction of a huge dam, 113 m (370 ft) high and 640 m (2,100 ft) long at Akosombo, a small town located near the Volta Gorge, about 113 km (70 miles) from the sea. The Volta Lake which extends upriver for about 400 km (250 miles) has a total area of 8,480 sq.km (3,275 sq. miles) and is one of the largest man-made lakes in the world. The lake drowned the sites of 700 villages, thereby displacing about 80,000 people who have since been resettled in 52 new villages located along the shores of the lake.

Apart from providing power for industry and domestic use, the Volta River Project has made other contributions to the development of the economy of Ghana. The lake is a major fishing ground and provides a means of transportation in an area which has very poor road communications. Finally, water from the lake is used for irrigating farmland in the dry Accra plains where the production of sugarcane, groundnuts and rice on a commercial scale is now possible. The development of cattle-ranching on the Accra plains has also been considered since water can be tapped from the Volta Lake.

Table 19—Exports of primary products from Ghana ('000 cedis)

	1966	1967	1968	1969	1970	1971	1972	1973*
Cocoa	103,000	130,700	185,600	219,700	300,399	195,066	289,058	344,833
Logs	10,880	12,700	16,260	39,100	19,875	20,536	42,292	88,551
Sawn timber	9,980	9,660	12,300		17,096	12,217	21,173	41,173
Bauxite	1,490	1,590	1,490	1,390	1,280	2,290	2,680	2,574
Manganese ore	9,800	9,200	10,500	7,000	7,200	9,640	10,075	7,315
Diamonds	10,840	12,640	17,430	13,870	14,470	11,750	18,640	13,063
Gold	17,050	20,970	25,790	25,670	26,690	28,450	50,440	70,106

*Provisional figures.

Source: *Africa South of the Sahara*, Europa Publications, 1975.

MANUFACTURING INDUSTRIES

With the commissioning of the Volta Dam in 1966, Ghana now produces more power than it needs (some power has been sold to Togo and Benin since 1970), and is therefore in a position to supply the necessary motive power for industrialization. The country is rich in raw materials, including minerals, but there are still problems of capital and lack of certain types of skilled manpower.

The first industries in Ghana were concerned with the processing of agricultural produce for export. As early as 1951, the government set up an Industrial Development Corporation (IDC) which was charged with the task of creating and managing industrial enterprises either wholly or with private investors. The IDC established many medium-scale and large-scale industries at Accra, Sekondi-Takoradi and Kumasi, but like most government corporations in Ghana (and Nigeria) the IDC did not pay its way, and was exposed to much interference by politicians. It was disbanded in 1961.

Ghana, like most developing countries, has placed much emphasis on import substitution of non-durable consumer goods, so as to conserve foreign exchange for use in importing capital goods and for certain basic necessities which cannot be produced in the country. Industrial growth was rapid before 1961 but since that year the growth rate has been slow. Table 20 shows the performance of the industrial sector between 1962 and 1968. The increase in output at current prices is impressive but this is due

to the rising prices of production. However, the contribution of manufacturing to the national income increased from 4 per cent in 1962 to almost 11 per cent in 1968. Make a careful study of Table 21 and notice the marked increase in the domestic production of textiles, processed food, and footwear between 1963 and 1968. The increase was low in beverages.

The VALCO alumina smelter at Tema is by far the largest industrial concern in Ghana. Many other large-scale and medium-scale industries are concentrated in the Accra-Tema area, which is a major destination for migrants from all over Ghana. Some of the more important industries are beer-brewing and distilling of spirits, vehicle assembly, soft drinks, cigarettes, cement and cotton textiles. Petroleum products have been refined using imported crude oil since 1963. Kumasi is another important industrial centre where beer, soft drinks, biscuits and textiles are manufactured.

Industries connected with the processing of local raw materials have increased since 1961. The major ones include the plywood factory at Sambreboi, margarine and soap at Tema, manufacture of fish-meal at Accra (Christianborg) and of lime juice at Abakrampa.

POPULATION AND SETTLEMENT

In 1970, the population of Ghana was 8.5 million as compared with 6.7 million in 1960, giving an annual rate of increase of 2.4 per cent. The economi-

Table 20—Growth of manufacturing production in Ghana

Gross output (million cedis)	1962	1963	1964	1965	1966	1967	1968
Current prices	71.4	93.1	107.0	120.1	142.0	170.7	219.2
1962 constant price	71.4	87.8	94.7	95.4	107.4	120.3	145.6
Real growth rate (%)	26.0	23.0	8.0	0.8	12.6	12.6	21.0
Share in GNP (%)	4.0	5.0	5.5	6.4	7.7	8.8	10.6

Table 21—Domestic production and imports of some manufactured goods in Ghana (million cedis)

	1963		1966		1968	
	Domestic	Imports	Domestic	Imports	Domestic	Imports
Processed food	4.3	46.0	10.8	29.1	21.8	34.2
Tobacco	14.6	1.5	20.5	1.4	26.2	3.9
Beverages	13.9	0.9	21.5	1.0	23.1	1.2
Textiles	1.7	35.1	7.0	25.7	25.8	21.6
Footwear	3.3	3.3	7.0	1.7	21.3	0.4
Paper & paper products	0.8	4.7	2.8	5.6	6.1	7.7
Chemical products	10.1	19.2	16.5	16.6	21.2	48.3
Petroleum products	2.0	14.8	5.2	9.7	6.4	21.5

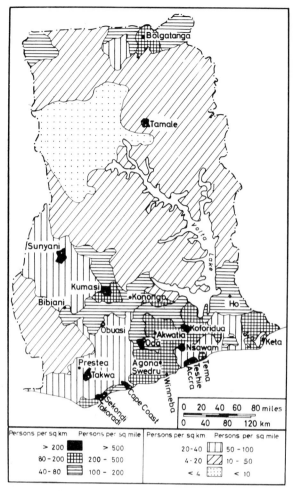

FIG. 19.4—Ghana: distribution of population

region and the Mole-Dagbani (16 per cent) of the northern region.

Distribution of population

Make a close study of Fig. 19.4, which shows the population density based on the 1960 census of Ghana. You will notice that most of the people live in the south, which is the most developed and richest part of the country. The areas of high density of over 78 persons per sq.km (200 persons per sq. mile) are located along the coast and in parts of the Ashanti cocoa belt. Notice too the small area of high density in the north-west corner of the country. The Volta Basin and parts of the forest belt are virtually uninhabited.

Areas of very low population densities are generally associated with difficult environment and lack of resources. They include tsetse fly infested areas like the Afram plains, areas where water is scarce in the dry season as well as those given to extensive flooding during the rainy season and areas like the Volta Basin which have very infertile soils. The forest reserves are of course uninhabited except by forest guards, hence the low population densities of districts where the forest reserves are located.

Recent migrations

There is a considerable movement of population in Ghana involving internal migrations from one rural area to another, rural-urban migrations and the immigration of foreign nationals largely from Upper Volta, Nigeria and Togo. In 1960 for example 537,000 foreign-born persons were enumerated during the census but there were also many Ghanaian-born dependents of persons of foreign origin, hence the large alien population of over 850,000 in 1960. The mass expulsion of aliens in 1969/70 when about 800,000 people were forced to leave the country has drastically reduced the foreign population although many seasonal migrants from Upper Volta still go to work in the cocoa belt.

Internal migration within Ghana is directed towards the better developed south and south-west, the migrants originating from the Frafra district of the north-east and from the Krobo and Ewe areas of the east. One interesting fact about internal migration in the country is that in spite of the rapid rate of urbanization, over 70 per cent of migrants aged 15 years and above went to rural areas in 1960. The indication is that this situation will not change much before 1980 in view of the high rate of urban unemployment and the higher wages now paid in cocoa farms as a result of labour shortage following the expulsion of aliens. The estimated number of internal migrants in

cally active population, that is those above 15 years of age accounted for about 40 per cent of the total population and of these, 61 per cent were engaged in agriculture while 31 per cent worked in service establishments. The number of wage-earners in 1970 was about 420,000 out of a total working population of over 3.4 million. Most Ghanaians are therefore self-employed.

Ghana is inhabited by peoples who belong to many different ethnic groups, the most numerous of which are the Akan-speaking peoples (44 per cent) who inhabit most of the southern half of the country. The Akans have a matrilineal kinship system although there are certain cultural and linguistic differences between the various sub-groups, of which the Ashanti-Ahafo, the Fante and the Brong are the most prominent. The other important ethnic groups are the Ewes (13 per cent) who live in the south-east of Ghana, the Ga-Adangbe (8 per cent) of the Accra

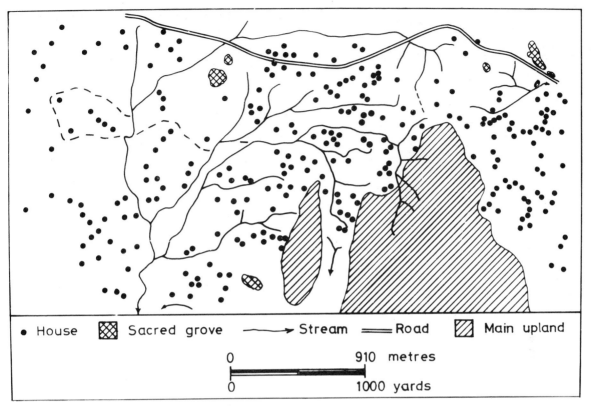

FIG. 19.5—Ghana: dispersed settlement near Bolgatanga

1960 was 600,000, a third of which worked as wage-earners in agricultural enterprises, including private cocoa farms. The rest were self-employed migrant farmers, miners and petty traders.

There has also been an increasing flow of people from rural areas to the growing mining and industrial towns of the south. About 58 per cent of the increase in urban population 1948–60 (from 532,720 to 1,551,200) is attributed to migration from rural areas while 42 per cent was due to natural increase.

Rural settlements

Ghana is a country of small villages and in 1970 as much as 48 per cent of the total population of 8.5 million lived in settlements of less than 1,000 persons. The coastal belt is characterized by small nucleated fishing villages while the forest people live in large nucleated villages which are surrounded by extensive areas of farmland. Since the introduction of cocoa, the large forest villages have continued to diminish in size as farmers disperse to set up smaller cocoa villages all over the forest belt. In the area colonized by the Krobo migrant cocoa farmers, a new and interesting type of village, the *huza* type of settlement (Fig. 6.2) has come into being. (See plate 73.)

In the far north, rural settlements consist of dispersed compounds scattered over a wide area of cultivated land. The dispersed settlement around Bolgatanga (Fig. 19.5) is a typical example. It is interesting to note that the dispersed settlement in north-eastern Ghana is associated with areas having a high population density as well as a patrilineal system of land inheritance; the same conditions which exist in the areas of dispersed rural settlements in Nigeria (Tivland, central Iboland and the Ikot-Ekpene-Abak area of the Cross River State).

The new resettlement villages of the Volta Lake Basin are in a class by themselves. The sites of these villages were selected after careful studies by the Volta Resettlement Authority, which provided some help in the form of money and building materials towards the construction of houses. In a sense these are artificial villages and it is not surprising that some of them have folded up while the size of others has diminished since there are very limited opportunities for the inhabitants.

Urbanization and towns

The urban population of Ghana in 1921 was 179,000 or 8 per cent of the total population, increasing to 1.5

157

million or 23 per cent of the population in 1960. In 1970, a total of 2.4 million people or 29 per cent of the population lived in urban areas. The growth of the urban population has therefore been quite considerable during the last fifty years, and it is necessary to recall here that this increase is still largely accounted for by net migration from rural areas.

About 129 cities and towns were designated as urban areas in 1970. The three important and growing urban centres are Accra-Tema, Sekondi-Takoradi and Kumasi and together these three cities accounted for 46 per cent of the total urban population. Most of the other 'census towns' exert very little urban influence on their surrounding rural areas and some of them are losing population to these three major centres.

Accra (636,067) is the capital and largest city in Ghana. It was formerly one of the main sea ports of the country but since 1961, the new port of Tema has served as the main gateway into Accra and Ghana. Apart from its administrative functions, Accra is the principal seat of learning and the commercial hub of the country. Industrial establishments are few and development is slow since most industrialists prefer to locate near the port facilities at Tema. The main industries of Accra are beer-brewing, fruit-canning, printing, light engineering and the manufacture of soap and margarine. (See plate 72.)

With its well-lit dual carriageways and many roundabouts, Accra is one of the most beautiful towns in West Africa. The residential areas are neatly laid out and the houses consist mainly of bungalows with beautiful gardens and steel gates. It has good road and railway connections with other parts of the country and its ultra-modern airport opened in 1969 is the best equipped in West Africa.

Tema (35,000) is a part of the Accra Capital District and is located 29km (18 miles) east of Accra. It was formerly a small Ga-Adangbe fishing village but since 1961 it has become the premier port and most important industrial centre of the country. It has a railway and good road connection with Accra and the hydro-electric power station town of Akosombo.

The port complex includes a well-planned modern town with neat residential areas. The administrative district is located between the two main residential areas while the industrial district is located on both sides of the railway to Akosombo. The aluminium smelter which is located at the eastern end of the town is by far the largest industrial enterprise. Other major factories include an aluminium utensil works, an oil refinery, textile mills, assembly plants for lorries and cars, and a cocoa products factory.

Kumasi (340,000) is the second largest town in Ghana, and the capital of the old Ashanti Kingdom.

Its importance as a major collecting and distribution centre for cocoa and consumer goods respectively started with the introduction of cocoa and the extension of the railway to Kumasi in 1903. Kumasi is also an important railhead for transporting logs to Takoradi and various sawmills along the coast.

The industries of Kumasi include saw milling, a biscuit factory, the Star beer brewery, a furniture factory and a fibre bag factory which manufactures bags for packing cocoa. The opening in 1953 of the Kumasi College of Technology, now the University of Science and Technology has contributed considerably to the growing importance of the town.

Sekondi-Takoradi (128,000) is a twin city with a port at Takoradi, an 80-hectare (200-acre) artificial harbour which was opened in 1928. It has a very productive hinterland which produces cocoa, timber and a variety of minerals, and still handles a large proportion of the export trade of Ghana, although it has lost much of its import trade to the new port of Tema. The industrial establishments of Takoradi include a cocoa-processing plant, saw mills, a paper factory, a tobacco factory and a car assembly plant.

Sekondi is primarily a residential town about 6km (4 miles) east of Takoradi. It became important when the town was selected as the port and railway terminus to the goldfields of Tarkwa which were opened in 1901. The growth of Sekondi as a commercial centre was however terminated when the port of Takoradi was opened in 1928. The railhead was transferred to Takoradi and today Sekondi is largely an administrative centre which also houses some of the working population of Takoradi.

TRANSPORT

In pre-colonial and early colonial days, head porterage along established footpaths was the main form of transport although donkeys were commonly used in the north. Water transport was limited to the use of canoes along the lagoons and navigable stretches of the Volta and Ankobra Rivers. These primitive forms of transport, which are rather slow and very demanding of human energy are still in use today in the more inaccessible parts of the country.

Early trade contact with Europe brought about the establishment of numerous primitive ports along the coast. Each port consisted of a fortified 'factory' or trading beach which later attracted population and became a town. In later years when roads and railways were built to link the coast with the interior, those coastal ports served by railways and roads emerged as major urban centres. The other coastal ports declined and many of them have since disappeared from the map.

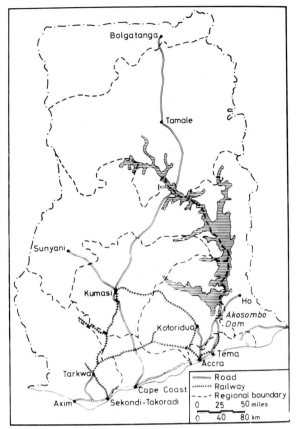

FIG. 19.6—Ghana: land transport and Lake Volta

The first railway was opened in 1901 to link the gold mines of Tarkwa with the port of Sekondi. Gold was also responsible for the construction of the Tarkwa-Prestea rail line. Another 'mineral line' was the Dunkwa-Awaso bauxite branch railroad which was opened in 1944. But while mineral exploitation prompted the building of the western railroads, it was cocoa that provided the main reason for the construction of the eastern line from Accra to Kumasi. The newest rail line links Accra to the new port of Tema from where it extends to the dam site at Akosombo (Fig. 19.6).

There are only 1,120km (700 miles) of railways as compared with over 32,000km (20,000 miles) of roads, most of which are not tarred. Note that the railways serve only the rich and rapidly developing south, which also has the best roads in the country. In north and central Ghana, most of the roads are not surfaced and may become impassable during the rainy season. It is hoped that the new Volta Lake will contribute immensely to solving the transport problems of parts of central Ghana.

It is significant that as in Nigeria, the roads were originally meant to serve as feeders to the govern-

ment-owned railways and not to compete with them. The rapid development of road transport since 1950 has meant a considerable loss of traffic to the railways. However, the Ghana railways have done very well as compared with the much longer Nigerian railroads, hence the decision in 1954 to build a double track along the very busy stretch from Takoradi to Tarkwa.

Apart from a few large transport firms, motor transport in Ghana is managed by local businessmen who usually prefer the multi-purpose mammy-wagon lorry called *tro-tro* in Ghana. An increasing number of passengers travelling by road now use buses while the lorries are largely restricted to carrying goods to the various ports of export.

Ghana Airways has a monopoly to operate internal air services which are restricted to Accra, Takoradi, Kumasi and Tamale. Accra has daily services to Lagos and London as well as regular services to other parts of Africa and Europe.

INTERNAL TRADE

As in other West African countries the market square is the most effective distributive agency for manufactured goods and foodstuffs in both the rural and urban areas of Ghana. Department stores and street vendors also play an important part in the retail trade of the major cities and towns. The Ghana National Trading Corporation (GNTC), created by the purchase of A. G. Leventis, has a chain of department stores in the main towns and since 1970 all forms of retail trade, including the textile trade formerly dominated by Syrians and Lebanese, have been indigenized.

There is a considerable trade in foodstuffs and cattle between the north and the main centres of population in the south. Yams and cattle come from the north to the south, which in turn supplies fish to north and central Ghana. As in the marketing of cocoa, a large number of middlemen are involved in the trade in foodstuffs. Between the farmer and the consumer, there may be three or four middlemen, hence the high prices of foodstuffs in the towns even though the prices paid to the farmers are low. The little shops run by the Food Distribution Corporation have been established so as to help reduce the high prices charged by food traders. The Corporation buys directly from the farmer at a fixed official price, but as of 1973, the trade in foodstuffs was still dominated by small scale independent traders.

Market women dominate the retail trade in foodstuffs as well as the trade in manufactured goods. The textile and grocery trade at Accra for example

PLATE 73—Compound at Navrongo, northern Ghana

are almost entirely in the hands of these market women who are also very influential in local politics.

FOREIGN TRADE

The principal exports of Ghana are cocoa, gold, timber, manganese and diamonds (see Table 19) while the minor exports include bauxite, palm kernels, copra and kola nuts. (Note that the exports are all primary products.) Cocoa is by far the most important export and between 1965 and 1970, cocoa beans and products accounted for 65 per cent by value of the total exports, as compared with 19 per cent for minerals and 10 per cent for timber. These exports go mainly to Great Britain, the United States of America, West Germany, the Netherlands and Japan. Some cocoa is also exported to the USSR and Canada.

Imports into Ghana consist mostly of manufactured goods such as motor vehicles and spare parts, petroleum products, cotton goods, chemicals and processed foods. The large amount of money (55 million cedis in 1969) spent on food imports is disturbing to the government in view of the annual deficit trade balance which averaged about 40 million cedis between 1960 and 1967. There was, however, an appreciable trade surplus in 1968 and 1970, (see Table 22), and the situation has since improved following the successful Grow More Food Campaign launched in 1972. The increase since 1960 in the range and quality of locally manufactured import-substitution goods such as cotton goods, plastic goods and smaller items like pomade, matches and candles has helped to reduce the import bills. The bulk of the imported goods come from Great Britain followed by Holland, Japan, West Germany and the United States of America.

Table 22—Trade balance of Ghana (million cedis)

	1964	1965	1966	1967	1968	1969	1970	1971	1972	1973*
Imports	243.2	320.0	251.2	261.5	314.0	354.4	419.1	443.1	393.3	525.9
Exports	229.2	223.4	191.2	245.1	338.0	333.3	467.4	357.5	564.4	730.4
Balance	−14.0	−96.4	−60.0	−16.4	+24.0	−21.1	+48.3	−85.6	+171.1	+204.5

Note: 3.00 cedis = ₦2.00.   *Provisional figures.

Chapter 20—The Republic of Guinea

PLATE 74—*Western edge of Futa Jallon, Guinea; upland rice is being cultivated on the lower slopes and in the wetter valley in the foreground bananas are being grown*

Guinea became independent of France in 1958 when the majority of the electorate voted against joining the Franco-African community which was established in October of that year. The independence of Guinea followed closely after that of Ghana, which took place a year earlier and was to be the beginning of the birth of new states which have since transformed the political map of West Africa. But the manner in which Guinea broke with France was not well received by the French government which proceeded to isolate the new state by cutting off trade and other ties with Guinea; withdrawing French civil servants and teachers and stopping aid to the young Republic. In the same year (1958), Guinea, the first French-speaking West African country to become independent, formed a short-lived political union with Ghana, also the first of the former colonies of British West Africa to attain full independence. The union was discontinued in 1960 but the two heads of state who had obtained independence for their countries continued to follow similar political ideals and when President Nkrumah of Ghana was overthrown in 1966 he sought and obtained political asylum in Guinea.

In 1972, the population of Guinea was estimated to be 5.14 million and the area which is about 246,000 sq.km. (95,000 sq. miles) is about the size of Ghana. This is a country of highlands which form the sources of many rivers including the Niger and Gambia Rivers. It is potentially very rich in agricultural and mineral resources and is now the largest world exporter of bauxite.

Guinea is bounded on the west by the Atlantic Ocean and the Portuguese-speaking young country of Guinea Bissau from where the abortive invasion of the Republic was launched in 1970 by the Portuguese. Its northern neighbours are Senegal and Mali, while the eastern part of the country is bordered by the Ivory Coast, Liberia and Sierra Leone.

RELIEF REGIONS AND DRAINAGE

The four relief regions of Guinea are (Fig. 20.1):
1) the coastal swamps and plain, 2) the Futa Jallon Highlands, 3) the Guinea Highlands, 4) the Upper Niger High Plains.

1. The coastal swamps and plain

The coast of Guinea Republic, like that of Guinea Bissau, shows many features of submergence. Most of its length of 272km (170 miles) is low-lying and is characterized by many drowned valley inlets and innumerable sandy islands. Tombo Island on which Conakry is built and the Los Islands (consisting of Tamara, Rooma, Kassa, Blanche, Cabris and Coral) off Conakry are remnants of old hard rocks. They have rich fertile soils and large deposits of bauxite. Mangrove swamps and marshes occur along most of the coast. The coastal plain, which has an average width of about 48km (30 miles), lies immediately behind the mangrove swamps. Much of it is flooded during the rainy season when the underlying sandstone strata become waterlogged. Extensive patches of lateritic soils occur all over the region.

2. The Futa Jallon Highlands

These highlands consist of plateau surfaces of sandstone which rise from the coastal plain as a series of steps, through which the rivers cut very narrow and steep-sided valleys. The eastern slopes which grade into the Upper Niger basin are more gentle, and the rivers flowing through them have shallower and wider valleys. Almost every valley is covered with dense forest vegetation, while the plateau surfaces are usually characterized by large areas of bare and hard lateritic crusts called *bowe* (i.e. no trees). The *bowe* are most extensive in the west but very bare in the north. The highest areas occur in the eastern part of the highlands which are also the most densely settled areas. In many places, hard rocks of volcanic origin occur as sills and dykes in the sandstone surfaces, giving rise to many impressive waterfalls. There is considerable seasonal variation in the volume of water in the rivers and only the larger rivers are perennial.

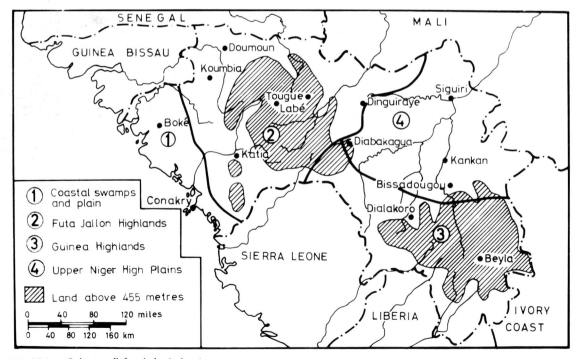

FIG. 20.1 — Guinea: relief and physical regions

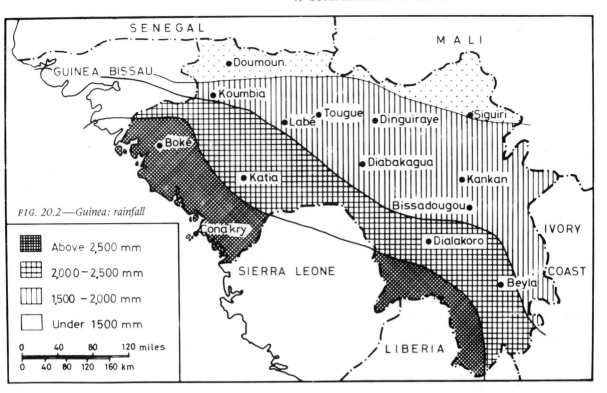

FIG. 20.2—Guinea: rainfall

Legend:
- Above 2,500 mm
- 2,000 – 2,500 mm
- 1,500 – 2,000 mm
- Under 1500 mm

```
0    40    80    120 miles
0  40  80  120  160 km
```

3. The Guinea Highlands

Unlike the Futa Jallon, which is contained almost entirely within the country, the Guinea Highlands extend southwards into Sierra Leone and Liberia and eastwards into the Ivory Coast. In rock composition and general character the Guinea Highlands, which consist of old crystalline rocks, differ markedly from the Futa Jallon Highlands. The highest points here are rock inselbergs, not flat-topped plateau surfaces. The rounded hills of this region, some of which are forested, remind one of parts of Ondo Province in Western Nigeria. Like the Futa Jallon, the Guinea Highlands are the source of many rivers including the headwaters of the Upper Niger. Some of the highest points in West Africa occur in this region where Mount Nuon 1,825m (or 6,083ft) and Mount Nimba 1,710m (or 5,695ft) are also located.

4. The Upper Niger High Plains

Almost the whole of this area of high plains is drained by the headwaters of the Upper Niger. The component rocks are similar to those of the Guinea Highlands but the general elevation, which is about 300m (1,000ft), is much less. Granitic outcrops and lateritic surfaces are very common, and it is these outcrops that have given rise to waterfalls which render the rivers useless for navigation.

CLIMATE AND VEGETATION

Climate

Relief is the most important factor affecting the climate of Guinea and in consequence, climatic regions are almost identical with relief regions. Temperatures are high all through the year, particularly along the coast which experiences very little seasonal change. The hottest month in the coastal areas is April which has an average maximum temperature of about 32°C (90°F) as compared with about 29°C (83°F) in August which is the coolest month. The lower temperatures and high humidity make the rainy season rather trying along the coast. The highlands experience a similar seasonal pattern of temperature changes but with greater variations in the diurnal and annual ranges.

The rainy season lasts from March to early December in the south but from early May to November in the north. The rainfall is heaviest on the coastal plains (4,320mm or 169in. at Conakry) and along the western slopes of the highlands, while the interior Niger High Plains which lie in the rain shadow of highlands are relatively dry (1,670mm or 66in. at Kouroussa). July and August receive the highest rainfall throughout the country and by early October when the ground is saturated and the rivers are full, floods are common (Fig. 20.2).

163

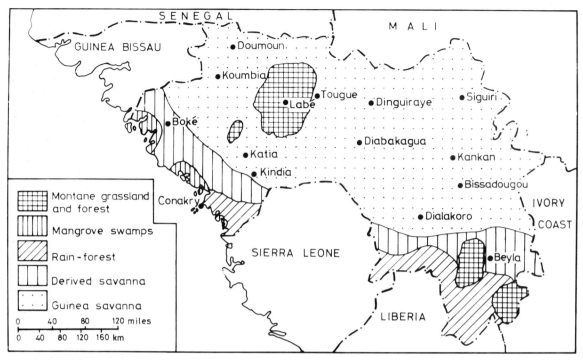

FIG. 20.3—Guinea: vegetation

Thunderstorms are frequent during the rainy season, particularly during the early part (April—June) and during the retreat of the rains (September—November). The dry season is normally cloudless but

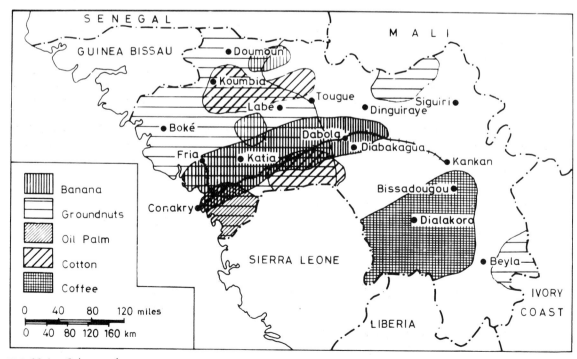

FIG. 20.4—Guinea: cash crops

PLATE 75—Swamp rice cultivation near Dubreka, Guinea

during the wet season heavy clouds cover the sky particularly in the coastal areas and on the windward slopes of the mountains.

Vegetation

Most of Guinea has a grass-woodland vegetation with dense forests along the Liberian and Ivory Coast borders. Dense forest remnants also occur in the more inaccessible parts of the high plateaux and peaks of Futa Jallon, but a greater part of the laterite capped plateaux has an open grass vegetation with fringing forests along streams and river valleys (Fig. 20.3 and plate 74).

Along the coast, the river mouths are bordered by dense mangrove woodlands but further inland the coastal areas support a dense forest vegetation. In the upper Niger Basin, which is much drier than the rest of the country, the vegetation grades from savanna woodland in the south to a more open grassland landscape in the north.

SOILS AND SOIL EROSION

Mangrove swamp soils occur along the coastal areas, parts of which have been reclaimed for rice cultivation. The coastal plains have rather sandy soils which become waterlogged after heavy rains. On the Futa Jallon the lateritic surfaces lack both humus and surface water except during rains, and are particularly infertile, although they support a dense population. Patches of richer soils associated with igneous intrusions, however, provide good farmland in such areas as the vicinity of Labe. The richest soils appear in the area of Basement Complex rocks in the Guinea Highlands and the Upper Niger High Plains.

The country as a whole has very thin soils and as a result of the heavy rainfall and exposure from bush fires there is considerable erosion, particularly along hill slopes. The areas most affected by soil erosion are the densely settled *bowe* of the Futa Jallon, and the heavily stocked highland areas which are relatively free from tsetse flies.

ECONOMIC ACTIVITIES

Agriculture

Farming is the main occupation of the people, about 80 per cent of whom obtain their living from cultivating rice, cassava, fonio (hungry rice), sweet potatoes and groundnuts as the major food crops. The export crops, which come primarily from the coastal region and the two highland areas, are bananas, palm kernels, coffee, groundnuts and pineapples. The Niger High Plains produce no important cash crop.

The expansion of swamp rice cultivation is one of the main features of agricultural development in Guinea. In the past, the country produced a small quantity of upland rice but swamp rice is now very important and widely cultivated, the total annual output averaging about 325,000 tons between 1965 and 1970. Along the coast the mangrove swamps have been reclaimed (plate 75) for rice cultivation and vast areas of inland freshwater swamps have also been reclaimed for rice farming. The 13,000 hectare (32,500 acre) rice project near Siquiri in the upper Niger region is the largest so far undertaken by the government, and it is aimed at reducing the importation of rice which cost the country as much as 1,546 million Guinea francs in 1962. Cassava is grown everywhere and so is maize, but millet and potatoes are grown mainly in the highlands and in the upper Niger Basin (Figs. 20.4 and 20.5).

Bananas account for about one-quarter of the export earnings and are grown almost exclusively on plantations located in the damp valleys of the two highland regions, the main producing areas being in the neighbourhood of the Sierra Leone boundary. The most common variety grown is the dwarf Chinese banana which was introduced into the country in 1898. About 80,000 tons of the fruit is produced every year, three-quarters of which is exported to France and other countries of Europe.

Other tree crops grown for export include oranges which are cultivated by small-holder farmers in the Futa Jallon Highlands as well as in large plantations such as the 500 hectare (1,250 acre) estate near Labe. Orange oil is also produced for export. Pineapples are grown mainly on well-drained slopes near Kindia, as well as in the coastal plain areas of Benty and Ousso. Large plantations of oil palms exist in the coastal plains, but coffee and much of the kola nuts come from the Guinea Highlands.

Livestock rearing

The highlands and the upper Niger Basin support more than 1.7 million cattle which are controlled by the nomadic Cattle Fulani. The dominant breed is the small humpless ndama which is immune to the tsetse fly. Guinea exports cattle to Sierra Leone and Liberia. The goat population is about 500,000 while the sheep number about 400,000, the main producing area for both being the Futa Jallon region. Donkeys and horses are kept in the upper Niger region.

Mining

Gold has been mined in Guinea for many centuries and is still obtained both by panning along river

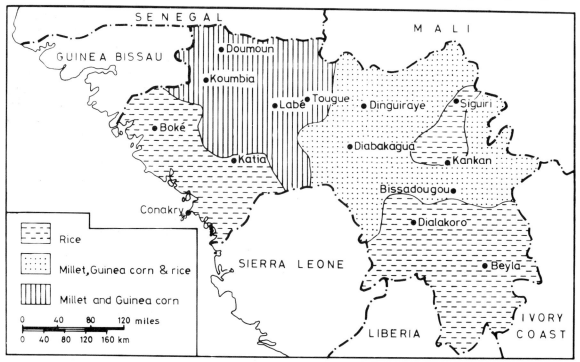

FIG. 20.5—Guinea: staple food crops

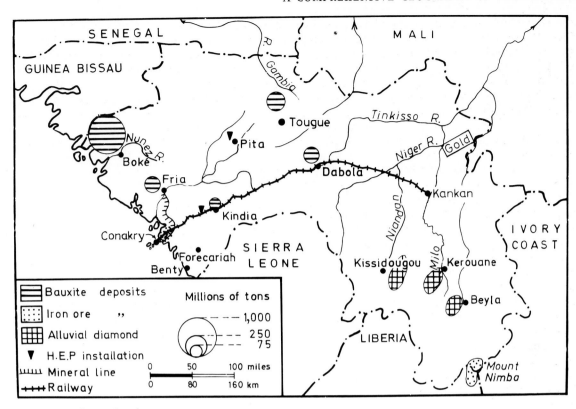

FIG. 20.6—Guinea: minerals

beds and by working veins in the bedrock. Much of the gold is worked by Africans who sink shafts of about 18m (60ft) deep in the bedrock. Mining is done on a family basis with the men digging up the gold-bearing gravels which are then washed by the women. Diamond is also worked by open-cast mining as well as by panning alluvial deposits along the tributaries of the Makona River.

The most important minerals, however, are bauxite and iron ore, both of which accounted for about 60 per cent of the total exports by value in 1970. Guinea is the largest producer of bauxite in Africa and the proven reserves show that Guinea possesses the world's third largest bauxite deposit. Mining started in 1951 on Kassa Island but the main centre of production in the Los Islands is on the Island of Tamara, following the closing down in 1967 of the Kassa Island mines which had become exhausted. On the mainland, bauxite is mined at Boke, Dabola and Kindia. In 1967, the country produced over 1,644,000 tons of bauxite ore, but exported only 250,000 tons of ore, the rest being processed locally into alumina at the Fria alumina plants before being exported. (See Fig. 20.6.)

Table 23—Mineral production in Guinea

	1960	1965	1966	1967	1968	1969	1970	1971	1972
Bauxite ('000 tons)	1,378	1,870	1,609	1,644	2,112	2,460	2,640	2,635	2,650
Alumina ('000 tons)	185	522	525	530	531	572	610	665	700
Iron ore ('000 tons)	776	755	610	701	—	—	—	—	—
Diamonds ('000 carats)	1,117	72	72	51	70	72	74	74	n.a.

Note: 1. Figures for bauxite include bauxite processed into alumina at Fria.

2. The figure for alumina has been steady at about 530,000 tons a year while output of bauxite has been increasing. The 1975 target for Boke mine is 2,300,000 tons of bauxite.

3. The Kaloum Peninsula iron ore deposit was abandoned in 1967, but mining has now begun on the richer and more extensive iron ore deposits at Mt Nimba.

Guinea also has very large reserves of iron ore. The 200 million ton reserve in the Kaloum Peninsula, one of the largest in the world, was first mined in 1953 and from 1960 it produced an average tonnage of 700,000 tons a year. The Kaloum deposit has an iron content of 50 to 55 per cent and was mined by the open-cast method until 1967 when the deposits were abandoned in favour of the much richer and more extensive deposits at Mount Nimba. Proven reserves of the Mt Nimba ore are estimated to be 300 million tons and the iron content is 65 to 67 per cent.

Table 23 shows the tonnage of minerals produced between 1960 and 1972. Mining has made great contributions to the rapidly growing economy and is largely responsible for the favourable balance of trade which Guinea has had in recent years. At Fria alone, the mines employed 1,500 people in 1967, 1,000 of them being Guinean nationals. The expansion of the mining sector is also responsible for the fact that the contribution of agricultural produce to the export trade of Guinea has fallen from 87 per cent in 1958 (i.e. at independence) to about 40 per cent in 1970.

Manufacturing

Largely because of the way Guinea became independent in 1958 the country has had to carry out her development programmes including industrialization without aid from her former colonial ruler, France. Indeed at independence, with the withdrawal of French personnel and equipment, the country faced considerable difficulties and her currency was left with no external support. Fortunately, the large bauxite and iron ore deposits in Guinea have brought in much of the necessary foreign exchange for buying industrial machinery.

Small-scale manufacturing by a combination of national and private enterprise has featured since independence and today the area lying between Conakry, Dubreka, Kindi and Coyah is developing into a major industrial zone. Industries in this area include textiles using imported raw cotton from America, cigarettes, and paint and brick works. There is a growing food and drink industry which manufactures beer, soft drinks and fruit juices. Chinese aid has enabled the country to establish a groundnut crushing factory at Dabola, a sugar refinery and a steel plant with an output of about 60,000 tons a year.

In addition to lack of capital for establishing industries, the poverty and small size of the country's market does not encourage industrial growth. There is also a great need to develop more hydro-electric power stations to provide adequate power not only for converting bauxite to alumina, but also for manufacturing aluminium metal. Guinea's break with France prevented the development of such a power station on the Konkoure River and it now appears that the project will be carried out with Russian aid. Two dams are to be built and these will provide a generating capacity of 1,720mW, which will be enough to manufacture 150,000 tons of aluminium each year.

POPULATION AND SETTLEMENT

Guinea has a population of about 4 million living in an area of 246,000 sq.km (95,000 sq. miles). This gives an average density of about 16.3 persons per sq. km (42 persons per sq. mile). The most densely settled areas are in the highest areas of the Futa Jallon, which have rather poor soils, but provide good pasture and a favourable climate for cattle-rearing. In these areas the Cattle Fulani population has become semi-settled, but the vast majority of people in the area are settled cultivators, many of whose ancestors were brought to work as slaves on Fulani farms. Other densely settled areas include the areas near the Liberian boundary, and the provinces of Boffa and Dabreka.

One of the very sparsely settled areas is the coastal swamp area which has an average density of less than 7.8 persons per sq.km (20 persons per sq. mile). Future reclamation of the swamps for rice cultivation is likely to result in a considerable increase in the population of this part of the country.

The Fulanis, who number over 900,000, constitute almost a quarter of the country's population. They are concentrated on the Futa Jallon Highlands where they live in small villages. Other large ethnic groups include the Malinkes (Mandingos) who number about 625,000, the Susus (275,000) and the Kissis (185,000).

Conakry (172,500) is the capital city and is located on Tombo Island which is connected to the mainland by a causeway similar to that connecting Iddo Island to Ebute Metta. It is a well-planned town with shady avenues and has a deep-water harbour which is sheltered by the Los Islands and by breakwaters. The trade of Conakry was relatively very small until 1952 when iron ore was first exported from the country. As the coastal terminus of the country's only railway, Conakry port handles the bulk of the country's export of bananas and other primary products. The airport is of international class and can handle all forms of air traffic.

Kindia (152,000) is an important railway town with railway workshops and a major collecting point

Table 24—Trade balance of Guinea (million Guinea francs [FG])

	1962	1963	1964	1965	1966	1967	1968
Imports	16,195	11,379	12,085	12,882	13,010	9,715	10,360
Exports	11,086	13,691	10,611	13,318	14,380	10,489	11,890
Balance	−5,109	+2,312	−1,474	+436	+1,370	+774	+1,530

Note: 1,000FG = ₦3.50.

for bananas. Its importance as a holiday resort for Frenchmen and other citizens of Conakry started in 1904 when the railway from Conakry reached Kindia. The Pasteur Medical Research Institute, which was established in 1925, and the agricultural experimental station established in 1930 are two of the most important institutions in the Kindia area.

Kankan (176,000), the eastern terminus of the country's only railroad, is located on the left bank of River Milo. It is also the terminus of the steamer service to Bamako and an important road centre. Its great accessibility has made it a major trading centre for kola nuts, palm produce and rice. It has a large agricultural research station which pays particular attention to cotton. Kankan has a medium-sized airport and a large modern hotel but apart from the high-class residential buildings which are occupied by Europeans, Lebanese and local senior civil servants, the outlook of the town is more that of a huge village of huts.

EXTERNAL TRADE

France is still an important trading partner of Guinea, but since independence in 1958 Guinea has sought markets for her primary products in China, Russia, the Netherlands and the United States of America. The chief exports are alumina and bauxite, fresh bananas, palm produce, coffee and iron ore. The main imports include cotton textiles, motor cars and parts, rice, petroleum products and industrial as well as agricultural machinery.

The trade figures given in Table 24 show that the country now has a favourable balance of trade, unlike most French-speaking countries in West Africa. The figures given in this table are, however, incomplete since a substantial proportion of the exports, including diamonds and foodstuffs, is smuggled out of the country. About half of the exports of Guinea go to the socialist countries and the United States of America while about a third goes to France. Guinea has a sizeable trade with the neighbouring West African countries. The annual exports of livestock and citrus fruits to neighbouring countries amount to about 1,000 million Guinea francs. The large amount of money expended in food imports (about 1,540 million FG for rice only) is a disturbing aspect of the economy of a country in which about 80 per cent of the people are engaged in farming. The Soviet Union, France, the United States of America and West Germany supply almost all the goods imported into Guinea.

Chapter 21—Guinea Bissau

PLATE 76 — *Village in Guinea Bissau*

Guinea Bissau is a small country with an area of 36,100 sq.km (13,940 sq. miles), about the same area as that of the Cross River State of Nigeria, 35,560 sq. km (13,730 sq. miles). But while the Cross River State of Nigeria had an estimated population of 3.6 million in 1972, the population of Guinea Bissau in the same year was estimated to be less than 600,000. There are therefore many more people in Ibadan city and twice as many in metropolitan Lagos as in the whole of Guinea Bissau, which is largely a land of estuaries and riverine swamps.

Until 1973, the country was administered as an overseas province by the Portuguese who, unlike other European colonialists, refused to grant independence to the territory. Fruitless appeals for political and social change started in earnest in 1956, and in 1963, the African leadership started

an armed revolt to liberate the country from Portuguese rule. Fighting continued after the country had been declared independent unilaterally by the freedom fighters on 24 September 1973. It was not until 1974, following the overthrow of the dictatorship in Portugal, that Guinea Bissau became free from Portuguese rule.

Portuguese interest in the country started in 1446 when it was first visited by Portuguese explorers. Then followed a long period of slave trade during which the Portuguese established a few trading posts along the coast. As late as 1915, Portuguese influence was largely restricted to the coastal strip, even though the Portuguese had claimed at the Berlin Conference in 1884—5 that they had established 'effective occupation' over the country. The African population was basically opposed to Portuguese intrusion and it was

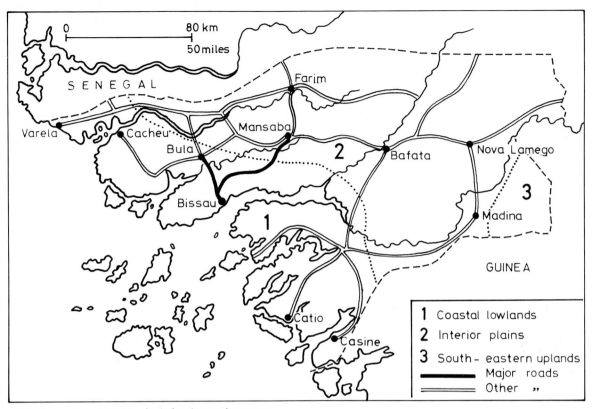

FIG. 21.1—Guinea Bissau: physical regions and transport

not until 1936 that Portuguese rule became established over the territory. In 1970 much of the territory had been captured by guerrilla forces of the liberation movement called PAIGC (i.e. African Independence Party for Guinea and Cape Verde) which had been recognized by the Organization of African Unity (OAU) and many socialist countries as the governing party in Guinea Bissau. The headquarters of the provisional government was in Conakry, pending the complete liberation of the country, when the government moved its headquarters to the capital city of Bissau.

PHYSICAL REGIONS

There are three distinct physical regions, and these are (Fig. 21.1): 1) the coastal lowlands and islands, 2) the interior plains, 3) the south-eastern uplands.

1. The coastal lowlands and islands

The numerous indentations along the coast are caused by a geologically recent invasion of the low-lying coastland by seawater, resulting in the creation of many river estuaries and swamps. The larger estuaries which provide deep and good waterways are those of the Cacine, Geba and Cacheu Rivers, and it is along these sheltered waterways that the capital city and port of Bissau as well as the two former capitals of Geba and Bolama are located. There are about sixty islands off the coast, some of which are very close to the mainland.

2. The interior plains

This region consists of extensive flat plains which are everywhere below 150m (500ft) above sea level. The river valleys are also flat and because of the low elevation of the land, the rivers meander their way into the sea. Severe flooding occurs during the rainy season and even during high tide in some areas. Further inland, in the area around Gabu, the land becomes more undulating as outcrops of lateritic rocks begin to appear.

3. The south-eastern uplands

This small region of high relief is a part of the foothills of the Futa Jallon highlands. It is characterized by more deeply incised river valleys which are separated by flat-topped laterite-capped interfluves, some of

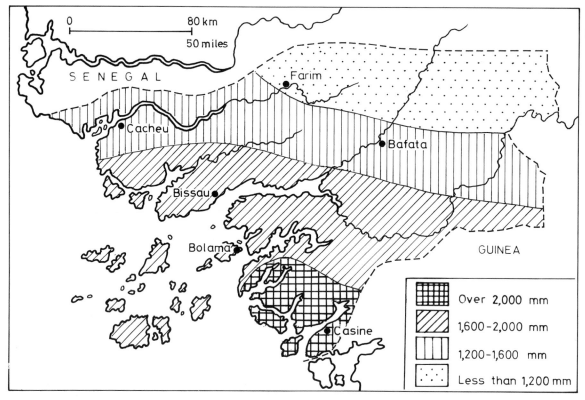

FIG. 21.2—Guinea Bissau: rainfall distribution

which exceed 180m (600ft) in height. These inter-fluves are a continuation of the *bowe* of Guinea Republic, and as in that country, they are practically bare of soils and useless for farming.

CLIMATE AND VEGETATION

Climate

The coastal areas receive very heavy rainfall during the months of June to October, when violent and continuous rains are characteristic. The wettest part is the southern half of the coastlands, which receives about 2,540mm (100in.), decreasing to about 1,780mm (70in.) in the interior. There is a marked dry season which lasts from December to May, and during which the dominant wind is the maritime trades, rather than the harmattan which blows for only a few weeks. The maximum mean monthly temperature in May, which is about the hottest month (just before the rains come), is 30°C (85°F), but there is very little variation throughout the year (Fig. 21.2).

Along the coast where swamp conditions prevail all through the year, the relative humidity is constantly high, often reaching saturation point.

Vegetation

Extensive areas of mangrove swamps occur along the coast and river estuaries as well as on some of the islands. As in Sierra Leone, some of these swamps have since been cleared for rice cultivation. The drier parts of the coastal region and the islands are covered with forests which give way to oil palm bush in the more densely settled areas. In the northern and eastern parts of the country which receive less rainfall, the vegetation consist of grass woodland in which the main tree species include the silk cotton tree, the baobab, the African mahogany and many varieties of acacia. In the highland area of the south-east, the vegetation consists of open savanna land-scape in which grass predominates, particularly on the hills. (See Fig. 21.3.)

ECONOMIC ACTIVITIES

Economic history

The coastal areas were settled by iron-using cultivators long before the Portuguese arrived during the 1440s. These early farmers produced both swamp and upland rice as well as marine salt which they sold

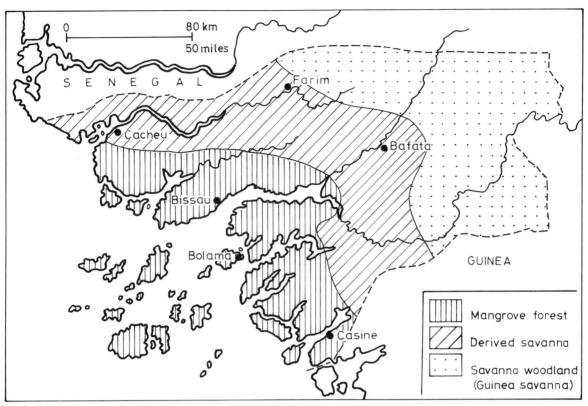

FIG. 21.3—Guinea Bissau: vegetation

to the people of the hinterland. During the early period of contact with Portugal, Guinea Bissau was a major source of slave labour for the cotton and indigo plantations as well as the cloth-weaving industry of the Cape Verde Islands. There was also a substantial trade in such commodities as kola nuts, ivory and wax, the last two items of which went to Europe.

Agriculture

Agricultural production is still largely on a subsistence basis although export-crop production has received increasing attention in recent years. In 1970, about 90 per cent of the population obtained a living from agriculture. Farming is still largely controlled by the indigenous population who produce rice, groundnuts, cassava, millet and palm oil as their main crops. Both swamp and upland rice are cultivated and the Balante people who live in the coastal and estuarine swamps are well known for their skill in reclaiming mangrove swamps for rice cultivation. Other crops produced for domestic consumption and for internal exchange include cassava, beans and millet (Fig. 21.4, p. 174).

Palm oil is produced both for local consumption

and for export, but almost all the palm kernel produced is exported and for many years, palm kernels have remained the second most important export by value. The main export by value is groundnut which are produced mainly in the grassland areas of the interior plains. In 1970, more than 65,000 tons of groundnuts were exported, the main centres of production being around Gabu, Farim and Bafata. An increasing proportion of the crop is now processed in the country before the oil is exported to Portugal.

Cattle rearing is important in the savanna north, although the coastal peoples also keep dwarf cattle in addition to pigs and sheep. In 1972, the cattle population was about 270,000 as compared with 150,000 pigs, 175,000 goats and 65,000 sheep. Protein foods are also obtained from fish, which abound in the estuaries and coastal swamps.

Forestry

The forests are rich in tropical hardwoods of which mahogany, and kapok are very common. Timber export is an important source of income to the country, the earning from timber being exceeded only by that from groundnuts and palm kernel. Poor transportation is a major handicap to the

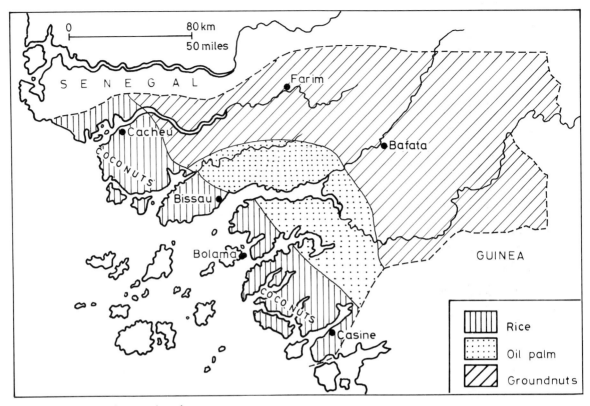

FIG. 21.4—Guinea Bissau: main cash crops

expansion of the export trade in timber. Beeswax is also an important forest product.

Industry

Industrial development is still very modest and largely restricted to the coastal areas. The capital city of Bissau is the only significant industrial area, the main industries being concerned with the processing of local agricultural products. The factories include mills for extracting groundnut oil and palm oil, plants for making soap and soft drinks as well as saw mills and brickworks.

POPULATION AND SETTLEMENT

In 1960, the total population of the country was 502,000, including over 10,000 Portuguese and 5,000 mulattoes, and the estimate for 1972 was under 600,000, which is still less than the population of Ibadan city. The main ethnic groups are the Balante (154,000) who live in the coastal and estuarine swamps and plains, the Manjaco (72,000) who live west of Bissau, the Fulanis (108,000) of the north-east, the Mandingo (64,000) who settle in the interior plains and south-eastern uplands and the Pepel (36,000) of Bissau Island. The Fulanis live a semi-nomadic life and occupy small villages consisting of temporary huts. They cultivate some groundnuts and millet, but their main occupation is cattle rearing. The Mandingo, who are Muslims like the Fulanis, also keep cattle but lead a more settled life. Mandingo villages are much larger and in addition to cattle-rearing, they cultivate groundnuts, cotton, vegetables and citrus fruits. The Mandingos are also known for their success in trading and for their role as smugglers.

Unlike the Fulanis and Mandingos of the interior, the coastal peoples are not Muslim but animist, although many of them have since adopted Christianity. The Balante are well known for their skill in reclaiming mangrove swamps for rice cultivation. They live in small villages but their houses are large and more durable. Most Balante families keep the small muturu cattle and pigs which provide manure for their farmlands. Fishing is also an important occupation, although the Manjaco are the specialist fishermen of Guinea Bissau. The collection of coconuts, oil palm fruits and products of the raffia palm is also a major source of income to the Manjaco and other coastal peoples.

Before the outbreak of armed resistance in 1963, the most densely settled areas were the Bafata and Cacheu districts where the population densities exceeded 46 persons per sq.km (120 persons per sq. mile). The coastal and estuarine swamps have always been sparsely settled and so are the northern districts where the density falls below 20 persons per sq.km (50 per sq. mile). Movements of refugees during the war of liberation altered the pattern of distribution of rural population, particularly in the Portuguese-controlled areas, where the people were concentrated in fortified and garrisoned villages. In the liberated areas, most villages did not shift although they were often subjected to air raids by the Portuguese airforce. The influx of Portuguese troops, estimated at over 2,000, resulted in considerable increase in the population of towns in the Portuguese-controlled areas, since most of the troops were based in the towns. The withdrawal of these troops after the formal recognition of Guinea Bissau by Portugal resulted in a sharp drop in the foreign European population of the country.

It is striking that the nationalist army consisted largely of the Balante, and the mulattoes or assimilados of the coastal areas, while the semi-feudal Muslim Fulani and Mandingos tended to support the Portuguese. The common language of the country is Guinean Creole, which was introduced by migrants from the Cape Verde Islands.

The capital city of Bissau (40,000)

Bissau, which has been the country's capital since 1941, was founded by the Portuguese in 1692. For many centuries it remained a small outpost battling against the hostility of the hinterland people. As late as 1915, Bissau was still described as a camp whose walls 'formed a triangle based on the sea' and whose people lived inside the walls, outside of which they were afraid of the 'fearsome' Pepel people.

Its growth into a modern town started about 1945 and today almost all the few manufacturing industries are located at Bissau. About 85 per cent of the import and export trade is handled at the port of Bissau. Places of interest include Fort Sao Jose, built in 1693, the Roman Catholic Cathedral and the Museum. The airport is located about 10km (6 miles) away.

Other towns

The other towns of importance are also located on river banks or estuaries. Such locations were favourable to the early trade in slaves and the later trade in palm oil and palm kernels. But as in the Niger Delta, some of these port-towns, such as Cacheu, Cacine and

Farim have declined in importance and size, following political and economic changes in the country since the Salazaar regime in Portugal. Cacheu, which was founded by the Portuguese in 1630 and was capital of Guinea Bissau until 1879, has, for example, declined so much that its population in 1960 was only 2,000. The first capital of the country was Geba which like Old Oyo is now in ruins.

At the same time the port-towns of Bafata (near Old Geba) and Canchungo have grown considerably in size. Bafata is located at the limit of navigation on the River Geba and has grown to become an important commercial town in the interior. Its population in 1960 was about 10,000.

TRANSPORT

The rivers Cacheu, Geba and Corubal provide a natural highway into the interior, and inland waterways remain important particularly during the rainy season when earth roads become impassable to motorized transport. Large ships can go as far as the head of each estuary at high tide.

In the coastal lowlands, swamp conditions make road construction very expensive, hence the continued dependence of the local population on canoe transport. The roads (about 3,570km or 2,220 miles in 1972 of which 420km or 260 miles were tarred) link the major towns and serve to supplement the waterways. Unfortunately most of the roads can only be used during the dry season. Guinea Bissau has no railways, but there are air-service connections with the towns of Bissau, Bintam, Bafata and Boloma.

FOREIGN TRADE

As a result of the political situation arising from the war of independence by PAIGC, Guinea Bissau was administered by two rival governments between 1963 and 1974. Table 25's figures (p. 176) refer to trade in the Portuguese-controlled areas of the country and it is important to realize that a considerable trade was also carried on between the liberated areas of Guinea Bissau and other countries.

Starting first with the trade between the Portuguese-controlled areas and other countries, it is clear from Table 25 that the trade balance of this part of the country was not only unfavourable but had become increasingly so since the outbreak of hostilities in 1963. As a result of the war and the large expenditure on arms, the value of imports in the Portuguese-controlled areas rose considerably after 1963, while the export figures declined. Local food production

Table 25—External trade of Portuguese-controlled areas of Guinea (1962–8) (N million)

	1962	1963	1964	1965	1966	1967	1968
Imports	7.8	9.4	10.0	9.8	11.8	11.0	11.8
Exports	4.4	3.8	3.6	2.4	2.0	2.2	2.0
Balance	−3.4	−5.6	−6.4	−7.4	−9.8	−8.8	−9.8

in these areas was inadequate and government had to import a considerable quantity of the food consumed by Portuguese soldiers and administrators.

In addition to vegetable products, food and beverages which top the import list, machinery, cotton textiles and petroleum products were the most important import commodities in the areas still controlled by Portugal. About 70 per cent of all imports by value came from Portugal and Portuguese 'Overseas Provinces', while the remaining 30 per cent was supplied by Great Britain, France and Japan. The exports, which consisted mainly of groundnuts (60 per cent) and palm kernel (30 per cent), went to Portugal (which took 75 per cent), West Germany, France and Britain.

The export trade of the liberated areas of the country was carried on largely through the Republic of Guinea although some kola nuts and palm oil were also sold directly to Senegal. Exports from these areas to the Republic of Guinea were valued at only N 52,500 in 1968, increasing to N 87,500 in 1971. The nationalist government therefore depended largely on foreign military aid to prosecute the war against Portugal.

Chapter 22—The Ivory Coast

PLATE 77—Aerial view of Abidjan, Ivory Coast

The Ivory Coast is the most prosperous of the French-speaking countries of West Africa but although it has a variety of resources and can afford to balance its budget, it relies heavily, like other French-speaking countries, on French aid and technical assistance. Indeed, its economy and senior civil service posts are still controlled by Frenchmen, who are now (1977) more numerous than at independence seventeen years ago. The Ivory Coast shares one border with Ghana and it is interesting to note some of the basic differences and similarities in the development of these two neighbouring countries. Both countries depend heavily on cocoa and other primary products for

earning foreign exchange and both have a relatively high *per capita* income, but while the economy of the Ivory Coast continues to grow, that of Ghana has stagnated since 1966 when President Nkrumah was overthrown. Ghana is, however, a truly African country whose politics and economy are controlled by the indigenous population, at least since the Aliens Act of 1970, but in the Ivory Coast, even the shop girls are French. As in Ghana, cocoa is produced almost entirely by peasant farmers, but almost all the banana crop comes from large plantations owned by private French companies, and at the present rate of educational development it appears that the

177

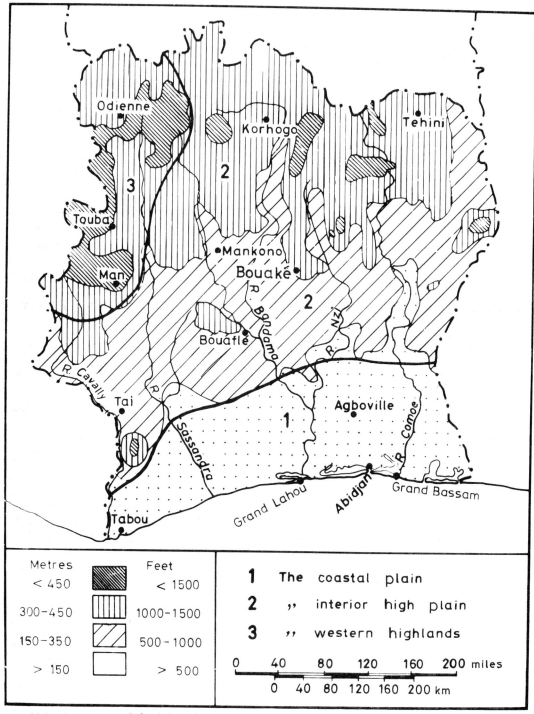

FIG. 22.1—Ivory Coast: relief and physical regions

Ivory Coast will continue to depend on French civil servants for a long time whereas the Ghana civil service has been Africanized since the late 1950s.

The country has an area of 322,500 sq.km (123,200 sq. miles), which is slightly less than half the size of the northern states of Nigeria, and a population of 4.6 million (1973). Its population is much smaller than Ghana's, although it is one third larger than Ghana.

PHYSICAL REGIONS

On the basis of land relief, the Ivory Coast can be divided into three natural regions. These are: 1) the coastal plain, 2) the interior high plains and, 3) the western highlands (Fig. 22.1).

1. The coastal plain

West of Fresco, the coastline is rocky and characterized by cliffs and headlands. The eastern coast is, however, fringed with lagoons which lie behind a continuous stretch of sandspit similar to that in the Lagos State of Nigeria. The only inlets through this sandspit are at Grand Lahou where the Bandama River enters the sea, at the mouth of the Comoe River at Grand Bassam, and at Assinie where the Bia River enters the sea through the Aby Lagoon. The lagoons, which are dotted with small islands, are narrow and shallow.

Away from the coastline and eastern lagoons, the region consists of low undulating plains which extend much farther inland than in any other West African country. A number of residual hills rise above these plains particularly in the region of the Cavally River, in the western and in the northern parts where the coastal plains give way to the interior high plains. The entire region, as well as the interior high plains is drained by parallel streams flowing in a north-south direction. The more important rivers are the Cavally, the Bandama and the Comoe Rivers.

2. The interior high plains

Inselberg landforms and shallow river valleys are common in this region which is underlain by very old hard rocks of the Basement Complex. The high plains have a general elevation of about 300m above sea level and are drained by seasonal rivers some of which become completely dry during the dry season. Lateritic soils which are usually difficult to cultivate occur over extensive areas.

3. The western highlands

This small region is an eastern extension of the Guinea Highlands which we came across in northern Liberia. The prominent relief features in the region include the Man Mountains with summits of over 900m (2,950ft) in the south, Mount Tiouri and Mount Seratigui in the north. The region, which has a much higher rainfall than the surrounding plains, is the source of many streams which flow either south into the sea or northwards to join the River Niger.

CLIMATE AND VEGETATION

Climate

The wettest part of the country is the south-west, which receives an annual rainfall of over 2,280mm (90in.) at Tabou, decreasing to 1,950mm (77in.) at Abidjan in the south-east. Along the coastal areas, the rain falls all through the year but with a marked dry season in August. The two rainiest months in the south, which has a double-maxima regime, are June and September. Along the northern part of the coastal plain region, the rainfall decreases to 1,270mm (50in.) a year and the little dry season becomes less marked. The driest month is January when less than 50mm (2in.) of rain falls (Fig. 22.2, p. 180).

North of latitude 8°N., that is, in the region of the interior high plains and the western highlands, the country experiences a one-maximum regime with the rainfall decreasing northwards to 1,280mm (51in.) at Firkessedugu. The relief effect of the western highlands, however, results in higher rainfall on the Man Mountains, 2,030mm (80in.) decreasing to about 1,530mm (60in.) in the region of Mount Tiouri in the north. It is this relatively heavy rainfall that has made it possible for high forest to survive in the valleys of the western highlands.

As in other parts of West Africa, the coastal areas have high temperatures and high humidity, the mean monthly maximum temperature at Tabou exceeding 27°C (80°F) throughout the year while the mean monthly minimum is never less than 22°C (72°F). Both the daily and monthly range are typically small along the coast but further inland in the area of Ferkessedougou which has higher maximum temperatures and lower minimum temperatures, both the daily and the monthly temperature ranges are much greater. March and April are the hottest months of the year.

Vegetation

Dense forest is the natural vegetation of the south but in many areas the original forest cover has since been replaced by planted forests of rubber, cocoa and oil palm trees. The slopes and valleys of the western highlands also support dense forest vegetation while the lagoons of the south-east support a dense growth of mangrove forests (Fig. 22.2, p. 178).

The rest of the country has a vegetation of Guinea grass-woodland which has been largely modified in the more densely populated areas. In the drier region of the interior high plains, areas with lateritic soils support a more open type of savanna vegetation while stream and river valleys stand out as areas of dense fringing forests.

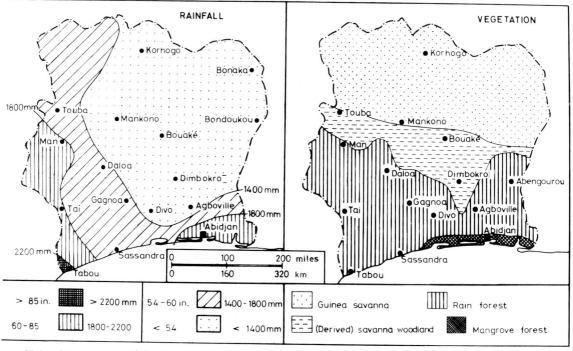

FIG. 22.2—Ivory Coast: rainfall and vegetation

ECONOMIC ACTIVITIES

The varied resources of the Ivory Coast have provided a solid basis for a healthy economic growth and today the country exports a variety of agricultural products but produces at the same time much of the food consumed by the local population. Manufacturing industries have been developed in recent years, but agriculture remains the backbone of the country's economy, providing employment for about 90 per cent of the population.

Agriculture

Since 1962, the government agricultural policy has been directed at diversifying export crops so as to reduce the country's reliance on coffee and to ensure the production of sufficient food for the people. Increasing attention has since been paid to the cultivation of oil palms, cotton, rubber, pineapples and sugarcane, while there has been a substantial decrease in the planting of bananas.

Unlike Ghana and Nigeria, where almost all the agricultural production is carried on by peasant farmers owning small farms, a large proportion of some agricultural exports from the Ivory Coast comes from large private plantations and estates owned by government corporations, although small-scale farmers dominate the production of certain crops. About

95 per cent of the country's cocoa, for example, is produced by small-scale farmers while 90 per cent of the banana crop comes from large European-owned plantations (Fig. 22.3).

The most important export crops produced are coffee and cocoa. Bananas, pineapples, cotton and palm produce are also exported. Coffee, which is a forest crop, was first grown in 1891 in the area near Elima but rapid expansion started after 1930 and today the Ivory Coast is the world's third largest producer of coffee, mostly of the *robusta* variety. Production is concentrated around Man, Dimbokro, Gagnoa, Bouake and Agboville and well over three quarters of the crop comes from African-owned farms. The crop enjoys a protected market in France and for many years up to 1970 it still accounted for more than one-third of the country's total export by value. The contribution of coffee to the export earnings has since declined, being about 28 per cent of the total export by value in 1972. The total amount of coffee produced in that year was 210,000 tons, while the income from coffee exports was 37,291 million francs CFA.

Cocoa is also very important and was introduced from Ghana in 1895. Early cultivation was carried out by European farmers but many African farmers adopted the crop after 1912, following the forced agricultural policy of the government which required that African farmers should plant specified amounts

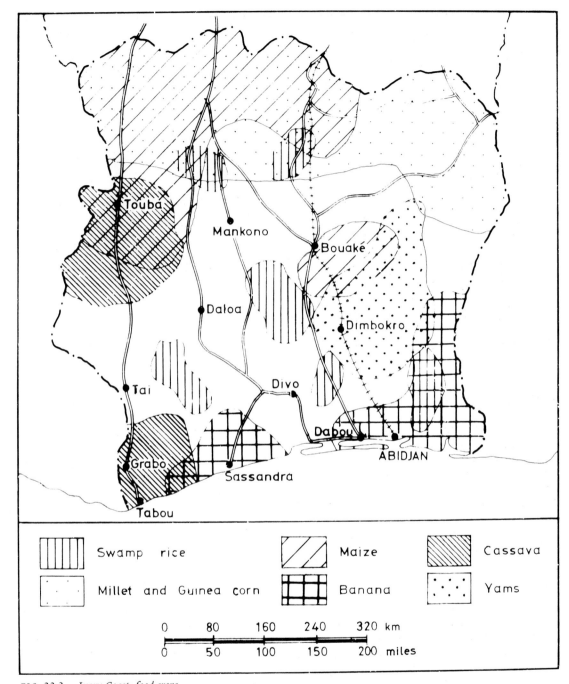

FIG. 22.3—Ivory Coast: food crops

of cocoa and other tree crops. The situation since 1960 is one in which the Ivory Coast alternates with Cameroon as the world's fourth largest producer of cocoa after Ghana, Nigeria, and Brazil. Coffee and cocoa are often grown by the same farmers but about half the cocoa produced in the country comes from the area near to the Ghana cocoa belt. African farmers produce well over 90 per cent of the total output of

181,000 tons (1973) which is about two-fifths that of Ghana. The growing importance of pineapples as an export crop is a significant achievement of the effort to diversify agricultural exports. In 1965, the export tonnage of pineapples reached the record figure of 40,000 tons, placing the crop as the third most important agricultural export for that year. The corresponding export tonnage for bananas was only

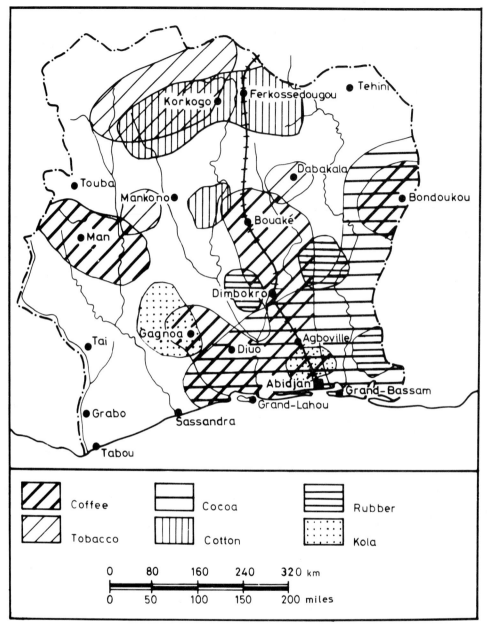

FIG. 22.4—Ivory Coast: export crops

15,000 tons, a considerable decline from 20,000 tons in 1950, when the production of pineapples for export had not yet started. The relative importance of pineapples has declined slightly and since 1966 the crop has remained fourth in the list of agricultural exports, that is after coffee, cocoa and bananas (Fig. 22.4).

The less important export crops include bananas, first grown for export in 1931 and produced almost exclusively by French farmers. The quick-maturing Chinese variety is grown, and the output of 140,000 tons (1965) is about one-third that of Guinea. The oil palm grows semi-wild as in other parts of the Guinea coastlands, but there are also a number of plantations owned by the government corporation, Sodepalm, as well as small-holder estates which have been made popular by financial support from the government. Kola nuts are grown for internal exchange while cotton is grown both for use in the local textiles factory at Bouake and for export.

Turning now to food production, we find that a great variety of crops is grown and that it is in the Ivory Coast that the rice zone of West Africa meets with the root-crop zone, the Bandama Valley being considered to be the dividing line. Rice is particularly important in the Sassandra and Bandama Valleys but local production is still inadequate to meet the country's demand and some rice is imported. Efforts to increase rice production include the construction of 108 hydraulic dams for irrigating rice fields, the building of canals and the distribution on credit of rice seeds, fertilizers and fencing materials to farmers.

Yams, plantains and cassava are the main staple crops east of the Bandama River while maize and guinea corn form the staples of the midlands and the far north. The fact that food production has been increasing, although at a slower rate compared with export crop production, is noteworthy. Root-crop production rose from 853,000 tons in 1950 to 2,210,000 tons in 1972 while the production of cereals (rice, maize, and millet) increased from 193,000 to 498,000 tons during the same period.

Forestry

Table 26 (p. 184) shows that timber is one of the main exports of the Ivory Coast, being the second most important earner of foreign exchange in 1967 and rising to the first position in 1972. The country has one of the greatest stands of timber in West Africa and timber was one of the earliest exports from the Ivory Coast. The best stands are in the sparsely populated south-west districts west of the Bandama River. In the more densely settled areas of the coastal plain, much of the natural forest cover has been destroyed by local farmers and French planters.

The most important species cut for export are mahogany and iroko. There is now a local paper factory using local softwood from the umbrella and silk cotton trees. It is located near Abidjan and produces more than 8,000 tons of brown paper every year. At present the timber industry is facing considerable competition from Ghana and Nigeria, while future expansion is greatly handicapped by the poor state of road transport.

Mining

Compared with neighbouring Liberia, the Ivory Coast is not rich in minerals. Diamonds are produced along the valley of River Bou which is a tributary of the Bandama River and at Seguela. In 1972, 330,000 carats of diamonds worth almost ₦5 million were produced. Other minerals which have been exploited on a small scale are gold, manganese and copper. Bauxite has been discovered in the region lying between the Sassandra and Bandama Rivers, about 80km (50 miles) from the coast, but the deposits have not yet been exploited (Fig. 22.5, p. 184).

Prospecting for iron ore in the Man region and for copper and molybdenum continues. Three oil companies, Esso, Shell and Erap, are also prospecting for oil in the sedimentary basins of the country.

Manufacturing

There have been remarkable developments in manufacturing since independence largely owing to the influx of capital and skill from France. During the colonial period, when Dakar was the industrial centre of French-speaking West Africa, manufacturing in Ivory Coast was almost limited to the processing of agricultural and forest products for export. The big coffee-exporting firms, including SCOA and CFAO, operated large coffee-processing factories in the early 1950s and in 1952 a Swiss company established a cocoa butter factory which was closed down in 1955 because it did not operate at a profit. Other pre-independence industries included several brickworks, a beer factory at Abidjan and a textile factory established in 1923 at Bouake. There were also several saw mills and oil mills producing both groundnut oil for the internal market and palm oil for export.

Table 26 shows the great progress made in the industrial sector between 1962 and 1968. Note the importance of food industries, wood and textiles in terms of value, number of employees and the wages paid. The figures have gone up considerably since then, and so has the range of manufactured goods. Items such as paints, soaps and detergents, cigarettes, bicycles and matches, amongst others are now made locally. The main industrial centre of Abidjan is the site of the local oil refinery and vehicle assembly plant for cars and lorries.

Most of the power used in industry comes from the hydro-electric power station on the Bia River with potential output of 100 million kW hours per annum.

POPULATION AND SETTLEMENT

In 1973, the population of the Ivory Coast was estimated to be 4.64 million. A large number of ethnic groups inhabit the country but the more numerous groups are the Agnis-Ashantis, the Mandes, the Dan-Gourous and the Voltaic groups which include the Bobos and the Lobis. The European population numbered about 12,000 in 1963 but the number has increased considerably since then, following the influx of French civil servants from Guinea into the Ivory Coast.

The average population density of the country is about 13.5 persons per sq.km (35 persons per square mile), but some areas, notably the north-east, the

Table 26—Manufacturing industries of Ivory Coast

	Turnover (million francs CFA)		Number of enterprises (1968)	No. of employees (1968)	Wages in 1968 (million francs CFA)
	1962	1968			
Food industries	5,900	20,400	97	6,480	1,500
Metals	1,900	6,200	30	1,860	800
Chemicals, Rubber	3,000	8,900	33	2,190	700
Wood	2,600	9,100	73	7,500	2,500
Textiles	2,200	10,200	24	5,410	1,400
Total	15,600	54,800	257	23,440	6,900

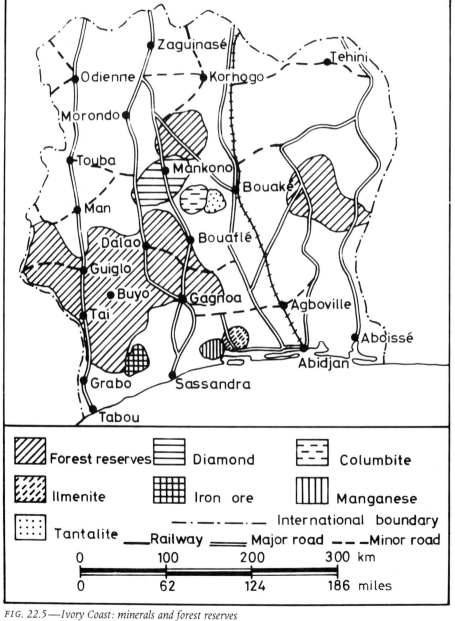

FIG. 22.5—Ivory Coast: minerals and forest reserves

PLATE 78—*Small village of Dianfla, Yamoussoukro district, Ivory Coast*

north-west and the south-west, and the province of Bondoukou are virtually uninhabited, have a density of less than 4 persons per sq.km (10 persons per square mile). The largest concentration of people is in the Man district, the Bouake, Korhogo and Abidjan districts and the rich agricultural area stretching from Dimbokro to Agboville. These densely settled areas have a population density of about 38.5 persons per sq.km (100 persons per sq. mile) which is relatively small compared with over 190 persons per sq.km (500 persons per sq. mile) for the densely settled areas of Upper Volta and Nigeria. The rest of the country has an average density of 10 to 20 persons per sq.km (25—50 per sq. mile) (Fig. 22.6, p. 186).

About 85 per cent of the population live in small villages and hamlets scattered all over the country but with a marked concentration in the grassland areas of the central and northern districts. There is however, an increasing movement of unskilled young people especially from the grassland north into the cities along the coast. (See plate 78.)

Ivory Coast is a labour-deficit country and has had to depend very much on foreign migrant labour for the development of plantation agriculture, the timber industry and manufacturing industries. In 1965 about

half the total labour force of the country consisted of foreigners, made up of 670,000 Africans and 30,000 non-Africans. Most of these migrants originated from Mali (220,000), Upper Volta (200,000) and Guinea (150,000). These foreign migrants constitute about 70 per cent of the unskilled labour force in the coffee and cocoa plantations and about 50 per cent of all urban workers. But although the country is in great need of more labour for the expansion of tree-crop production, there has been mounting unemployment in the urban areas. Civil service jobs in the cities are therefore largely reserved for the indigenous people, while foreign migrants who settle in urban areas are either self-employed or work for wages in private commercial and industrial firms.

Economic growth has been accompanied by a rapid increase in the urban population which rose from 160,000 in 1950 to about 915,000 in 1972. The main centres of attraction for rural-urban migrants are the growing industrial towns of Abidjan and Bouake. The wide range of social and economic opportunities offered by Abidjan have attracted very many migrants to this city. But while the number of non-agricultural jobs increased by 57 per cent between 1960 and 1967, the urban population increased much faster, by 115

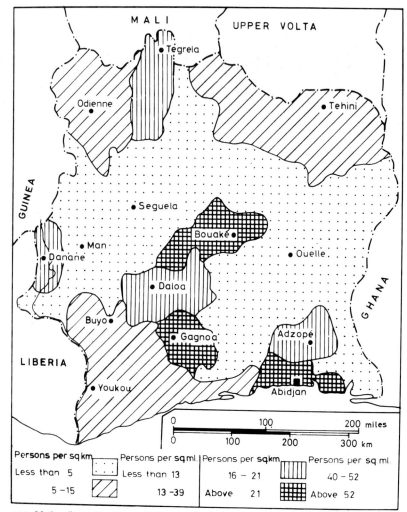

FIG. 22.6—*Ivory Coast: population distribution*

per cent in Abidjan. Hence the large and increasing number of urban unemployed in the country.

Abidjan (500,000), the capital and the country's major port (plate 77), handles practically all the export and import trade of the Ivory Coast as well as those of landlocked Upper Volta and Mali. The cutting of the Vridi·Canal in 1950 resulted in a 50 per cent increase in the traffic handled by the port whose deep water makes it possible for large ships to call at Abidjan. Abidjan is also the coastal terminal of the country's only railroad and has a large modern airport. During the last 50 years, the town has developed from a small fishing village to become a well-planned and important industrial centre, where local agricultural products are processed. Other important industrial establishments include engineering and printing works, soap and soft drinks factories and a beer brewery.

Bouake (100,000) is located on the highest point of

a small plateau just north of the forest belt and is an important collecting point for produce from the forest belt as well as from the savanna country lying north of the town. It is a railway town 315km (196 miles) from Abidjan and has good road connections with its hinterland. Bouake is well known for its local handicrafts. It is an important cotton ginning and weaving centre and has a large agricultural research station where livestock is kept. As a provincial headquarters it has a small airport and several educational institutions. Its textile factory produces cotton piece goods and a nearby factory ropes from sisal.

Sassandra is a small provincial headquarters located on a bay bearing the same name. It has a healthy site and a sheltered anchorage which has been developed into a small port which handles much of the timber and banana exports from the south-west. Sassandra is an important sawmilling centre which will develop with improved transportation to the hinterland.

TRANSPORT

Rapids and falls as well as marked fluctuations in water level have made the rivers virtually useless as a means of transport. There is also no form of animal transport since the whole country is tsetse-infested. The east coast lagoons therefore provide the only natural means of communication and are used by a considerable number of barges. The completion in 1950 of the Vridi Canal which links the Ebrie lagoon to the sea brought about a rapid increase in the trade of Abidjan.

As in Nigeria, the railway came before the road. The first and only railway from Abidjan reached Dimbokro in 1909 and was extended to Bouake in 1912. The terminus is now 1,138km (711 miles) away at Ouagadougou in Upper Volta which was once administered as part of the Ivory Coast.

Road building received much attention during the First World War when a number of roads were built to serve as feeders for the railway. Fig. 22.5 shows that the country is now served by a relatively dense network of roads, most of which are still untarred. All the main roads run north-south from the interior agricultural and mining districts to the coastal ports of Abidjan, Sassandra and Tabou.

A national airline, Air Ivoire was formed in 1963 to handle internal traffic, but apart from Abidjan which has a class 'A' international airport the other airports are suitable only for light planes.

EXTERNAL TRADE

Like the other French-speaking countries of West Africa, the Ivory Coast exports much of her primary produce to France which in turn supplies her with most manufactured goods. But unlike most French-speaking countries of West Africa which suffer from chronic trade deficits, the Ivory Coast has had a steady and favourable balance of trade (Table 27). This is largely a result of the relatively broad agricultural export base of the country and of favourable French prices for her coffee exports. Increased timber exports have also made trade more favourable.

The growing importance of the United States of America, Italy, West Germany and the Netherlands as markets for exports from Ivory Coast is noteworthy. In 1967, for example, the total exports by value to these four countries was greater than the exports to France, which took less than 40 per cent of the total exports for that year. This trend has been maintained in subsequent years. France, however, remains the main source of imports which consists primarily of capital equipment, consumer goods, machinery and food. About 50 per cent of the imports by value came from France in 1967, decreasing to 48 per cent in 1972. Other important sources of imports are the USA, West Germany and the Netherlands.

The percentage composition of the country's exports is shown in Table 28. Coffee remains as the most important export commodity although its relative importance, like that of cocoa, has declined.

Table 27—Trade balance of Ivory Coast (million francs CFA)

	1960	1965	1966	1967	1968	1969	1970	1971	1972
Imports	32,000	58,340	63,610	65,050	77,600	86,300	107,700	110,800	113,100
Exports	39,000	68,420	76,660	80,260	104,900	118,200	130,200	126,600	139,500
Balance	+ 7,000	+ 10,080	+ 13,050	+ 15,210	+ 27,300	+ 31,900	+ 22,500	+ 15,800	+ 26,400

Note: 1,000 francs CFA = ₦3.00

Table 28—Percentage composition of exports from Ivory Coast

	1960 (Percentage)	1967	1970 (Value in million francs CFA).	1972	1967	1970 (Percentage)	1972
Coffee	48	25,423	43,172	37,291	31.5	33.2	26.72
Cocoa	22	13,878	30,960	27,364	18	23.8	19.61
Timber	16	21,777	29,335	37,728	27	22.5	27.03
Bananas	4	3,038	3,208	3,456	4	2.5	2.47
Pineapples	2	2,448	3,810	?	3	2.9	?
Manganese	0	473	258	?	0.5	0.2	?
Others	8	13,226	19,457	?	16	14.9	?
Total	100	80,263	130,200	139,541	100	100	100

Chapter 23—The Republic of Liberia

PLATE 79—Central Monrovia, Liberia

The origin of Liberia dates back to 1822 when a group of freed slaves was settled at Monrovia through the efforts of the American Colonization Society. By 1847 when the country became independent, the number of settlers was about 3,000, but the territory which came to be administered by the settler population included an extensive hinterland inhabited by native African peoples. Liberia is therefore the oldest independent country in West Africa and in addition, it is the only country in West Africa which has not experienced any period of colonial rule. Its rate of development has not been very impressive and indeed, for the first one hundred years of its existence as an independent state, the country remained rather isolated while its economy and population showed very little sign of growth.

Until 1950, when the native Africans first took part in the government of the country, the affairs of Liberia were solely in the hands of the settler population who still dominate various aspects of the political, social and economic life of the country. Today, these settlers, who are often referred to as Americo-Liberians, are still concentrated in the coastal towns and plantations. Their number is put at about 25,000 out of a total population of about 1.5 million. The country is therefore one of the least populated in West Africa, its population being about the size of that of Lagos State while its land area of 111,000 sq.km (43,000 sq. miles) is about the size of Benue and Plateau States or thirty-one times the size of Lagos State.

RELIEF AND DRAINAGE

The simplified geological map of West Africa (Fig. 1.1) shows that almost the whole of Liberia is made

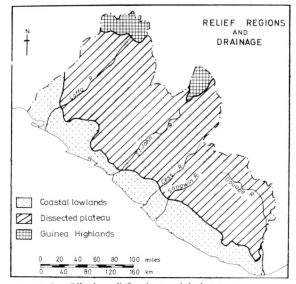

FIG. 23.1—Liberia: relief regions and drainage

up of old hard rocks of the Basement Complex similar to those in western and northern Nigeria. The land forms, which feature broad plains and erosional survivals as well as flat valleys, are also similar to the familiar scenes in northern Yorubaland. Considering the elevation and general character of the relief, the country can be divided into three major regions namely (Fig. 23.1): 1) the coastal lowlands, 2) the dissected plateau, 3) the Guinea Highlands.

1. The coastal lowlands

Liberia has a relatively long coastline which stretches for about 510km (320 miles) from north-west to south-east. There are only a few indentations—river estuaries and inlets to lagoons. Extensive stretches of sandbars formed by wave action are characteristic and it is behind these sandbars that the lagoons and mangrove swamps occur. In areas such as the Cape Mesurada, Grand Bassa and Cape Mount, where the hills come right down to the sea, the coast is characterized by bold cliffs and headlands similar to that at Freetown.

The coastal plain itself is a low-lying area which varies in width from 48 to 96km (30–60 miles). Like the rest of the country it is drained by parallel streams, most of which rise from the Guinea Highlands. The valleys of these streams are particularly broad in this region and given to regular flooding towards the end of the rainy season when areas of freshwater swamps occur in parts of the coastal plain.

2. The dissected plateau

A narrow range of high hills running across the country from north-west to south-east separates the coastal lowlands from the central dissected plateau, which has an average elevation of over 270m (900ft) above sea level. Further inland the plateau rises to heights of over 450m (1,500ft). Numerous tributary streams originate from this region, which has a rather complex relief featuring extensive hill masses and inselberg landscapes. It is in this hilly country that the main Liberian coffee farms are located. Much of the region is still undeveloped and isolated, since the numerous rivers draining it are hardly navigable.

3. The Guinea Highlands

In the northern parts of Lofa and Nimba counties, the land rises to over 1,200m (4,000ft) above sea level to form the southern foothills of the Guinea Highlands. This is a largely uninhabited and isolated mountainous region and is virtually undeveloped. The rivers are characterized by numerous rapids and falls as they descend from the highlands into the plateau region.

CLIMATE AND VEGETATION

The coastline of Liberia lies almost at right angles to the direction of the rain-bearing south-west winds and the coastal areas have therefore a very rainy climate, particularly along the north-west coastlands where the annual rainfall is about 3,560mm (140in.), decreasing to 2,540mm (100 in.) in the region of Cape Palmas. Highland areas along the coast, such as Cape Mount, record up to 5,080mm (200in.) a year, but further inland the rainfall decreases to just over 2,290mm (90in.) a year (Fig. 23.2, p. 190).

The rainy season starts from late April or early May and lasts until October or early November. There is a short break in the rains lasting from about the last week in July to the middle of August and as a result, Liberia has a double-maxima regime with the peaks occurring in July and September. Along the coast, the average monthly minimum temperature lies between 20–24°C (68–75°F). The hottest month is March, that is just before the rains come, while the lowest temperatures are recorded during the month of July when the rains are heaviest. The climate is characterized by small ranges in the annual and diurnal temperatures, and by high relative humidity all the year round.

Mangrove swamps occur along the coast, particularly in the area west of Monrovia and at the various river estuaries, but they are not as extensive as in neighbouring Sierra Leone. In the coastal plain region which has a rather hot, wet and humid climate, the vegetation is surprisingly very poor, consisting of light forest and savanna woodland except in the Firestone plantations which consist of large areas of rubber forests. The most extensive areas of high forest occur further inland in the region of the dissected plateau. The main forest reserves and forest concessions are located in this region, but particularly in the eastern counties of Grand Bassa, Kimba and Grand Gedeh. Parts of the Guinea Highlands are also rich in forest cover but in the more elevated areas, the vegetation consists of grass-woodlands.

ECONOMIC HISTORY

As a result of the poor economic situation during the first one hundred years of its history, Liberia was a great disappointment to many people in America and Africa. The Americo-Liberian did not possess the necessary skill to establish a successful settlement in the Liberian environment and right from the beginning they were not well received by the indigenous African population. There were virtually no roads in the interior.

Coffee and sugar provided the main source of earned income for the early settler and by 1850, trade relations with Europe had grown considerably as ships built near Monrovia and manned largely by the famous skilled Krumen of Liberia carried palm produce and coffee to England, Holland and Germany. The introduction of Liberian coffee into Brazil, which came to dominate the world market in this product, and the fall in world prices of cocoa, palm produce and sugar brought a grave economic crisis in the 1870s, a crisis which was to last for more than 60 years. In 1926, however, things started to improve following the establishment of the world's rubber plantation at Harbel near Monrovia by the Firestone company of America. More development projects were started when President Taubman came to power in 1944 and since 1951 the mining of iron ore and other minerals have contributed considerably to the country's economic growth. The strategic importance of Liberia during the Second World War brought about some major developments in the economy following the establishment of an American military base in Liberia. Amongst other things a large and modern airport was built at Robertsfield while the United States Navy constructed the deep-water commercial port at Monrovia.

AGRICULTURE

Like other countries in West Africa, Liberia is basically an agricultural country with more than 80 per cent of the population obtaining their livelihood from farming. Traditional agriculture in which the vast majority of the people produce food crops on small

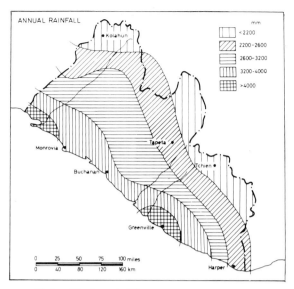

FIG. 23.2—Liberia: rainfall

farms under the method of bush fallowing exists side by side with large-scale plantation agriculture where modern methods of farming are used to produce tree crops for export.

Upland rice and cassava are the main subsistence crops but although most farmers cultivate rice, the country does not produce enough to feed itself and as late as 1969 as much as 50,000 tons of rice, valued at ₦5.8 million was imported into the country. Plans to reduce the country's dependence on imported food include the expansion of swamp rice by making use of the mangrove swamps which, unlike in Sierra Leone, have so far seen little developement. Under its recent 'Operation Production' policy, the government has already enlisted the help of FAO and Nationalist Chinese rice experts to assist the Department of Agriculture in starting some swamp rice projects similar to the mechanized rice project established by the Liberian Produce Marketing Corporation near the Makona River. Land is plentiful and an estimated 288,000 hectares (720,000 acres) of freshwater swamps suitable for the rice cultivation are available. In addition another 360,000 hectares (900,000 acres) of land situated along valley floors are considered suitable for irrigated rice farming. Other crops grown on peasant farms include yams, sweet potatoes, and variety of fruits and vegetables. Sugarcane is also grown, partly for making sugar and partly for making local rum.

Rubber is easily the most important export crop and most rich Liberians have some interest in rubber production. As in Nigeria, the earliest production of rubber in Liberia was from wild plants and it was not until 1907 that the first rubber plantation (abandoned

FIG. 23.3—Liberia: transportation and tree-crop areas

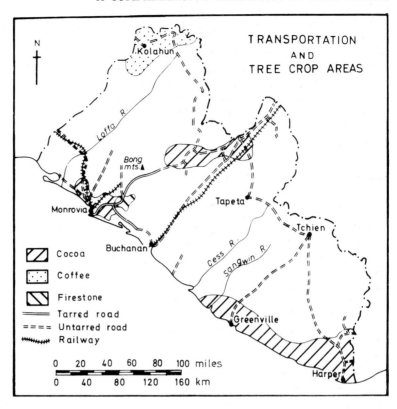

in 1920 because of poor prices) was established on Mount Barclay). The Firestone rubber concession of about 405,000 hectares (1 million acres) was granted in 1926 and consists of a very large estate at Harbel (near Robertsfield) on the Farmington River and a much smaller estate on the Cavally River which enters the sea at Cape Palmas. Many local farmers also plant rubber and by 1968 there were over 3,800 private rubber farmers each usually owning about 10 hectares (25 acres) and employing 5 to 10 labourers. In 1972 the country exported 85,000 tons of rubber, a third of which came from smallholdings owned by Africans. Both the plantations and the peasants cultivate high-yielding varieties and this has made it possible for the country to achieve a high yield of 184 kg per hectare (1,000 lbs. per acre), which is more than three times the average yield in Nigeria (less than 55kg per hectare or 300 lbs per acre). The total number of people employed in the rubber industry in 1972 was 40,000, about 14,000 of whom worked in the two Firestone plantations.

Other export crops include coffee which was the main export until 1880, when Brazil started to dominate the world market. The main variety grown is *robusta* and the main producing areas are around Gbaruga and Ganta. Cocoa is of little importance and is grown in scattered farms in the south-east, although there are a few large estates near Sakripi and the Cess River. Palm oil and kernels are produced all over the country, the main centres of production being west of the Cess River. Crops of the interior include cotton, groundnuts and kola nuts, the latter being exported to Guinea.

LIVESTOCK

Environmental conditions prevent the keeping of cattle but sheep and goats are numerous. Most of the cattle slaughtered in the country come from Mali and Guinea and between these countries and Liberia there exists a trade in cattle and kola nuts, the organization of which is similar in some ways to the one between western and northern Nigeria. Attempts to increase the supply of protein foods include the expansion of commercial poultry farming and it is now possible to obtain adequate supplies of poultry and fresh eggs all through the year. The Department of Agriculture has also established a branch to supervise the raising of cattle, pigs and rabbits for meat. In 1972, a Swiss company opened a factory to produce bacon, ham and sausages, food items which were formerly all imported from abroad.

FISHING

Small-scale coastal fishing is dominated by the Fante and Kru people and it is only in recent years that large-scale commercial fishing has been started. The largest fishing company is the Mesurado Fishing Company which owns a small fleet and catches about 10,000 tons of fish a year. The company owns a modern cold store, with a fish-processing plant in Monrovia and has about fifteen cold stores in the interior. The overall production of fish in 1972 was about 17,000 tons including fish from fish-farms and freshwater fishing in the interior.

FORESTRY

The area under forest is estimated to be 5.6 million hectares (13.8 million acres), and out of this, 1.6 million hectares (3.9 million acres) have been set aside as forest reserves while about 1.2 million hectares (2.9 million acres) are now being exploited by foreign concessions. Most of the concessions (about 60 per cent) lie in the eastern half of the country and according to an inventory of the existing forest reserves in 1967, there are more than 235 species of timber trees, at least 60 of which are in marketable quantities, although only 11 of them are known in the world market. Exploitation of these forests has so far been handicapped by the lack of good roads and vast areas still remain inaccessible. Most of the timber is exported as logs although 19 saw mills were in operation in 1973. There is also a scheme to establish a wood-processing factory which would provide facilities for producing plywood and hardboard (Fig. 23.4).

MINING

Liberia possesses a wide variety of minerals but only gold, iron ore and diamonds have so far been exploited (Fig. 23.5). Deposits of mica, lead, manganese, graphite, columbite and other minerals have been discovered in various parts of the country, but further investigation is required to show whether it will be economical to exploit them. (See plate 80.)

Iron ore is by far the most important mineral produced in Liberia and as the most important export commodity it provides the main source of income for the country (Table 29). Mining started at Bomi Hills in 1951 when 195,000 tons of ore were produced and before 1965 Liberia had become the largest iron ore producing country in Africa and the third world exporter, its iron ore output being about 4 per cent of the world total output. The Bomi Hills deposits are exploited by the Liberian Mining Company, an American company which produces about 3 million tons of iron ore a year. The total reserves of iron ore in this area are estimated to be about 120 million tons about 20 million tons of which consist of very rich ore containing up to 68 per cent of iron. The other

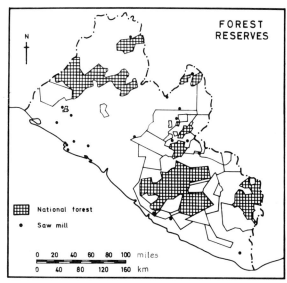

FIG. 23.4—Liberia: forest reserves

mines are the Mano River mine on the Sierra Leone border, the LAMCO mine at Mt Nimba near the Guinean border with an annual production of over 10 million tons and Bong Range mine which started production in 1965. The Bong Range mine is located in a 780sq.km (300 sq. miles) concession area 80km (50 miles) north-east of Monrovia and was opened in 1961 by the National Iron Ore Company. With an estimated reserve of 250 million tons of ore, it produced about 22.4 million tons in 1972. The ore from Bong Range is concentrated at the mine and shipped in the form of 'ready to use' pellets which are highly favoured by European consumers. The total ore reserve for the country is put at 650 million tons with an average iron content of 60 per cent.

Alluvial gold has been worked for many years from small placers along stream beds but production is small, being valued at less than $86,400 (₦72,000) in 1969. Diamond is much more important and is obtained from alluvial flats along the Bar and Joblong Rivers. In 1972 the country exported 890,000 carats of diamond valued at $31.7 million (₦26.4 million). Amongst other things, mining employs over 10,000 native workers, the labour force at Bomi Hills being over 2,500. In 1972, the mining sector contributed about 70 per cent of the export earnings of Liberia and was by far the main source of government revenue. The total investment in Liberia's mines at the end of that year was about $2,000 million (₦1,666 million).

MANUFACTURING INDUSTRIES

Manufacturing is still not much developed. In 1969 it contributed only 3 per cent of the gross domestic

PLATE 80—Iron ore mine at Nimba, Liberia

product. The most important industry is the $8.4 million (₦7 million) oil refinery near Monrovia with a daily capacity of 10,000 barrels of crude oil. It produces all grades of petrol, jet fuel, diesel oil, fuel oil and asphalt. There is also a chemical and explosives plant and a paint factory. The food and drink industry plants include a brewery, a distillery, a fish plant and factories producing various soft drinks. Finally, there are such industries as soap-making and furniture-making which make use of local raw materials. But although Liberia produces so much rubber, there is as yet no tyre factory utilizing local rubber as in Nigeria. Rather, Liberian rubber supplies the tyre factory in Ghana which has a much larger internal market. Many more industries, including a wig, confectionery and a paper conversion plant, have been proposed but the small size of the Liberian market is a major factor which does not encourage industrialization.

POPULATION AND SETTLEMENT

During the 1962 census (the first in the country's history), the population of Liberia was 1.01 million but in 1974, the population was 1.5 million. Considered as a whole, the country is very sparsely populated and indeed it is the small size of its population that constitutes one of the major factors inhibiting the development of the economy. Shortage of labour has been felt not only in the rapidly expanding iron ore mines

but also in the plantations and timber concessions. In 1957 for example the government had to close down some diamond mines in order to stop a diamond rush which threatened to worsen the labour situation in the plantations and iron ore mines. The small size of its internal market is also a serious limiting factor to the establishment of viable manufacturing industries. The average population density

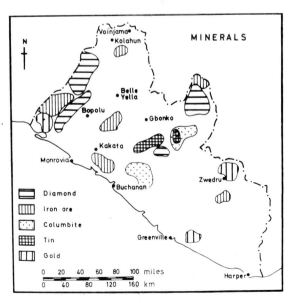

FIG. 23.5—Liberia: minerals

193

for the country is less than 15 persons per sq.km (40 persons per sq. mile) but vast areas of the interior are uninhabited. The main concentrations of people are in the areas around the capital city of Monrovia, the Firestone and Bomi concessions and around the provincial towns (Fig. 23.6).

The Americo-Liberians, whose number is estimated at 25,000, are economically the most dominant group in the country. More than half of them live in the capital city of Monrovia while the rest also live along the coast. For more than one hundred years, this group dominated the politics and economy of the country. The group had very little contact with the people of the heartland, who often regarded the Americo-Liberians as foreign intruders. Relations between the group and the native inhabitants of the country have improved greatly since President Taubman came to power in 1944, but there is still a lot to be done to bridge the educational and cultural gap between the indigenous population and the Americo-Liberians.

Other important groups inhabiting the country include the famous Krumen of the south-eastern coast who are a seafaring people, the Gissi, Gola, Kpwesi and the Mandingos of the north. With the exception of the Mandingos who are predominantly Muslims, the other groups are animists, although an increasing number have adopted the Christian faith.

Recent developments in the Liberian economy have brought about considerable movements of population to the towns as well as to the foreign-operated rubber, iron ore and timber concessions. There is a greater influx to the mines since the mining companies offer higher wages and better housing. These migrations have tended to worsen the food deficit situation in the country and at present, agricultural enterprises such as the Firestone rubber plantations are obliged to import rice to feed their workers. Government policy towards population movements is one of encouraging the urban unemployed to return to the land and since 1964 a vagrancy law which allows mining companies to evict excess population from their workers' villages, has been in operation.

Monrovia

Monrovia is the capital and by far the largest town in the country. It has a population of over 45,000 people and has a neat grid-pattern layout which reminds one of American cities. Its harbour which was opened in 1948 has deep-water wharves capable of handling large ocean-going ships. It is provided with modern equipment for the mechanical loading of

FIG. 23.6—Liberia: population density

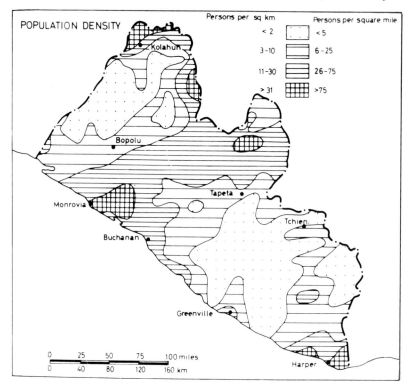

iron ore from the Bomi Hills mines and has the great advantage of being the only free port in West Africa in that no duty is payable for goods transferred from one ship to another or stored in warehouses to await shipment by another vessel. It has a small local airport which connects it with the country's international airport at Robertsville. (See plate 79.)

Provincial towns and other settlements

A few other urban centres exist along the coast and in the provincial administrative headquarters where most of the literate Liberians live. Outside these urban centres, settlement consists of small villages and hamlets. The street village in particular is widespread but contact between villages in the interior is still limited, owing to the poor state of transportation.

TRANSPORTATION

One of the main factors inhibiting the rapid development of the economy has been the poor state of transportation in the country. During the first one hundred years of its existence there were virtually no roads except in the Monrovia district. Communication was largely by human porters using footpaths, since rapids and falls limit navigation on the rivers to only short stretches near the coast.

Remarkable improvements in transportation have taken place since the opening by the American Navy of the deep-water port at Monrovia in 1942. The first railway in the country is the 75km (47 miles) line built by the Liberian Mining Company in 1950 to evacuate iron ore from the Bomi Hills to Monrovia for export. This line has since been extended by 72km (45 miles) to tap the iron ore at Mano River near the Sierra Leone border and once again the cost of construction was borne by an iron ore mining company, this time the National Iron Ore Company. The other two railway lines, one from Bong Range to Monrovia, 80km (50 miles) and the second from Mt Nimba to Buchanan, 270km (168 miles) were also built and are operated by iron ore mining companies, who have also contributed to road development in the country. Mining, and to a lesser extent plantation agriculture, have brought about great improvements in the transportation system of the country. Apart from the roads built and maintained by these companies, the increased revenue earned from mining and agriculture has enabled the government to build more roads to link the more productive parts of the country with the capital. The length of the road network doubled between 1958 to 1968, when the country had 3,680km (2,300 miles) of road, about 370km of which had been tarred. One-third of these were built by private concession.

The international airport at Robertsfield handles regular services from other parts of West Africa and from provincial towns in the country. Internal flights are handled by the Liberian National Airways.

There has been very little development of sea and river transport in Liberia. Only a few small vessels engage in coastal trade although a new shipping company, the Lone Star Shipping Line, has been formed to encourage trade among the major coastal towns of Monrovia, Buchanan, Greenville and Harper. Presently, most of the maritime communication of Liberia is with other countries. The freeport of Monrovia serves as an important transhipment centre to other countries including Guinea and Mali. The total registered tonnage of ships flying the Liberian flag is over 23 million tons, and this makes Liberia the largest 'maritime' nation in the world. Almost all the ships, however, belong to foreign countries who have been attracted to fly the Liberian flag because of the small registration fee and the small annual tax charged by the government.

FOREIGN TRADE

The ten-year period beginning from 1960 saw a rapid growth in the economy of Liberia and the main export figures for a part of this period are given in Table 29 (p. 196). Study these figures carefully and notice the steady growth in the value of earnings from iron ore and the fluctuations in the earnings from rubber and diamonds. The value of timber exports has been increasing, amounting to $8.16 million (₦6.8 million) in 1972.

It is also clear from Table 30 (p. 196) that the country now has an increasingly favourable balance of trade, thanks to earnings from iron ore, rubber, timber and diamonds.

The trade figures given in Table 30 are certainly impressive particularly when we take into consideration the extremely poor state of Liberia's economy during the period up to 1955. But the export trade is dominated by foreign firms who of course take most of their profits out of the country. The people of the hinterland are still to benefit from the new growth in the economy. Thus while the export trade of Liberia is generally greater than that of Guinea Republic, for example, the people of rural Guinea are more involved in the production of their country's wealth and share much more in its profits than is the case in Liberia.

America remains the largest single market for Liberian exports although its share has fallen from 28 per cent in 1969 to 22 per cent in 1971. The share of the EEC countries in 1971 was 57 per cent. Japan is another important trading partner. An increasing number of vehicles and electrical equipment now come from Japan which is an important buyer of iron ore from Liberia. West Germany and Britain are the other main trading partners. Trade with neighbouring West African countries is negligible. In 1970, for example, only 1 per cent of the exports of Liberia was sent to Guinea and Ivory Coast.

Table 29—Value of major exports from Liberia (in million $)

Commodity	1964	1965	1966	1967	1968	1969	1970	1971	1972	1973
Iron ore	80.6	96.0	106.3	115.1	118.1	137.0	159.0	160.6	182.7	196.7
Rubber	29.7	29.0	27.0	26.6	25.5	30.4	36.1	32.2	29.1	42.9
Diamonds*	1.6	1.4	3.1	5.4	9.1	8.8	4.1	28.2	31.7	49.3
Coffee	6.0	1.7	5.8	2.5	2.9	2.5	3.3	4.0	4.6	4.9
Palm kernel	0.8	2.1	1.6	1.8	1.9	1.4	1.8	2.2	0.4	0.2
Timber	—	—	—	—	1.5	6.9	4.9	8.0	8.2	?
Cocoa	0.6	0.2	0.5	0.6	1.3	1.6	1.0	1.3	1.5	1.9
Others	?	0.5	1.4	1.2	1.6	?	?	?	—	—
Re-exports	?	4.5	4.8	5.6	6.9	?	?	?	—	—
Total	125.7	135.4	150.5	158.8	169.0	195.9	213.7	246.6	269.8	324.0

*Trade Figures published in 1974 showed a substantial revaluation of diamond exports from $5.7 to $28.2 million for 1971 and from $6.3 to $31.7 million for 1972.

Table 30—Trade balance of Liberia (million $)

	1964	1965	1966	1967	1968	1969	1970	1971	1972	1973
Exports	125.7	135.4	150.5	158.8	169.0	195.9	213.7	246.6	269.8	324.0
Imports	111.2	104.8	113.7	125.2	108.5	114.7	149.7	162.4	178.7	193.5
Trade Balance	14.5	30.6	36.8	33.6	60.6	81.2	64.0	84.2	91.1	130.5
Total Trade	236.9	240.2	264.2	284.0	277.5	310.6	363.4	419.0	448.5	517.5

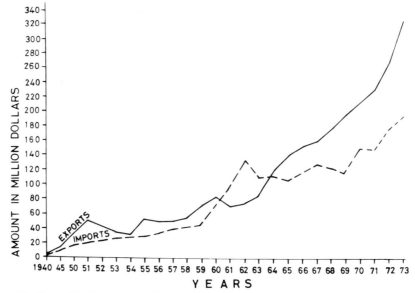

FIG. 23.7—Liberia: exports and imports

Chapter 24—The Republic of Mali

PLATE 81 — Dogon village near Songhai, Mali. The Dogon are the direct descendants of Iron Age people who lived here

With an area of about 1,240,000 sq.km (478,800 sq. miles), Mali is the second largest country in West Africa (second only to Niger Republic). Like Niger Republic, it is a landlocked country, much of which consists of desert wastes. In 1973, the total population was estimated to be 5.4 million giving an average of slightly over 4 persons per sq.km (10 persons per sq. mile) for the whole country. As plate 81 shows, Mali is the cradle of an ancient civilization which flourished for many centuries in the region of the Niger Valley, and has a long period of recorded history.

Ancient empires associated with the country include ancient Ghana (fourth to eleventh century A.D.) Songhai (ninth to sixteenth century A.D.) ancient Mali (eleventh to seventeenth century A.D.) and the Fulani Empire of Macina which flourished during the nineteenth century A.D. Almost all these empires had regular trade and cultural contacts with Africa north of the Sahara, from where Islam was introduced and it was from Mali that people migrated to settle in the areas which today constitute the Republics of Ghana, Ivory Coast and Sierra Leone.

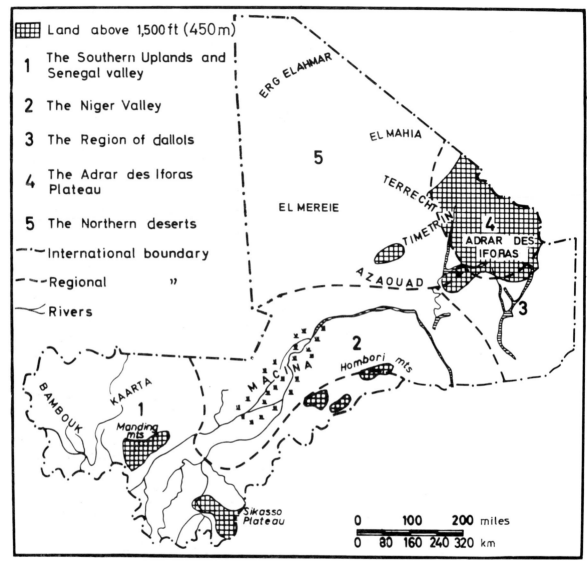

FIG. 24.1—Mali: relief and physical regions

PHYSICAL FEATURES AND RELIEF REGIONS

During the colonial period Mali was one of the territories of French West Africa and was then called French Sudan. It became independent, assuming the name of Sudanese Republic in November 1958 and in April 1959 it joined with Senegal to form the short-lived Mali Federation. On 20 June 1960, Senegal seceded from the union while the Sudanese Republic assumed the new title of Republic of Mali.

PHYSICAL FEATURES AND RELIEF REGIONS

Most of Mali consists of a flat and monotonous plain which rarely exceeds 330m (1,100ft) above sea level. A number of prominent sandstone highlands called

mountains, which are characterized by steep escarpments occur in the south (Fig. 24.1). These include the Manding Mountains just west of Bamako, the Mina Mountains which are a westward extension of the Sikasso Highlands of Upper Volta, the Bandiagara Highlands (lying between Bandiagara and Koro) and the Hombori Mountains which lie just west of Hombori. All these highlands occur in the region of the southern uplands and Senegal Valley. Outside this region, the only prominent highland area consists of the dissected high-plateau region called the Adrar des Iforas, which is developed on very old hard rocks.

The only permanent rivers are the Niger, the Senegal and the Bani. There are also many other small seasonal rivers draining either into the Niger or the Senegal Valley, but these are dry water courses for most of the year. Because of the open character of the valleys of these rivers, extensive flooding is common towards the end of the rainy season when the rivers overflow their banks. Surface drainage is virtually absent in the rest of the country although the wadis (or dallols) usually flow for a few days each year. The most prominent of these dry valleys are the Timlesi and the Dallol Bosso.

The main relief regions of Mali are (Fig. 24.1): 1) the southern uplands and Senegal Valley, 2) the Niger Valley, 3) the region of dallols, 4) the Adrar des Iforas, 5) the northern deserts.

1. The southern uplands and Senegal Valley

This is a region of gently sloping high plains, flat-topped sandstone hills rising above the plains and sandstone mountains with prominent escarpments. The best known of these mountain scarps is the steep eastern edge of the Bandiagara Mountains. The average height of this escarpment is 180m (600ft), about the same as that of the Enugu-Nsukka escarpment, and, as in the case of the Enugu escarpment, the lower slopes of the Bandiagara scarp is lined with springs and villages. The slopes of the Hombori Mountains are, however, much steeper, rising in some places to over 300m (1,000ft) above the surrounding plains. Apart from the Manding Mountains, the western part of this region consists of a lower plateau surface which is flat and monotonous, except near Yelimane where a few highlands occur. Low sand dunes and desert conditions begin to appear north of the line joining Nioro to Nara.

This region is by far the best watered and most suitable for settlement, and it is in this region that the capital city of Bamako and the town of Kayes are located. The western part drains into the Senegal Valley while the eastern part drains into the Niger Valley. Falls and rapids are common along the valleys of the numerous fast streams that drain this region.

2. The Niger Valley

In an essentially very dry country most of which is desert waste and in which the wettest parts receive no more than about 1,020mm (40in.) of rain per annum, the Niger and its tributaries are indispensable for human and animal life. It provides water for irrigation and stock, as well as large quantities of fish and a highway for navigation. The population of the country is therefore concentrated along the Niger River which is as important to Mali as the Nile is to Egypt. (See plate 82.)

The region described in this section begins at Segou and continues along the river banks and floodplains up to the border with Niger Republic. The most interesting part of the region is the inland Niger Delta which lies between Diafara and Timbuktu. The delta occupies an ancient lake basin which like Lake Chad was an inland drainage basin until it was drained when its waters were captured by the lower Niger. The whole of the delta region is inudated every year at high water when floodwaters come down from the upper Niger, and since the river gradient is negligible, the river channels are easily diverted during floods and by wind-borne sand.

The area is characterized by a series of lakes which are linked by a network of river channels. With the exception of Lake Faguibine, which is the biggest lake, the larger lakes, including Lakes Garou and Niangay, lie on the right bank and in the far north of the delta region. Lake Faguibine is located west of Timbuktu and at high water it measures about 80km (50 miles) long, 19km (12 miles) wide, and 30m (100ft) deep. The only hilly area in this region is the Goundam district where outliers of sandstone hills rise to heights of between 60–90m (200–300ft) above the surrounding plains.

A few kilometres below the river port of Kabara, the inland delta ends as the river becomes re-united. Its volume is much diminished and at low water it is fordable at many places.

The river floodplains, including the entire region of the inland delta are surrounded by the vast plain of Macina which is a semi-desert country of riverine sands deposited by the Niger in the distant past. Fixed dunes are common all over the Macina plain, much of which is also characterized by lateritic surfaces.

3. The region of dallols

This region, which lies between the Adrar des Iforas and the Niger Valley, is dry (less than 200mm (8in.) of rain at Menaka) and very much dissected by steep-sided wadis (dry valleys) draining into the Niger Valley. The largest of these wadis is the Dallol Bosso which takes the name of Azaouak in this region. Their physical characteristics, which include steep sides which are dissected by water channels and flat floors covered with riverine sands, testify to the important role of running water in the formation of desert landforms. They are thought to have been formed by running water when the climate was more humid and by the occasional flash floods which occur in the Sahara every few years. During the rains, the wadis, which are usually bordered by belts of fixed sand dunes become marshy hollows. Flat-topped lateritic capped hills (*mesas*) occur on the interfluves and north of Menaka, there is a group of hills with an average height of about 90m (300ft) above the surrounding plains.

4. The Adrar des Iforas

East of the Timlesi Valley a series of prominent steep hills, including the Adrar Achaoulene and the Adrar Tachdait, form the western foothills of the great highland area called the Adrar des Iforas. The massif, which has an average elevation of 600m (2,000ft) above sea level, is a southern extension of the great Ahaggar Massif in Algeria. It consists of old intrusive rocks and is highly dissected, most of it draining into the Timlesi Valley. The uplands are completely barren and uninhabited but there are wells and some vegetation in the gorges which provide habitation for some Tuareg families.

5. The northern deserts

The northern deserts begin immediately north of the Timbuktu-Bourem road as the vast plain of Azaoud which stretches northwards for about 160km (100 miles). In the north-east regions of Timetrin and Ter-recht, the landscape becomes rugged as barren and rocky outcrops with steep slopes begin to appear. There is a total lack of water, particularly in the barren limestone district of Adjour, but in other places in the north-east, shallow wells abound in the sand-filled dry valleys or wadis which rise from the Adrar des Iforas.

The sandy trough of the Timlesi Valley, which has an average width of 48km (30 miles), lies in the eastern part of this sub-region. The valley, which is 272 km (170 miles) long, joins the Niger Valley at Gao and provides a good example of a dry valley which was formed when the area had a wetter climate.

West of the route from Araouane to Taoudenni, the northern deserts consist of vast areas of dunes and rocky wastes. Barkhan dunes are particularly numerous in the El Mereie and El Krenachich districts. North of Taoudenni, that is in the northern tip of the country, the landscape becomes more broken and low *mesas* are common.

CLIMATE AND VEGETATION

Rainfall

Both the total annual rainfall and the length of the rainy season decrease northwards and westwards from the region of the upper Niger Basin. At Sikasso and Bamako in the south the rainy season begins in May and continues till October (6 months), decreas-

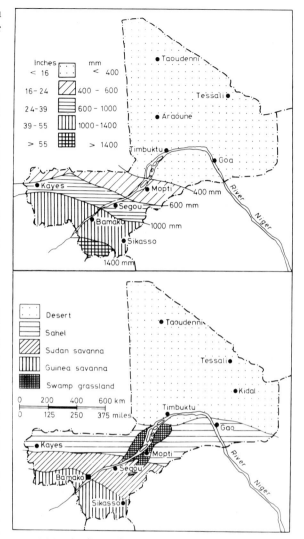

FIG. 24.2—Mali: rainfall and vegetation maps

ing to five months at Kayes in the west and four months at Mopti in the region of the inland delta. The total annual rainfall for Sikasso is 1,400mm (55 in.), decreasing to 760mm (30in.) at Kayes and 510mm (20in.) at Mopti. The rainiest month throughout the country is August and as a rule, the rain falls in short violent showers which usually come in the afternoon (see Fig. 24.2).

North of latitude 19°N., on which Araouane is located, there is an almost complete lack of rain, and the little rain that falls is very irregular. Araouane itself has an annual total rainfall of less than 50mm (2in.) but the more southerly towns of Gao and Menaka have 250mm and 200mm (10 and 8in.) respectively. It is therefore only in the far south, that is, in the region of the upper Niger Basin, that farming can be carried out without irrigation, although the irregularity of the rains has made it necessary for farmers in the south to irrigate their crops.

Although the northern desert may receive no rain for several years, there are also years when violent thunderstorms give rise to disastrous floods. At such times, the wadis are completely filled with water and people and cattle may be drowned within minutes of the onset of the storm. Houses and crops in the oases may be completely washed out during these storms, which provide the main source of water for replenishing the wells.

Temperature

The hottest parts of Mali are in the drier north where the cloudless sky allows the direct rays of the sun to reach the ground unimpeded. In the north, the hottest months are April–October when the daily maximum temperature exceeds 38°C (100°F), the harmattan season (November–March) being slightly cooler. In the far south, the rainfall is heavy enough to lower July and August temperatures below those of the harmattan months of November–February.

As a rule, the annual range increases from south to north, and so does the daily range. There is a rapid rise of temperature at sunrise and an equally rapid fall at sunset. The daily range is greatest during the dry season when it may be as much as 18°C (65°F).

Vegetation

There are three vegetational zones and working from north to south, these are the desert, thorn shrub and grass-woodland (Fig. 24.2). By far the greater part of the country is desert, consisting of sand dunes which may be mobile or fixed. Apart from a few small spiny trees and shrubs, plant life is lacking for most of the year. There is, however, a considerable growth and flowering of annuals in the southern desert immediately after rain, when the summits of stable dunes and some hollows are covered with woody vegetation. Important species include acacias, salt bush (*Salvadora persica*) and asclepiad (*Leptadenia spartium*) which is regarded as good camel food.

Thorn shrubs occur in the central part of the country and are best developed along watercourses and marshy depressions. This is the main area where gum-producing acacias grow alongside such other trees as the African myrrh, which yields gum-resin and the sennas (*Cassia spp.*). Other important trees, found mainly in the fringing forests, are the tamarind (*Tamarindus indica*), the sausage tree (*Kigelia africana*) and the West African ebony tree (*Diospyros mespiliformis*).

Grass-woodlands occur mainly in the south and consist of extensive grasslands with occasional clumps of trees. The shea-butter tree (*Butyrospermum parkii*) and the African locust bean (*Parkia biglobosa*) are the commonest trees in the south of this zone. In marshy areas, the raffia palm and Indian bamboos (*Oxytenanthera abyssinica*) are common while the hills are virtually bare of vegetation. Fringing forests with tall fig trees occur along the banks of streams and rivers but grass predominates on the plateau surfaces.

ECONOMIC ACTIVITIES

Although Mali is often referred to as the land of livestock, the cultivation of food crops is by far the most important economic activity in the country. Livestock comes next followed by fishing, forestry and mining. There is as yet little industrial activity.

Agriculture

About 80 per cent of the population are peasant farmers and two-thirds of the area under cultivation is devoted to guinea corn and millet. Cultivation is restricted to the south and the Niger Valley where water for irrigation is available although there are a few scattered areas of farmland in the oases.

Millet is by far the most important food crop (850,000 tons a year) and in recent years, the country has been able to produce more rice than it requires. The main rice-producing areas are in the inland delta where large-scale irrigation works exist. Annual production is now put at 180,000 tons. Other important crops grown largely on small peasant farms include maize (78,000 tons), cassava (150,000 tons), shea-butter trees, vegetables and fruits. Cotton is produced both under irrigation (about 35 per cent) and on un-irrigated fields (about 65 per cent), the main areas producing unirrigated cotton being the districts of San, Sikasso and Koutiala. Availability of transport restricts groundnut cultivation to areas located near the railway from Bamako to Kayes and along roads suitable for motorized transport (Fig. 24.3, p. 202).

The inland delta irrigation scheme

The Niger Project, which is called the Office du Niger in Mali, is probably the largest scheme of the colonial period in West Africa. The original plan of the scheme, which started in 1932, was to develop the huge delta region for irrigated cotton with rice as a secondary crop. It aimed at putting under cultivation nearly 0.5 million hectares of cotton fields and another 0.4 million hectares (1.2 million acres) of rice fields, a goal which has still not been attained forty years after

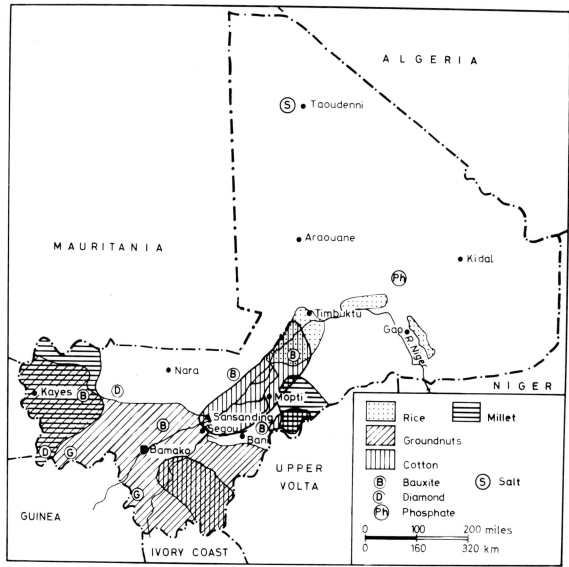

FIG. 24.3—Mali: major crops and minerals

the project started. About 800,000 settlers to be recruited from all over French-speaking West Africa were required for the project, which at independence in 1960 had cost about 22,000 million francs CFA (i.e. about ₦66 million) (see Fig. 24.6, p. 208).

The main dam above Sansanding was completed in 1947. It is 805m (2,640ft) long and has 490 small sluice gates and an irrigation canal which feeds a number of smaller canals that lead into the cultivated fields. Colonists or settlers are provided with 10 hectares (25 acres) of land, houses, compound-lands for farming, animals and simple farm implements, which they keep for as long as they remain on the scheme. Each settler is also provided with initial seeds, food and basic training and his main farmland

is prepared with machinery. He pays a fixed annual fee from the harvests of his holding and may market whatever crop is left through any other organization.

By 1963, only 40,000 hectares (98,800 acres) had been irrigated and there were 35,000 settlers. Rice became the main crop as from about 1949, following a considerable modification of the original plan. The cost of transporting cotton to Dakar was prohibitive and by 1950 at least 60 per cent of the irrigated area was under rice as compared with about 15 per cent under cotton. Up till 1952, when the project showed a small profit for the first time, it had been operating at a loss although the settlers earn a cash income estimated to be ten times as much as the average Mali peasant farmer. As a result of the higher standard of living, the project has attracted many more colonists than can be accommodated and by 1953 more than 2,500 applicants had been turned down. This is a great contrast to the experience of the farm settlement scheme in Nigeria where it is becoming increasingly difficult to attract settlers to existing farm settlements.

In 1961, the Office du Niger came under the direct control of the government of the newly independent state of Mali which has since embarked upon the expansion of the area under cotton and sugarcane.

Other irrigation schemes

In addition to the ambitious delta scheme of the Office du Niger, the Mali Ministry of Agriculture has also established a number of small irrigation projects along the Niger, Bani and Senegal valleys. The main schemes are located between the Diaka and the Niger Rivers, the Pondory region between the Niger and the Bani Rivers and the San and Mopti districts. The aim of the Ministry is to produce more food crops, including rice, guinea corn and millet under irrigation. These small schemes have proved much cheaper to run and by 1955 the total area under irrigation was about three times the area irrigated under the schemes of the Office du Niger.

Livestock

The livestock population of Mali is only exceeded by that of Nigeria. In 1971, the cattle population was put at 5.3 million as compared with 6 million sheep, 5.6 million goats and half a million donkeys. There were also 175,000 horses, 217,000 camels and 33,000 pigs. Cattlerearing is concentrated on the highland areas in the south and east since the tsetse fly prevents cattlekeeping in the well-watered lowland areas of the inland delta. The main cattle centres are therefore at Gao, Mopti Ségou, Bamako and Kayes. Notice the comparatively small number of pigs. Mali is predominantly a Muslim country and the pigs are kept in the non-Muslim areas of the south (Fig. 24.4, p. 204).

Mali is the main supplier of cattle, sheep and goats to the neighbouring countries of Senegal, Ivory Coast and Ghana. Mali also supplies up to 30,000 cattle and about 90,000 sheep and goats to Nigeria every year. This trade is certain to decline greatly following the reported loss of 1,740,000 cattle and 4,471,000 sheep and goats during the severe drought of 1973/4.

Forestry

The main forest products are gum Arabic from the drier north, shea-butter and various products from the silk cotton and tamarind trees. The silk cotton tree provides tannin from its bark, while the flowers and seeds are used for medicine and food respectively. Tannin is also obtained from the tamarind tree which is also an important host for silk worms which provide silk for women's clothes. Shea-butter trees are now cultivated, although wild stands are still important.

Fishing

River fishing is an important occupation along the Niger and Senegal Valleys. All the riverine people fish for food but there are also professional fishermen in the region of the inland delta who fish for the market. Prominent amongst the professional group are the Bozos and Somonos of the Macina region and the Sorkawas who live further down the River Niger. The main fishing grounds are in the lakes and creeks of the floodplains and not in the main river beds. Fishing is highly seasonal and since it depends on the flooding periods, which vary along the courses of the main rivers, the professional fishermen are essentially migratory. Fishing equipment includes basket traps, cast nets, seine nets and harpoons. Dried fish is an important item of international trade and is sold to the neighbouring countries of Upper Volta, Ivory Coast and Ghana. The largest fish market is at Dioro.

Mining

Salt has been mined for many centuries and featured prominently in the trans-Sahara trade. Some of the more ancient workings at Terhazza have since been abandoned and today the main salt mines are at Taoudenni where rock salt is cut and transported by camel caravan to Timbuktu and Gao. Local production has declined considerably following the importation of better-refined and often much cheaper salt from Senegal and Europe, which together supply about 75 per cent of Mali's salt requirements.

Gold was also an important trade commodity in the days of the trans-Sahara trade, but most of it came from outside Mali. Today local supplies come from panning river gravels in the Upper Niger and Senegal valleys.

Other minerals include bauxite in the Kayes area, (see Fig. 24.3) iron ore in various places but particularly near Kayes (as magnetite) and between Kayes and Bamako (non-phosphoric haematite). Manganese occurs in large quantities (3.5 million tons) in the south-east of Gao. Oil drilling has been in progress near Taoudenni but no finds have yet been reported.

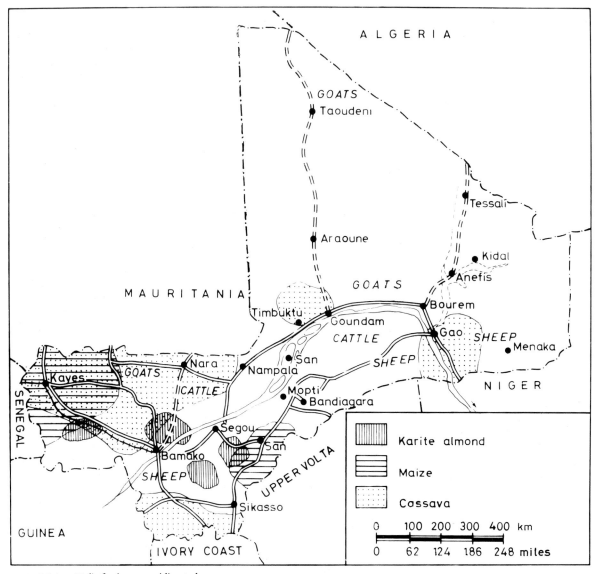

FIG. 24.4—*Mali: food crops and livestock*

Manufacturing industries

Manufacturing is largely confined to the processing of local agricultural products. Of the nine rice mills with a total capacity of 60,000 tons, four are under the management of the Office du Niger. There are three cotton ginneries and two oil mills for extracting cotton seed oil and groundnut oil. Other agriculturally based industries include a sugar refinery, a meat factory with refrigeration plant, and textile mills. In 1965, a cigarette factory was opened at Bamako which also has a plastic shoes factory, a radio assembly plant (1966), a match factory and a ceramic works (1967).

The first textile mill at Ségou was built in 1968 while

the second one is located at Bamako. Other industries include cement works, a brewery (1,500,000 litres), a shoe factory and a soft drinks factory. A second sugar refinery has been proposed and there are plans for establishing bicycle and motor-cycle assembly plants. Most of the industries are owned by the state and are generally badly managed. Indeed, apart from those industrial projects financed by China (which also supplies technical aid), especially the textile factory at Ségou, the cigarette and match factory, and the sugar refinery, the other industries hardly make profits.

Mali has a rather small internal market and cannot therefore support large viable industries. Power for industry has also been a major problem, but the new

204

(1966) small hydro-electric plant near Bamako has helped to solve the power problem of that city.

Recent economic history

Apart from the large-scale irrigation project of the Office du Niger which has turned out to be a huge drain on investment capital there was very little development in Mali during the colonial period. At independence, therefore, the government became actively involved in developing all sectors of the economy. It did this by creating statutory corporations and discouraging private enterprise even by nationals of Mali. Between 1961 and 1966, the state's share in the agricultural sector increased from 20 to 66 per cent and private commerce decreased from 45 to 8 per cent. Many petty traders resented the government's action in taking over retail trade just as transporters became antagonistic to the complete take-over of road transport by the Régie des Transports du Mali.

One result of government policy to control all sectors of the economy was the rapid rise in public expenditure. But government found it difficult to raise the necessary revenue since the vast majority of the people are still outside the market economy and are therefore unable to pay tax. The creation of an independent currency in 1962 which meant that Mali had left the franc zone created more problems since government could not support the amount of paper money printed. Rapid inflation followed. French aid was virtually stopped and between 1962 and 1967 Mali had to turn to the socialist countries for aid.

Lack of finance has been the main factor hampering the development of a socialist economy in the country. In 1964 a 2,000 million francs CFA credit was given by IMF, followed by long-term credits for equipment from the Soviet Union (32,000 million francs CFA) and China (7,000 million). Yet the external debt continued to increase, reaching 5,000 million francs CFA in 1967, when the government decided to return to the franc zone. Devaluation of the Mali franc followed while France gave substantial aid to the country. The balance of payment problems, however, continued and it is thought that government austerity measures to improve the financial situation contributed to the army coup that toppled the administration of Modibo Keita in 1968.

POPULATION AND SETTLEMENT

In 1973, the population of Mali was estimated to be 5.4 million including about 2,600 Frenchmen. The most numerous African people include the Bambara (1.2 million), Fulanis (450,000), Markas or Sarakoles (350,000) and Songhais (260,000) (Fig. 24.5, p. 207). Other prominent groups are the Mossi (325,000), Tuaregs (250,000), Senoufo (350,000) and the Arabs (100,000). About 75 per cent of the people are Muslims while about 20 per cent still practise traditional religions. The Christian population is small and has declined considerably since independence following the decline in the French population from 7,500 in 1961 to 2,600 in 1967.

Most of the people (over 85 per cent) settle in the comparatively fertile southern part of the country which has better water supplies. Areas of concentration include the Niger Valley above Timbuktu and the Senegal Valley. The desert north has very few permanent inhabitants, consisting mostly of Tuaregs, Fulanis, and Arabs, who are essentially nomadic cattle herders.

The main towns and villages are located in the south, in the regions of the Niger Valley and the southern uplands, and the Senegal Valley. In the region of the inland delta the villages and hamlets are built on levees which rise above the highest flood levels. Both the pastoral Fulani and professional fishermen, whose migration along the Niger floodplain is influenced by flood periods along the Niger, live in temporary camps.

Bamako (200,000), the capital city, is located on the Niger. It was founded as far back as 1650 but remained a village for a very long time and had a population of only 800 in 1883 when the French occupied the settlement. Its growth started in 1908 when the railway from Dakar reached the town, which was then established as the adminstrative headquarters of what was then the territory of French Sudan. Bamako is well served with roads and has a new large airport and a 346,000 hectare (854,620 acre) national park. It is now the main industrial area of the country and its factories include a textile mill, a brewery, a bicycle and motor assembly plant, a radio assembly plant and a plastic shoe factory.

Kayes (32,000) is situated at the head of navigation on the Senegal River. It is said to be one of the hottest places in the world. From 1892–1907, Kayes was the capital of the country and today it is the main market centre for the south-west region.

Ségou (32,000) was the capital of the Bambara Empire which flourished in the seventeenth and eighteenth centuries. It is now an important administrative and commercial centre. In recent years, Ségou has attracted a number of agriculturally based industries including a large textile mill (1968), a cotton ginnery and a cotton oil mill.

Timbuktu (15,000) is a town of declining importance. It was founded as far back as AD 1100 and during the fourteenth to sixteenth centuries it was a

PLATE 82—River Niger at Mopti, Mali

flourishing commercial city of over 100,000 inhabitants. At this period, Timbuktu was a major terminal point for the western trans-Sahara caravan route as well as an important Islamic cultural centre with its own university. The town was once located on the bank of the Niger, but is now 7.2km (4 miles) away from the river bank to which it is connected by a canal to the river port of Kabara. It is still an important market for distributing the salt mined at Taoudenni.

Other important ancient towns

Amongst the ancient towns of Mali which have suffered considerable decline in importance and population are Djenne (8,200), which was founded in 1250 and served for a long time as the most important trading town of the Mali Empire, and Gao, founded in the seventh century A.D. From 1010 to 1591 Gao served as the capital of the Songhai Empire and is still the terminal point for the trans-Saharan route passing through the Adrar des Iforas. Its population in 1968 was 15,500 and its main source of income is traditional crafts.

TRANSPORT

There has been remarkable development in road, river and air transport since 1960. During the seven-year period ending in 1967, 15,000 million francs CFA (₦45 million) were invested in road construction, while another 5,000 million francs CFA (₦15 million) were spent in the construction of airports and in improving river transport.

The transport network of the country is shown in Fig. 24.5. In 1973 there were more than 13,000km (8,000 miles) of roads, about 4,800km (3,000 miles) of which consisted of tracks suitable for motorized transport only during the dry season. Road transport is controlled by a national company, the Régie des Transports du Mali, the performance of which has been as disappointing as that of state-owned manufacturing industries.

A single-track railway built between 1881 and 1906, joins the national capital to Dakar, through Kayes (on the Senegal River). This railway is now the most important means for transporting exports to and imports from Dakar. In 1967/8 it carried about 703,000 passengers and 226,000 tons of cargo.

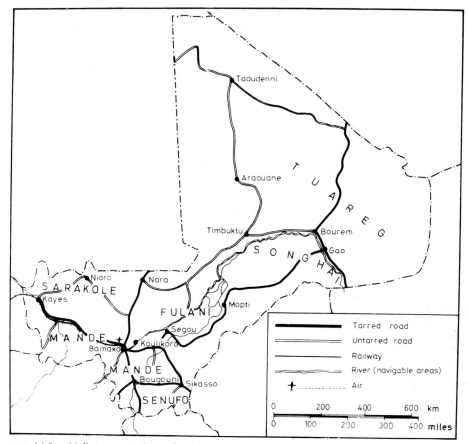

FIG. 24.5—*Mali: transportation and peoples*

Its rolling stock consisted of 23 diesel engines, 36 passenger and 240 goods coaches. There is a plan to extend the railway from Bamako to Kouroussa in Guinea.

Both the River Niger and the Senegal River are used for local traffic. The Upper Niger is navigable between Bamako and Kouroussa (in Guinea) for a distance of 352km (219 miles) and between Kouli-koro and Ansongo for 1,400 km (870 miles). The Upper Senegal is used by small boats as far as Kayes from July to September. As with road transport, internal waterway traffic is controlled by a government agency which runs a number of cargo boats, motor barges and tugs.

There are twelve public airports but the only international airport is at the capital city of Bamako.

Table 31—Principal external trade commodities of Mali (million Mali francs)

Imports	1965	1968	1970	1972	Exports	1965	1968	1970	1972
Textiles and clothing	2,257	2,395	2,164	2,200	Live cattle	1,109	664	4,686	4,700
Food, beverages and tobacco	1,807	3,202	6,092	14,300	Live sheep and goats	86	40	1,242	
Iron and steel products	435	881	813	—	Fish (salted and dried)	772	691	1,409	960
Machinery etc.	585	687	1,445	6,400	Groundnuts	555	562	1,513	2,150
Vehicles and parts	267	1,018	1,676	3,700	Cotton	644	2,099	3,760	7,900
Petroleum products	394	947	1,776	4,100					

Note: 1,000 Mali francs = ₦1.50

Source: *United Nations E.C.A. Statistical Yearbook*, 1973, Part 2, West Africa.

1972 figures from *Africa South of the Sahara*, Europa Publications, 1975.

Air Mali, a state-owned corporation operates internal flights and daily flights to neighbouring French-speaking West African countries. The state airline also provides weekly services to Paris and North Africa.

EXTERNAL TRADE

The export trade of Mali falls into two categories, the first of which consists of the traditional exports of livestock and dried fish to the neighbouring countries of Senegal, Ivory Coast, Upper Volta and Ghana. The second group of exports consists of cotton and vegetable oils which go mainly to France, the Soviet Union and China.

On the import list, the main items are motor vehicles and spare parts, machinery and electrical equipment, textiles, food and tobacco, and iron and steel products. France, Senegal, Ivory Coast, the Soviet Union and China are the main suppliers of import goods. The values of the principal imports and exports for selected years are given in Table 31.

Since independence, Mali has always had an unfavourable balance of trade and in view of the importance of live animals in the export trade of the country, the trade deficit has increased considerably following the disastrous, Sahelian drought of 1973/4, when the country lost 1.7 million cattle and 4.5 million sheep and goats.

Table 32—Trade balance of Mali (million Mali francs)

	1965	1966	1967	1968	1969	1970	1971	1972
Imports	10,600	8,900	12,800	16,900	20,100	26,200	30,500	35,700
Exports	3,900	3,200	4,100	5,300 →	8,700	18,200	19,600	17,200
Balance	− 6,700	− 5,700	− 8,700	− 11,600	− 11,400	− 8,000	− 10,900	− 18,500

Note: 1,000 Mali francs = ₦ 1.50

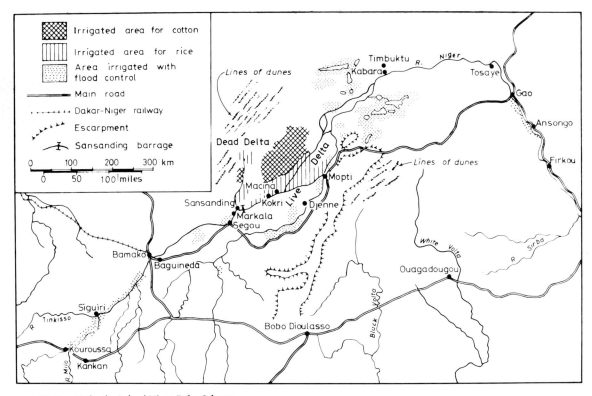

FIG. 24.6—Mali: the Inland Niger Delta Scheme

Chapter 25—The Republic of Mauritania

PLATE 83—*Nouakchott, capital of Mauritania*

The Islamic Republic of Mauritania gained its independence from France in November 1960 after more than fifty years of French rule. It has an area of 1.1 million sq.km (420,000 sq. miles), almost all of which is desert country, and a population of about 1,500,000 all of whom are Muslims. Mauritania has extensive reserves of rich iron ore deposits and is the second largest producer of iron ore in Africa (after Liberia). It provides major tourist centres for international travellers and has surprisingly varied resources in spite of the fact that much of it is desert. On the west, it is bounded by the Atlantic Ocean and on the south by the French-speaking Republic of Senegal. The eastern boundary is shared with Mali while the northern boundary borders on Algeria and Rio de Oro.

Contact with Europe started in the fifteenth century when the Portuguese came for slaves—the slave trade later gave way to the trade in gum Arabic. Because of its extreme aridity, the country is a region of difficulty which is very sparsely settled. Its budget always showed a deficit until 1963 when the export of iron ore started, and today this commodity is the main source of foreign exchange earnings. In the north and central districts, the people who call themselves Bidanes (whites) are predominantly nomadic cattle-rearers, but in the south, there are many settled agriculturalists.

209

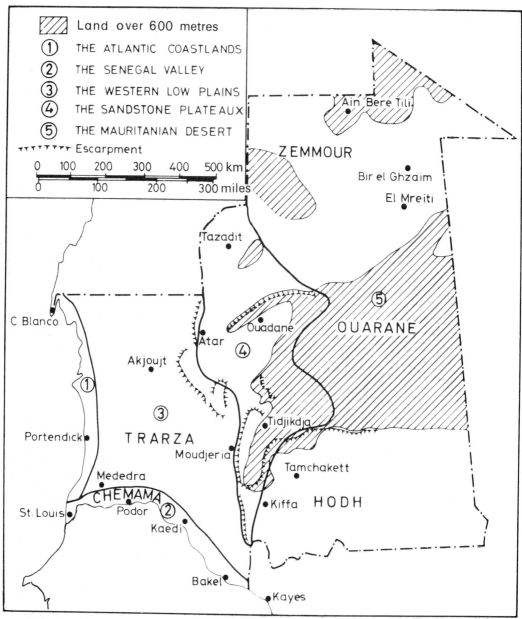

Land over 600 metres

1. THE ATLANTIC COASTLANDS
2. THE SENEGAL VALLEY
3. THE WESTERN LOW PLAINS
4. THE SANDSTONE PLATEAUX
5. THE MAURITANIAN DESERT

Escarpment

FIG. 25.1—Mauritania: relief regions

THE PHYSICAL LANDSCAPE

The 150m (500ft) contour line divides the country into a low-lying plateau in the west and south and a region of higher plateau surfaces in north and east. Many major relief features have a general north-east to south-west trend. One of these landforms consists of a series of westward facing escarpments which separate extensive and monotonous plateau surfaces. The plateau surfaces are characterized by numerous hills or the survivals of erosion, some of

which are very rich in minerals, a good example being the iron mountains of the Kedia d'Idjil which now produces about 10 million tons of iron ore annually.

The main physical regions are: 1) the Atlantic coastlands, 2) the Senegal Valley, 3) the western low plains, 4) the sandstone plateaux, 5) the Mauritanian Desert. (See Fig. 25.1.)

1. The Atlantic coastlands

The coastline is remarkably smooth and behind it

lies an area of mobile sand dunes which give way further inland to a narrow depression running all the way south to St Louis. In its northern parts the depression is characterized by a string of salt marshes which are thought to be remnants of former lagoons. These marshes contain water during the rains, but during the long dry season the depressions consist of salt-encrusted mud flats. South of Nouakchott the seasonal saline marshes give way to clay depressions which remain marshy all through the year. One of these marshes, the Toumba Marsh is 16km (10 miles) long and is located about 3km (2 miles) from the shore.

2. The Senegal Valley

This is the most fertile region where most of the millet and rice consumed in the country is cultivated. The regular flooding of the Senegal Valley keeps the soil fertile and makes this region the best-watered in the country. Several permanent lakes of which Lake Cayor is the largest occur in this region and are normally swollen during the rains, when most of the depressions become swamps and the numerous dry valleys carry running water.

3. The western low plains

East of the north-south coastal depression of salt marshes, the landscape consists of extensive flat plains which stretch inland to the western edge of the Rachid-Moudjeria sandstone escarpment. In the southern districts of Trarza and Brakna, the plains are underlain by clayey formations which appear in the form of depressions separated by lines of stable sand dunes with a north-east to south-west trend. Many of these depressions are waterlogged during the rainy season when there are many shallow lakes and seasonal streams. In the northern district of Akjoujt, the plains become more open as the vegetation becomes sparser. The numerous sand dunes become mobile unlike in the wetter south.

4. The sandstone plateaux

A bold escarpment marks the western edge of the plateaux which occupy much of central Mauritania. This is a very arid region of rocky wastes and loose sand. As in the Nsukka-Udi escarpment, the scarp slopes, which may rise to over 60m (200ft) above the plains, are broken into several flat-topped hills by ravines which carry water from springs rising at the foot of the escarpments. Water from such springs has made it possible for such oasis settlements as Atar, Rachid and Tichit to survive.

5. The Mauritanian Desert

The entire northern and eastern districts of Mauritania consist of desert country which is low and sandy in the south, but rises gradually northwards where the sandy wastes give place to broken and rocky landscapes. The Zemmour district in particular is characterized by granitic hills which occur as dome-shaped inselbergs or as flat-topped hills called *mesas*. In the southern part, the land drops suddenly to form a high basin which is occupied by sand dunes.

CLIMATE AND WATER SUPPLIES

The two features which dominate the climate of this dry country are 1) the persistence of the north-easterly harmattan winds, and 2) the great variation between day and night temperatures, which is caused by the complete absence of clouds. The harmattan is essentially a dry and dusty wind which blows for most of the year except along the coast where its influence is felt only in December and January. It is particularly severe in the afternoons when wind speeds of up to 16km/h (10mph) are common. Along the coast, moister westerly winds bring some rainfall while sea breezes help to make the coastal climate more pleasant.

All over the country, rainfall is very scanty and most unreliable. The rainiest area is the Senegal Valley where Selibaby records more than 730mm (28in.) per annum, decreasing downstream to 440mm (17in.) at Kaedi. The rest of the country, except the southern half of the coastal areas, has a rainfall of less than 100mm (4in.) and is therefore essentially a desert. Along the Senegal Valley, July and August are the rainiest months but along the coast, the heaviest rains occur in August and September. The humid marine winds bring very little rain and over most of central Mauritania, the main source of rain consists of occasional storms which fill up depressions and may cause extensive floods in areas underlain by clayey rocks. In the west and south, heavy dew at night provides an important source of moisture. There is virtually no rain in the desert region of northern and eastern Mauritania.

Temperatures remain high throughout the year, particularly in the south and in the interior. Cooler conditions prevail along the coast which is exposed to the influence of the cool Canary current such that Nouadhibou (Port Etienne) on the coast has a much cooler temperature than the plateau settlement of Atar.

In view of the scanty nature of the rainfall and excessive evaporation, the need for water is very great and its availability is a major location factor for any form of economic development except for mining. Generally, the best-watered areas are the Senegal Valley and the southern clay depressions where underground water may be obtained at depths of about 18m (60ft), and at depths of up to 90m (295ft) in areas covered by sand dunes. The western low plains have large reserves of underground water, but at great depths of about 210m (690ft). Water from deep wells and a few earth dams have made possible the extension of the area under cultivation.

VEGETATION

The Senegal Valley has a vegetation of brushwood with clusters of dum palms, acacias and other trees. Further north, that is, in the region of the western low plains, the landscape consists of old sand dunes which have since been stabilized by forests of acacias, brushwood thickets and tall grass. Along the coast, or sub-Canarian region, the typical vegetation consists of larger bushes of tamarisk on the ridges separating the salt marshes which support a vegetation of dwarf acacias and high grass.

The rest of the country is completely bare of vegetation during the dry season, but after heavy rains the soil is covered with shrubs and grass tufts. In clay depressions and on rock outcrops, a grass savanna vegetation with large tufted grass is characteristic. Along the wadis or dry river valleys where the water table is very near the surface a denser vegetation of acacias and a few other species occurs. In the far north, woody and herbaceous Mediterranean plants thrive along these dry valleys.

Parts of the Zemmour Hills have a richer vegetation of acacias and shrubs as compared with the surrounding plains. The relatively more luxuriant grass vegetation on these hills has made the areas important for stock-rearing.

POPULATION AND SETTLEMENT

The population of Mauritania is estimated to be about 1.2 million (1972), of which more than three-quarters (800,000) are Moors who are essentially a group of nomadic herders, except for a small number who are fishermen along the northern coast of the country. The Moors are characterized as intelligent, quarrelsome, crafty and cruel. They live a rather simple life and their diet is modest, consisting of millet, dates and camel milk. They live in tents made of camel skins and wander from one waterhole and sparse pasturage to another, taking with them their herds of sheep, camels and goats.

The other prominent ethnic groups in the country

are the Tukulors (75,000), the Fulanis (45,000) and the Sarakoles (35,000). The Tukulors have interbred so much with such ethnic groups as the Wolofs, Bambaras and Mandingos that it is not easy to distinguish them as a group apart from the fact that all of them speak the Fulani language. In addition they have a caste and class system associated with the occupations of farming, fishing and crafts making. The Sarakoles are a Negro group who were formerly a warrior group thought to have founded the ancient empire of Ghana. Today most of them have settled down as farmers and traders while some have taken to cattlebreeding.

Most of the population is concentrated in the south where 80 per cent of the people occupy 7 per cent of the land area of the country. Of these, about 20 per cent live in the Senegal Valley while 30 per cent occupy the south-eastern part of the Hodh region which forms the southern part of the Mauritanian Desert. The rest of the country is virtually uninhabited, consisting of rocky and sandy wasteland.

Only 10 per cent of the population live in towns, of which the most important are Nouakchott (45,000), Fort Derik, formerly Fort Gouraud (12,000), Nouadhibou, formerly Port Etienne (11,000), Kaedi (9,500) and Atar (10,000).

The capital city of Nouakchott

Nuoakchott became the capital of Mauritania in 1957. Its lighter-harbour port with facilities for handling copper exports from Akjoujt was developed into a deep-water harbour during the early 1970s. Important government buildings retain the traditional Berber style of architecture but the city is modern and well planned. One of the country's two international airports is located in the city which has regular air connections with Dakar and Paris. The small industrial area near the harbour has a seawater distilling plant and a power station which supply the city with water and electricity. (See plate 83.)

Other towns

Other towns of significance include the iron-ore exporting port-town of Nouadhibou (11,000), the river port of Rosso (10,000), Atar (10,000) and Kaedi (9,500). Nouadhibou, which until 1969 was called Port Etienne, was a fishing port since its founding in 1905 until 1961, when it also became the port of export for iron ore from the Fort Gouraud area. It is now linked to the ore-fields by a railway which supplies the town with drinking water tapped from a subterranean basin located 64km (40 miles) away. It is much more industrialized than the capital city of Nouakchott and is served by an international airport.

Rosso is an important ferry port on the Senegal River and has become the main gateway from Senegal into Mauritania. Old Rosso was destroyed by floodwaters when a dyke was broken in 1950 and the present town was rebuilt shortly after. It has a mixed African population; the most numerous groups are Moors, Wolofs and Tekruri.

The oasis town of Atar (10,000) is the most important town in the north and since 1968, it has been the administrative capital of the northern half of the country. It is essentially an oriental settlement in character and its large market place is considered to be the most important in the western Sahara.

ECONOMIC ACTIVITIES

Agriculture

Traditional agriculture is restricted to a few areas owing to the extremely dry conditions which prevail over most of the country. Its contribution to the national economy (GDP) is less than 40 per cent even though 90 per cent of the people obtain their livelihood from agriculture, with 70 per cent depending on stock rearing. In terms of the number of people employed, agriculture remains, as in other countries of West Africa, the most important sector of the economy. In 1971 there were over 2,700,000 cattle, 5,350,000 goats and sheep, 700,000 camels, 300,000 donkeys and 24,000 horses. Sheep and goats are most numerous along the coast while the main camel area is around Akjoujt. Exports of livestock to Mali, Senegal and Ivory Coast remain an important source of cash income to a large section of the population.

Arable farming is important in such favoured districts as the Senegal Valley and the areas where water is available for irrigation. Millet and dates (which are cultivated in the oases) are the main crops but beans, maize and sweet potatoes are also important. In 1971 the country produced about 80,000 tons of millet, 15,000 tons of dates and 10,000 tons of beans. Recent developments in arable farming include the cultivation of cotton and rice in the Senegal Valley near Boghe and the expansion of paddy rice cultivation in the region of the Senegal Delta. (See Fig. 25.2.)

Forestry

Gum Arabic, which is obtained from the *Acacia senegal* and *Acacia arabica*, is the most important forest product (Fig. 25.3, p. 214). The gum, which is used in cooking, in the textile industries and in the manufacture of dyestuffs and drugs, is obtained by

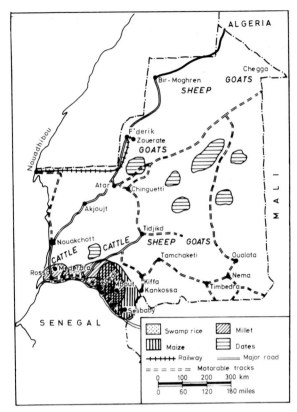

FIG. 25.2—*Mauritania: food crops, livestock and transportation*

tearing strips of bark from the trees which begin to yield from their fifth year. Trarza and Brakna are the main producing areas and almost all the 7,000 tons produced every year is exported to France.

Fishing

The continental shelf lying between Nouakchott and Nouadhibou (Port-Etienne) is one of the world's important fishing gounds. Fishing vessels from various countries including Japan, Italy, Portugal, France and the USSR take about 250,000 tons of fish every year from the area. In 1969 only 30,000 tons of the catch was landed and processed at Nouadhibou for consumption in Africa as well as for export. Since 1967, the Mauritanian government has maintained its own fishing fleet. Inland fishing on the Senegal River is also important, the annual catch being estimated at 15,000 tons.

Mining

Mauritania has extensive and rich reserves of valuable minerals including iron ore, copper and

213

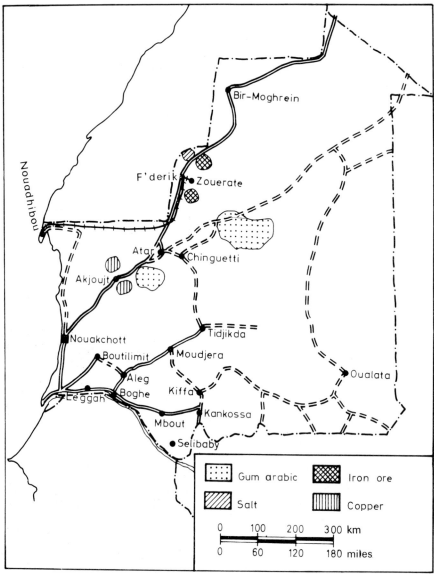

FIG. 25.3—*Mauritania: minerals and gum Arabic*

salt. Mining started in 1960 with the opening of the Fort Gouraud, now Fort Derik, iron-fields. Since then minerals have become the most important export. In 1972 for example, iron ore accounted for 74 per cent of the total exports by value. (See Fig. 25.3.)

The main iron ore deposits are the rich haematite ores of the Fort Derik area, with estimated reserves of 250 million tons of ore of 63 per cent iron content. In 1966, that is, six years after mining started, Mauritania was already the second largest producer of iron ore in Africa (next to Liberia). A 672km (418 miles) railway links the mines to the port of Nouadhibou, which has been provided with special facilities for handling the ore. (See plate 84.)

Several other iron ore deposits of medium grade have been located in various parts of the country, but the only other major mines in the country are the copper mines which are located near Akjoujt. The estimated copper ore reserve is about 500,000 tons of smelted copper and the ore, which is obtained by both open-cast and underground methods, is exported through the new port of Nouakchott.

Phosphate deposits have been located in the area around Kaedi and gypsum in the Nouakchott area, but mining has not yet started. A small quantity of salt (700 tons per annum) is produced near Fort Derik while the search for mineral oil continues on land off the coast.

Manufacturing

There are no large-scale modern industries other than those associated with mining and the processing of fish and other sea foods at Nouadhibou. In addition to canning fish for export, the fish-processing plants manufacture fish meal and operate cold-storage houses for the exporting of frozen fish. The refrigerated slaughter house at Nouadhibou supplies skins to an affiliated tannery plant at Kaedi. Proposed industries include a textile mill near Rosso, a match factory and a steel plant at Nouadhibou.

TRANSPORTATION

The development of road and rail transport (see Fig. 25.2) in recent years has been closely associated with mining. The 672km (418 miles) rail-road from Zouerate to Nouadhibou for example was built in 1961–3 to evacuate iron ore to the port of export, although it also serves to carry drinking water to the two terminal towns.

The principal highway is the 1,380km (858 miles) transmountain road which runs south-north through Nouakchott, Akjoujt, Atar and Fort Derik to the

PLATE 84— Iron ore mine near Fort Derik (Fort Gouraud), Mauritania

Table 33—Principal exports of Mauritania (million francs CFA)

	1966	1967	1968	1969	1970	1971	1972
Iron ore	15,834	15,820	15,816	17,349	21,490	20,847	19,894
Fish	618	932	935	1,134	2,029	2,137	2,842
Others	637	704	963	1,079	1,161	3,098	4,223
Total	17,089	17,456	17,714	19,562	24,680	26,082	26,959

Table 34—Trade balance of Mauritania (million francs CFA)

	1965	1966	1967	1968	1969	1970	1971	1972
Imports	6,140	5,678	9,105	8,713	10,963	15,516	17,496	17,895
Exports	14,219	17,089	17,456	17,714	19,562	24,680	26,082	26,959
Balance	+8,079	+11,411	+8,351	+9,001	+8,599	+9,164	+8,586	+9,064

Note: 1,000 francs CFA = ₦3.00

Algerian border. Most of the existing roads consist of unpaved desert tracks and it was not until 1967—70 that the first tarred road (208km, 130 miles) was built from Nouakchott to Rosso. The total road system is about 8,000km (4,975 miles), most of which can only be used during the dry season.

River transport is important along the southern border where the Senegal River provides a natural highway for evacuating agricultural products. The ore and fishing port of Nouadhibou and the lighter port of Nouakchott are also used by cargo boats and passenger liners.

Internal air transport services are not well developed and are controlled by the government sponsored 'Air Mauritanie' founded in 1963. Only the two airports of Nouakchott and Nouadhibou are equipped with facilities to handle international flights, which are mainly by UTA and Air Afrique.

FOREIGN TRADE

Up till 1963, Mauritania, like most French-speaking countries in West Africa had a negative trade balance in which the value of imports was about double that of exports. The mining and exporting of mineral ores has since changed the situation, and since 1964 the country has had a favourable balance of trade (Tables 33, 34). Iron ore is by far the most important export, accounting for 74 per cent by value of all export products in 1972. The value of cattle exports to Senegal, Mali and Ivory Coast is about 2,000 million francs CFA a year, making livestock the second most important export of the country. The other important exports are copper, fish and fish products, and gum Arabic. The major imports include machinery, motor vehicles, foodstuffs and fuel oil. France supplies a large proportion of imported goods (45 per cent), followed by the United States and Great Britain. The largest proportion of total exports, however, goes to Great Britain (26 per cent) followed by West Germany (20 per cent) and France (19 per cent).

Chapter 26—Niger Republic

PLATE 85 — View of Agadèz, Niger

Niger Republic, like Nigeria, takes its name from the River Niger on whose left bank is located the capital city of Niamey. The country also shares much of its southern boundary with Nigeria and has a population of about 2 million Hausas who also constitute one of the largest ethnic groups in Nigeria. These and the trade contact between the two countries are what they have in common. In other respects the two countries are very different. With an area of 1,267,000 sq.km (or 489,000 sq. miles), Niger Republic is much larger than Nigeria but its total population of about 4 million is only 5 per cent of that of Nigeria which is by far the richer and more developed country. Niger is landlocked and extremely arid, about three-quarters of the country being desert, most of which is uninhabited.

RELIEF AND DRAINAGE

Niger Republic consists of a rather flat and monotonous plain of about 450m (1,500ft) above sea level, with a few mountainous areas in the Air and north-eastern districts. Much of the plain is made up of sedimentary rocks but the mountains are developed on old hard rocks with volcanic lava. The main physical regions are (Fig. 26.1, p. 218): 1) the Niger Valley, 2) the region of dallols, 3) Tagama and the southern plains, 4) the eastern desert, 5) Air and the northern mountains.

1. The Niger Valley

No more than 480km (300 miles) of the River Niger's 4,180km (2,600 miles) length passes through Niger

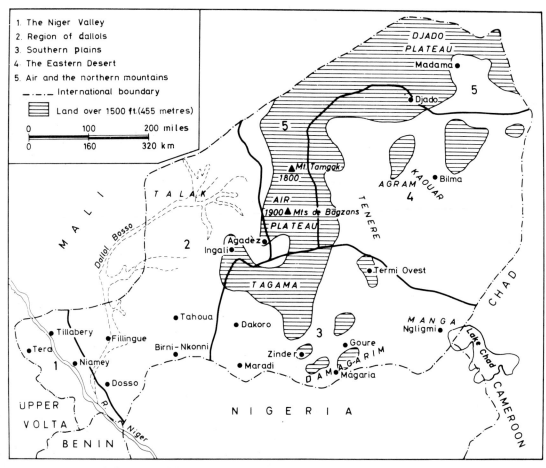

FIG. 26.1—Niger: relief regions and drainage

Republic. Several rapids occur within this short stretch and the valley which is split into several channels by rocky islands and sandbanks is very similar to the stretch between Bussa and Jebba. The Niger flood passes through this section of the valley during the dry season and makes it possible for the cultivation of dry-season crops shortly after the floods have subsided. South of Niamey, the valley widens out to form extensive open plains. Flat plains cut up by wide, shallow dry valleys characterize the uplands bordering the Niger Valley.

2. The region of dallols

The southern part of this region consists of sandstone and clay plains, parts of which are covered with hard lateritic soils. There are two major relief features, the first of which consists of wide, shallow but steep-sided dry valleys (dallols) draining into the Niger Valley. Surface drainage is absent but these dallols, the largest of which include the Dallol Bosso

and the Dallol Foga, formerly contained running water when the climate of the Sahara was more humid. The second major relief feature is the flat-topped hills (*mesas*) with steep sides and tops capped by a hard layer of laterite (Fig. 26.2). These hills are found scattered all over the plains.

3. Tagama and the southern plains

Apart from the eastern extremity which forms part of the Lake Chad Depression, this region is a northward extension of the high plains of Hausaland in Nigeria. The far western part is a dissected limestone country with numerous low flat-topped hills, capped with hard layers of laterite. Much of the region is dry and waterless, the main drainage system being that of the Goulbi Kaba which flows into River Rima. Some perennial lakes occur in the Damagrim district around Zinder, where the water table is high (2 metres, or 6ft), and several small tributaries of the Goulbi Kaba rise from this district. The

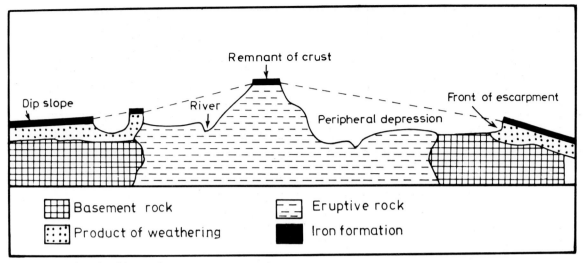

FIG. 26.2—Niger: lateritic capped mesa

valleys of these tributaries like that of the main river are filled with sand for most of the year. Temporary lakes form in the sand-filled valleys during the rainy season when much of the Chad Depression is flooded. In many localities, granite inselbergs rise like islands through the sands.

In the Tagama district, the land rises to much greater heights while the landscape is characterized by wide, dry valleys which are usually covered with a thin layer of sand.

4. The eastern desert

North of the Chad Depression, there is a continuous stretch of sand dunes, giving way to a stony desert landscape in the Bilma region. The desert surface is broken by a few prominent groups of hills such as the Termet Hills in the south, and the Fachi Hills, west of Bilma.

5. Air and the northern mountains

The Air Mountains cover an area of about 400km (250 miles) from north to south and 240km (150 miles) from east to west. The region consists of a vast massif of young volcanic rocks which have been dissected by wide sandy valleys, the peaks rising to well over 600m (2,000ft) above the general level of the land. The main mountain groups include the Tarazit 1,040m (3,410ft) and the Tamgak 1,476m (4,840ft). Most of Air drains into the great Tessela-mane Depression, where several valleys meet to form the upper reaches of the Dallol Bosso. Valleys (wadis) draining eastwards are usually shorter and soon disappear under the sands of Tenere which mark the beginning of the eastern desert.

The northern mountains form part of the broken highland country lying between the higher mountains of Ahaggar and Tibetsi. Deeply incised wadis, cut by occasional rainstorms, separate extensive plateau surfaces whose tops rise to about 900m (3,000ft).

CLIMATE AND VEGETATION

Climate

Desert climate prevails, except in the extreme south which has a dry sudan or sahel-type climate. There are two clearly marked seasons in the south, the dry season (October–April) and the rainy season (May–September). The length of the rainy season, the reliability of the rainfall and the amount of rain decreases northwards and eastwards, and north of latitude 20°N. there is virtually no rain for periods of several years. Temperatures are always high, with diurnal ranges of up to 16.7°C (30°F) in Agadèz. Low relative humidities and clear skies are characteristic except during parts of the rainy season.

In the far north, the harmattan blows persistently all through the year, but in the south, it is interrupted for a period by the moisture-laden southwest winds whose influence and duration decreases northwards. Haze is common during the harmattan when stationary objects are quickly covered by dust and advancing dunes.

The rain generally comes in the afternoon as torrential thunderstorms. Much erosion is accomplished as the storm water sweeps across the sandy valleys and often much damage is done to crops, houses and roads.

PLATE 86a—Flat-topped hills (or mesas) and the flood plain of the Niger River at Niamey, Niger

Vegetation

As in other parts of West Africa, the vegetation types which are closely associated with climatic conditions are arranged in clearly marked west-east belts. Grass-woodland in which trees are scattered singly or in groups is the vegetation of the south. Dum palms appear in large numbers south of Maradi where fringing or gallery woodlands are also common along river valleys. North of latitude 12°N. and extending to 15°N., thorn-land vegetation of trees and shrubs with spines predominates. Denser tree growth, featuring the borassus palm, several species of acacias and other spiny trees, occur in many of the dallols and other areas with a high water table. Low scrub grows on the lateritic surfaces of the southern high plains.

The rest of the country, that is, about three-quarters of its area, is desert, much of which is completely bare of closed vegetation. In areas where underground watercourses raise the water table near to the surface, such as along some wadis, a closed vegetation of small trees and bushes thrives. Woody plants also grow in areas where the date palm is the dominant vegetation. Another desert area with patches of closed vegetation featuring several species of acacias, the dum palm and soapberry trees, occurs in the Air Massif whose higher altitude accounts for its greater rainfall. The vegetation of Air is certainly sahelian and includes groves of date palm around the few villages. (See plate 86a.)

ECONOMIC ACTIVITIES

Most of the country is agriculturally unproductive because of the dry climate. Farming is restricted to the floodplains and nearby uplands of the far south, and the oases. No major economic mineral deposits have been discovered and the salt from Bilma, formerly sent to northern Nigeria, is no longer mined. This is a tsetse-free country and cattle rearing is common except where conditions are too dry. The country is generally poor, and does not produce much for export.

Animal rearing

Cattle rearing is the most important occupation amongst the Tuaregs who like the Cow Fulanis are a nomadic people. There were about 2.7 million cattle in 1971, the chief breeds of which include

As may be expected the Air Mountains, like other mountains, have a modified climate compared with the surrounding plains. The rainfall for instance is heavier while the temperatures are lower.

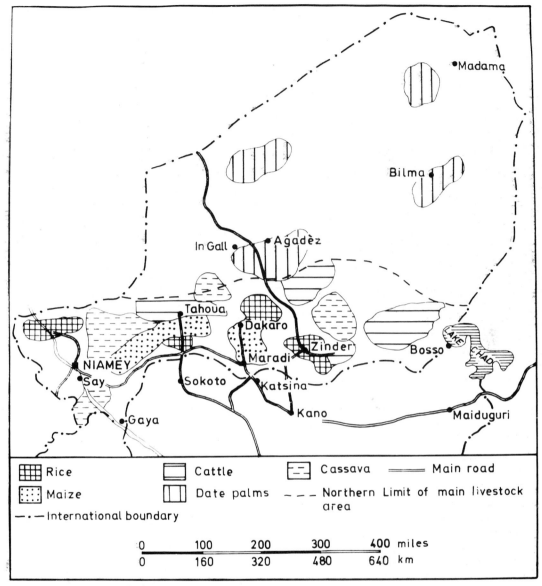

FIG. 26.3—Niger: staple food crops

the Borroro Zebu and the White Fulani. The combined goat and sheep population in 1971 was estimated to be 5.3 million. These animals are concentrated mainly in the Hausa areas of the Niger-Nigeria borderlands. Other domesticated animals include horses, donkeys and camels. Livestock production is estimated to be growing at the rate of 3 per cent a year, and most of the animals are sold in Nigeria.

Farming

Food-crop production covers most of the cultivated land which is only 3 per cent of the country. The quick-maturing millet (bulrush millet), which requires just a little rain in the early stages of growth, is the main staple food, closely followed by guinea corn. Bulrush millet takes only three months to mature and is more widespread whereas guinea corn is restricted to the region of the Niger-Nigeria borderlands. In the region of the Niger Valley, irrigated rice, maize, groundnuts and wheat are cultivated. Other crops grown in the south are barley, cassava, cotton and tobacco. (See Fig. 26.3.)

Groundnut production has increased considerably since 1960 and groundnuts as well as groundnut products constitute the most important export by

221

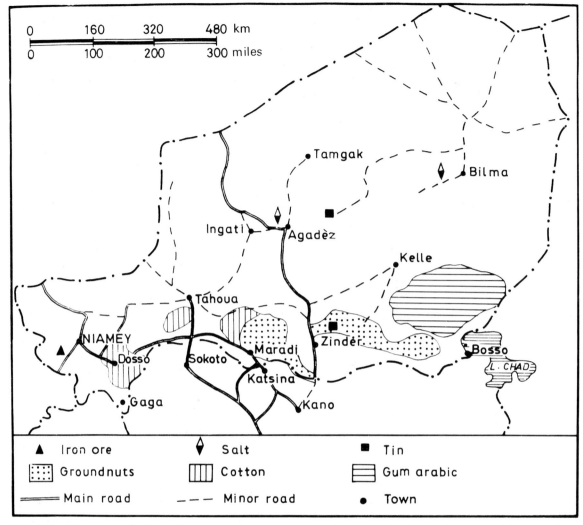

FIG. 26.4—*Niger: mineral and export crops*

value. The main groundnut-producing areas are in the Hausa homelands around Zinder and Maradi. Cotton production has been less successful and production is likely to remain insignificant until there is a substantial development of irrigation.

Date palms are the most important crops raised in the oases. Irrigation based on well water permits the cultivation of wheat and millet in fields where date palms grow. Some dates are exported but the main export crop is groundnuts followed by cotton.

Mining

The mining sector of the economy is not yet well developed, and minerals contribute very little to the national economy. No more than 80 tons of iron ore is mined at Air, although there are several deposits of low-grade iron ore in the country. Production of uranium at Arlit started in 1971. Mining problems include the high cost of power and the poor state of transportation. (See Fig. 26.4.)

Manufacturing industries

There is very little industrial development. In 1970, for example, manufacturing accounted for only 3 per cent of the national income, while agriculture contributed about 67 per cent. Niger is poor in minerals and power resources which could have formed a basis for manufacturing. Transportation is also poor and the internal market is too small to support even medium-sized factory industries. In 1970 less than 2,000 people were employed in manufacturing.

A number of import-substitution industries have,

however, been established since 1965. Two of these industries, the groundnut oil factory (24,000 tons capacity) in Niamey and the cotton ginneries are essentially mills processing local farm products. Industries producing manufactured goods which were formerly all imported include the textile factory (2,000 tons), the Malbaza cement works (35,000 tons) and a tile and brick factory. Other manufactures include flour milling (4,000 tons), soap and detergent, beer and soft drinks, canned tomatoes plastic shoes and utensils. A radio assembly factory has also been built at Niamey.

Other occupations

River fishing along the Niger is important and yields an estimated 8,000 tons of fish a year, some of which is exported to Nigeria and Upper Volta. Fishing is also an important occupation of the people living near Lake Chad. Local crafts industries featuring the production of leather poufs, blankets of camel hair, skin bags and perfumes employ a much larger number of people than either the fishing or factory industries. The Hausa people who make these crafts are also known for their trading activities. Items of trade distributed by the itinerant Hausa trader include local crafts, kola nuts from Western Nigeria and a large range of low-order manufactured goods which are readily smuggled across the Niger-Nigeria border.

POPULATION AND SETTLEMENT

In 1973 the population of Niger was estimated to be 4.3 million. Most of the people live in the south, along the Niger-Nigeria boundary and only about 20 per cent of the population live in the vast desert regions of the north where their main occupation is nomadic cattle rearing. The cattle-rearers are mostly Tuaregs and Fulanis while the Hausas are predominantly settled cultivators.

Apart from the Hausas, who number about 2 million, the other important ethnic groups are the Djerma-Songhai (948,000), the Fulanis (426,000) and Tuaregs (120,000). The Djerma-Songhai who settle in the south-west of Niger are hoe cultivators. Most of the 50,000 migrants from Niger to Ghana and Benin are Djerma-Songhai people. A large number of Hausa migrant farmers are also attracted to settle and farm in the Sokoto Province of Nigeria where soils and climatic conditions are more favourable.

The development of education was very slow during the colonial period, but since 1960, the number of children in schools has increased greatly. The number of primary school attendants rose from 35,000 in 1962 to over 82,000 in 1970 when 13 per cent of the school-age population were in school as compared with 5 per cent in 1962. The increase in the number of school-leavers has also meant an increase in the number of migrants into the towns and rising urban unemployment since no more than 23,000 people were wage- and salary-earners in 1970.

In 1970, however, only 4 per cent of the people lived in the main urban centres of the country, consisting of Niamey, Zinder, Maradi and Tahove. The rest of the population live in rural villages. The only other urban centres are the oasis town of Bilma and the important Saharan trade centre of Agadèz (plate 85).

Niamey (102,000), a river town, is located in the most densely settled part of the country. This is one of the main reasons why the capital was transferred from Zinder to Niamey in 1926. Before that date, Niamey was a small native village, but it has since grown to be an important administrative and transportation centre. It is connected by river, road and air to other parts of Niger and French-speaking West Africa. Niamey is the southern terminus of the trans-Saharan bus service to Gao and Colomb Becher. Industrial establishments in the town include a frozen meat plant, cotton gineries, furniture factories and a brick factory.

Maradi (29,000). The new town of Maradi was built shortly after the old town was destroyed by floods in 1945. Unlike the old town which was located on the floodplain of River Maradi, the new town is sited on high ground overlooking the floodplains which are still cultivated. Although houses in the new town are still largely of mud, the town, which has very wide streets, is clean and well planned.

Maradi is the administrative headquarters of the province that bears its name. It has an important market and is a major collecting point for groundnuts, hides and skins which are exported through Nigeria. A small factory processes groundnut oil for the local market.

Zinder (36,000), a predominantly Hausa town was the capital of Niger from 1900 to 1926. It is still the military headquarters and the commercial capital of the country. Like Kano in Nigeria, Zinder is noted for the skill of its craftsmen who make good blankets from camel hair, goat hair and wool. Some of its well-known trade goods are hides and skins and crafts made from leather, skin and wood. Zinder is also a market for gum Arabic, groundnuts and horses (plate 86b).

PLATE 86b—Sultan and mosque at Birni, Zinder, Niger

Table 35—Trade balance of Niger (million francs CFA)

	1960	1965	1966	1967	1968	1969	1970	1971	1972	1973
Imports	3,207	9,297	11,115	11,352	10,237	12,570	16,213	14,975	16,576	15,281
Exports	3,108	6,250	8,574	8,226	7,125	6,250	8,795	10,552	13,712	12,698
Balance	−99	−3,047	−2,541	−3,126	−3,112	−6,320	−7,418	−4,423	−2,864	−2,583

Note: 1,000 francs CFA = ₦3.00.

TRANSPORTATION AND EXTERNAL TRADE

Niger is a landlocked country which trades with the outside world through the Nigerian port of Lagos and the Benin port of Cotonou. The only good roads are found in the south, but most of them are earth roads, which may be closed to heavy traffic after a rainstorm. Camel transport is still an important means of carrying kola nuts, millet and imported goods to the more remote settlements.

The trans-Saharan trade which was important in the past is virtually dead. Groundnuts and groundnut oil provide about three-quarters of the export earnings, and between 1960 and 1970, the value of groundnut exports rose from 3,000 to 6,000 million francs CFA. Annual export figures vary considerably depending on climatic conditions. The second most important export commodity consists of live animals, mainly cattle, sheep and goats, which are sent to Nigeria, Benin and Ghana. The record of live animals exported is rather unreliable but average annual figures are estimated to be 180,000 cattle valued at 12,000 francs CFA each and 520,000 sheep and goats valued at 2,000 francs CFA each. The estimated income from livestock export is therefore 3,200 million francs CFA although the recorded figure rarely exceeds 850 million francs CFA.

A considerable illegal trade in smuggled goods goes on between the Hausa population on both sides of the Niger-Nigeria boundary which is very difficult to police. As a result of this illegal trade, the official trade statistics given in Table 35 represent about 70 per cent of the actual trade figures.

France buys almost all the groundnut exports of Niger and in return supplies most of the imported manufactured goods. The main imports include cotton textiles, machinery, petroleum products and motor vehicles and spare parts.

Chapter 27—Nigeria: I. The Natural Environment

The Federal Republic of Nigeria is by far the most populous country in Africa. In 1963 it had a population of 56 million, increasing to over 71 million in 1973. If we accept the United Nations estimated population of Africa to be 344 million in 1970, it means that out of every five Africans, at least one person is a Nigerian. Considering the West African scene, we find that Nigeria, which has a total area of 923,800 sq.km (357,000 sq. miles), occupies only 14 per cent of the land area of West Africa, but supports more than 60 per cent of the total population.

Nigeria lies approximately between latitudes 4°N. and 14°N., and between longitudes 13°E. and 15°E. It is bordered on the north, east and west by the French-speaking countries of Niger, Cameroon, and Benin, while the Gulf of Guinea, an arm of the Atlantic Ocean forms the southern boundary. The total length of the coastline is about 800km (500 miles) while the longest distance as the crow flies is about 1,120km (700 miles) from north to south and 1,200km (750 miles) from east to west.

Like other West African countries, Nigeria is a creation of the colonial period which started during the late nineteenth century. The history of the country as one political unit, however, dates from 1914 when the two protectorates of Northern and Southern Nigeria were first administered together under the governorship of Sir Frederick Lugard. Nigeria became independent of British rule in October 1960 and three years later, the country adopted a republican constitution, but remained a member of the (British) Commonwealth of Nations. seventeen years after independence, Nigeria still has strong economic ties with Britain, although Russia, Japan, France, West Germany and the United States of America have since emerged as important trading partners. English is still the official language and is likely to remain so since many people consider it unnecessary to attempt to enforce the adoption of any of the main languages—Ibo, Hausa and Yoruba—as an official language.

The first six years of independence was a period of considerable uncertainty born out of suspicion and fear of domination of the country by particular ethnic groups. The series of political crises and events culminating in the military coup of 1966 and the bloody civil war of 1967–70 can be traced back to these fears. The creation of twelve states in 1967 by the military regime was aimed at removing these fears and establishing a stable political entity. This aim has been largely achieved particularly after the creation of seven more states in 1976. The bitter experiences of the civil war years and the present might of the Nigerian army appear to suggest that no section of the country will attempt to secede in future, but there is still a lot to be done to make the various peoples of the country think of themselves first as Nigerians rather than as Hausas, Ibos, Yorubas, Edos, Ibibios and Kanuris.

PHYSICAL REGIONS AND LANDFORMS

Although Nigeria is only the fourth largest country in West Africa, it has a much greater variety of physical landscapes as compared with the larger countries of Mali, Niger and Mauritania. It is for this reason that we recognize as many as twelve physical regions in the country. The regions are (Fig. 27.1, p. 226):

1. The coastal creeks and lagoons
2. The Niger Delta
3. The coastal plain
4. The western or Oyo plains
5. The scarplands of south-central Nigeria
6. The Cross River Basin
7. The Niger-Benue Valley
8. The Jos and Biu Plateaux
9. The high plains of Hausaland
10. The Sokoto-Rima plains
11. The Chad Basin
12. The eastern mountains.

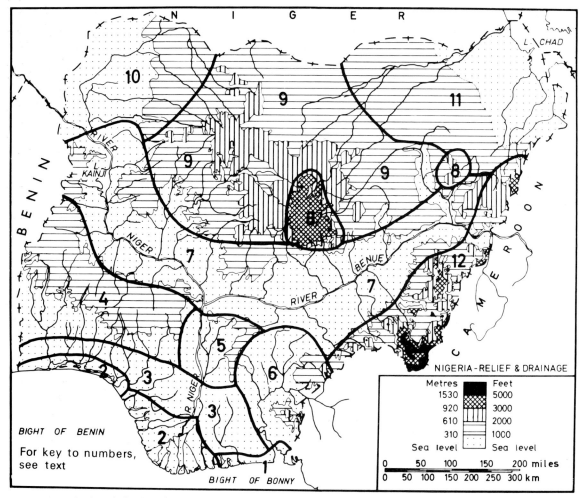

FIG. 27.1—Nigeria: relief and physical regions

1. The coastal creeks and lagoons

A maze of creeks, rivers and lagoons occurs along the Nigerian coast on both sides of the Niger Delta. Like the Niger Delta, the creeks and lagoons region provided the first points of trade contact with Europe and it is in these two regions that Nigeria's seaports (old and new) are located. The creeks and lagoons provided an important means of transportation at a time when road transport was not well developed and although some of these water channels have been silted up, it is still possible to navigate from Badagry to Calabar along these inland waterways, without getting into the open sea.

This is a low-lying region of about 30m (100ft) above sea level, rising to 45m (150ft) along the northern boundary. West of the Niger Delta, the region consists of lagoons and swamps which are separated from the open sea by a strip of sandy land which varies in width from about 2–16km. (1–10 miles). The Lagos entrance is the only major outlet through which the lagoons and creeks drain into the open sea. The section lying east of the Niger Delta consists of creeks and swamps which stretch from Opobo town, through the Cross River estuary, to the border with Cameroon.

The whole region is very poorly drained particularly during the rainy season when the rivers and creeks overflow their banks. The submergence of the riverside vegetation by floods produces a rather dull and monotonous landscape while the inundation of footpaths and dry-season roads increases the degree of isolation between the villages.

2. The Niger Delta

The Niger Delta, like the creeks and lagoons region, is a low-lying region which is cut up by a complicated system of natural water channels through which the River Niger finds its way into the sea. It is made up of three distinct sub-regions and these are: the freshwater zone, the mangrove swamps and the zone of coastal sand and beach ridges. The freshwater zone which starts from the apex of the delta, just below the town of Aboh, is essentially an extension of the lower Niger floodplains. The numerous water channels in this zone are bordered by natural levees which are of great topographical interest. These levees provide the site for most of the settlements in the zone as well as limited farmland for cultivating yams, cassava, cocoyams, vegetables and plantains (see Fig. 27.2).

Mangrove swamps covering about 10,360 sq.km (4,000 sq. miles), which are generally muddy and unsuitable for settlement, occur immediately south of the freshwater swamp zone. A few islands of solid red earth which are above floodwater all through the year appear in parts of the zone and have provided sites for many settlements, including Tombia, Degema and Buguma. A narrow strip of sandy beaches and beach ridges which varies in width from a few metres to 16km (10 miles) separates the mangrove swamps from the open sea. The older port-towns of Bonny, Brass, Akassa and Forcados were built on these sandy beaches which are virtually useless for food-crop cultivation.

In addition to natural levees, ox-bow lakes and other lakes as well as abandoned meander loops, caused by the continual changing of river courses, are common landforms in the Niger Delta. The high rainfall of this region, coupled with the abundance of surface water and the level character of the landscape, creates a serious problem of poor drainage and too much water, which combine to make road construction a very difficult task.

3. The coastal plain

The coastal plain is a region of gently undulating landscapes which are developed on young sedimentary rocks. It has an average elevation of about 90m (300ft) above sea level and covers more extensive areas in the Bendel and the four eastern States but a rather narrow tract in the Western States of Lagos, Ogun and Ondo States. Only a few permanent streams flow across this region of porous sands and almost all these streams originate outside the region. In the eastern districts of Owerri, Aba, Abak, Ikot Ekpene and Uyo, the distance between permanent

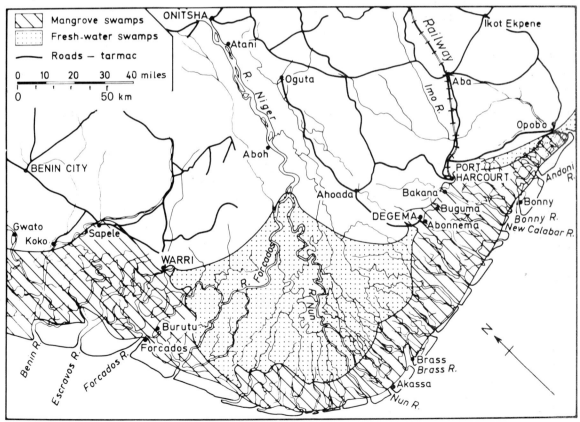

FIG. 27.2—Nigeria: the Niger Delta

streams exceeds 12km (8 miles) and many villages suffer from acute water shortage during the dry season. Numerous dry valleys constitute the dominant landforms in the region.

4. The western or Oyo plains

The whole of this region is underlain by old metamorphic rocks which outcrop to form high hills in many districts. The land surface is undulating and descends from an altitude of 480m (1,600ft) in Ekiti district in the north to 120m (400ft) in Ondo and Ijebu districts in the south. In the open grassland areas of Oyo, the characteristic landscape consists of extensive plains broken by steep-sided inselbergs (dome-shaped hills) which occur singly or in groups. The inselbergs are particularly numerous in the Ekiti, Akure and Ondo divisions where they attain greater heights than in the Ibadan and Oyo divisions. The Idanre Hills, which attain heights of over 900m (3,000ft), are the most prominent inselbergs in Yorubaland. A number of prominent ridges which are elongated in a north-south direction feature in the area east of Ilesha, a good example being the 600m (2,000ft) Oke Messi-Efon Alaiye ridge.

The region is drained by many north-south flowing rivers including the Ogun, Oshun and Shasha Rivers. These and other large rivers flow all the year round, but show a marked drop in volume during the dry season. The smaller tributaries, on the other hand, are dry each year for periods varying from a few weeks to three months. The valleys of these rivers are generally much more deeply incised than those of rivers in the coastal plain.

This region is the most developed area of its size in the country. Most people live in urban centres and the southern part constitutes the cocoa belt of Nigeria.

5. The scarplands of south-central Nigeria

Although a greater part of this region lies east of the lower Niger Valley, it is important to realize that the Ishan Plateau and the much lower Asaba Plateau are a westward extension of the scarplands which are usually considered to be made up of the Udi-Nsukka Plateau and the Awka-Orlu uplands. The physical characteristics of Ishan Plateau in particular, such as the level topography, the sandstone hills and the numerous dry valleys, are very similar to those of the Udi-Nsukka Plateau. (See Fig. 27.3 opposite.)

There are three major dip slopes and three escarpments in this composite region of plateau surfaces separated by river floodplains. The first escarpment consists of the steep slope separating the Ishan Plateau

from the lower Niger Valley. Beyond the Niger Valley, the land rises gradually east of Onitsha to form the Awka-Orlu uplands (better described as the Agulu-Nanka Plateau) which terminates in another east-facing escarpment lying west of the Mamu River Valley. Finally we come to the main Udi-Nsukka Plateau which has a general elevation of 300m (1,000 ft) above sea level. The steep escarpment which forms the eastern edge of this plateau is one of the most prominent landforms in Nigeria. It is heavily dissected by headwaters of rivers flowing into the Cross River. In some areas the sharp-edged spurs projecting into the Cross River plain have been breached by erosion to form sandstone outliers of which the Juju Rock at Uwani, Enugu, is the best example.

All the three plateau surfaces are dotted with numerous residual hills and ridges which often occur in groups to form saucer-shaped depressions similar to the one in which the Nsukka campus of the University of Nigeria is built. Most of the hills are dome-shaped although many of them have flat tops. There are only a few permanent streams, most of the valleys being dry throughout the year.

Extensive areas of this region have since been rendered useless for farming as a result of accelerated soil erosion by wind and running water. The scarp slopes in particular are ravaged by gaping erosion gullies such as those at Agulu, Nanka, Nsudde and Ukehe.

6. The Cross River Basin

The Cross River Basin is a composite region made up of the vast low-lying Cross River plains and the two eastern highland areas of Obudu and Oban Hills. The plains extend eastwards for about 80km (50 miles) from the foot of the Enugu escarpment and cover about 320km (200 miles) from north to south. The underlying rocks consist predominantly of shales with patches of sandstone which forms occasional ridges. Many isolated hills and ridges formed by igneous intrusions appear in Afikpo district and near Leffin in Abakaliki division. Extensive patches of clay depressions occur all over the plains. During the rainy season, these depressions contain stagnant water and since the early 1950s these seasonal swamps have been utilized for cultivating swamp rice.

South of the line joining Okigwi to Afikpo, the Cross River Basin consists of a dissected hill country characterized by many very steep-sided valleys cut up by streams flowing into the Enyong Creek, a tributary of the Cross River. The dendritic stream network of this district is striking and so is the oversized valley of the Enyong Creek which is a misfit stream whose headwaters have been captured by the Imo River at a point close to Umuahia.

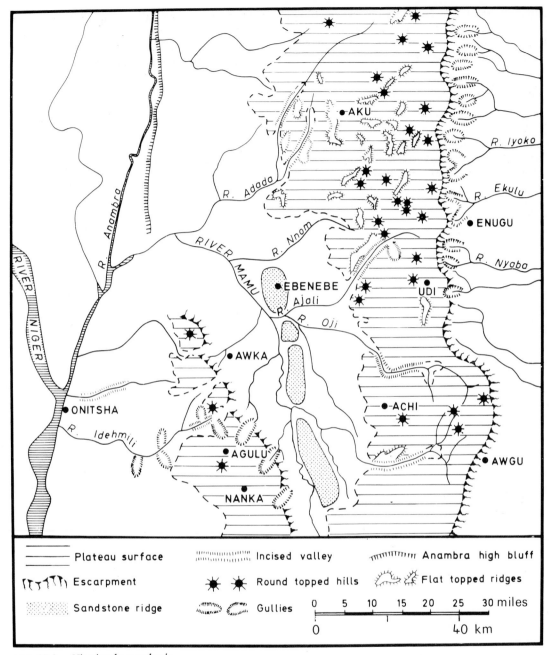

FIG. 27.3—Nigeria: the scarplands

The two highland areas of Obudu and Oban represent the highest surfaces in the region. The 900m (3,000ft) Oban Hills consist of a mass of steep-sided hills separated by valleys and ravines cut by swift streams. Rapids and waterfalls are common features in this district which is highly forested while the Obudu Plateau which is over 1,200m (4,000ft) high is covered with grass.

7. The Niger-Benue Valley

Between Yelwa and Jebba, the Niger cuts its valley through crystalline rocks and its course is therefore characterized by rapids which impede navigation. Along this section of the valley, blocks of these crystalline rocks protrude through the river-bed to form rocky islands. Below Jebba which is still the effective head of navigation, the Niger Valley is cut through

229

sedimentary rocks, and like the Benue River, which also flows through an area of sedimentary rocks, this section of the Niger Valley is free from rapids. Remnants of volcanic cones and lava occur along the Benue Valley between Ibi and Makurdi where the river is confined to a relatively narrow valley. The rest of the Niger-Benue Valley is characterized by extensive floodplains and alluvial swamps which are potential swamp ricefields. Large scale irrigation for sugarcane and rice is however so far restricted to the Niger Valley districts of Kabba and Niger provinces.

The 1,295 sq.km (500 sq. miles) man-made lake behind the Kainji Dam is one of the largest in Africa and is a major landform in the country. Although the dam was built primarily to generate hydro-electricity for industrial and domestic use, it has also served to control the annual flooding of the lower Niger Valley while the lake has become a major source of fish for the region, as well as water for irrigation.

8. The Jos and Biu Plateaux

The Jos Plateau is an erosion relic which covers an area of about 7,780 sq. km (3,000 sq. miles) and has a general elevation of about 1,260m (4,200ft) above sea level. It is bordered by an irregular margin with gentle slopes except in the southern border which is characterized by a regular margin with very steep slopes. The highest surfaces occur near Ngell and Bukuru. Massive outcrops of granitic rocks appear in various localities to break the monotony of the vast open plains of this region. There are also many extinct volcanic cones with well-preserved craters and crater lakes near Panyam, Vom and Miango. As a major watershed and the source of many streams flowing into Lake Chad, where the Niger, the Benue and the Gongola originate, the Jos Plateau has come to be regarded as the hydrological centre of Nigeria.

The Biu Plateau is built on rocks similar to those of the Jos Plateau and its surface is also characterized by numerous inselbergs and extinct volcanic cones. It is a much smaller region and has a general elevation which is less than 900m (3,000ft).

9. The high plains of Hausaland

This region consists of wide plains drained by mature rivers flowing through broad shallow valleys. The general elevation is about 600m (2,000ft), rising to over 810m (2,700ft) in the Zaria district and over 1,050m (3,500ft) towards the foothills of the Jos Plateau. The most conspicuous relief features in the region are the isolated or massed inselbergs which rise abruptly above the general level of the plains. The most important perennial river is the Kaduna River, which flows

through a broad rocky valley. Most of the other streams dry up completely during the dry season, but are given to extensive floods during the later part of the rainy season.

10. The Sokoto-Rima plains

The Sokoto River and its tributaries constitute the main relief feature of this region. The main river flows through a flat-bottomed trench-like valley between two steep and heavily eroded escarpments. In certain areas like Goronjo, the cliffs bordering the river valley exceed 30m (100ft). Soil erosion at the headwaters of the Sokoto-Rima system has resulted in the silting up of the valley floors, giving rise to increasing flood heights. The periodic destruction of settlements and farms by floodwaters is largely responsible for the migration of villages from the floodplains to the nearby sandstone plateau.

The northern and western parts of the region consist of a plateau of sandstone capped by a rather resistant layer of lateritic ironstone. It is this lateritic capping that has given rise to the many flat-topped hills found in areas where the plateau has been broken by river erosion. In the drier areas north and north-east of Sokoto town, the relief of the sandstone plateau is more uniform since many of the depressions and smaller valleys have been covered up by large deposits of wind-blown sands.

11. The Chad Basin

The vast open plain of this region is developed on young sedimentary rocks consisting mainly of clays with some sand horizons and gravels. In many places the clays become very dark as a result of the accumulation of organic matter and are then referred to as *firki*, the so-called black cotton soils of Bornu. In areas where the clays are exposed, they become plastic and saturated with water during the rainy season, when such areas are converted into swamps, from which numerous small streams emerge. During the dry season, the *firki* dries up and the swamps give way to a hard and brittle surface with numerous cracks. Water is generally scarce at this time of the year, although the water table remains high, hence the digging of numerous shallow ponds to supply water for man and beast. In central Bornu, the clay formation is covered by sandy drifts which may be up to 90m (300ft) thick and under which lateritic ironstone is formed.

The average elevation of the Basin is 300m (1,000ft) above sea level, the elevation of the lake being 240m (800ft). The uniform aspect of the landscape is striking, particularly during the rainy season when vast areas are flooded. The roads to Kukawa and Dikwa

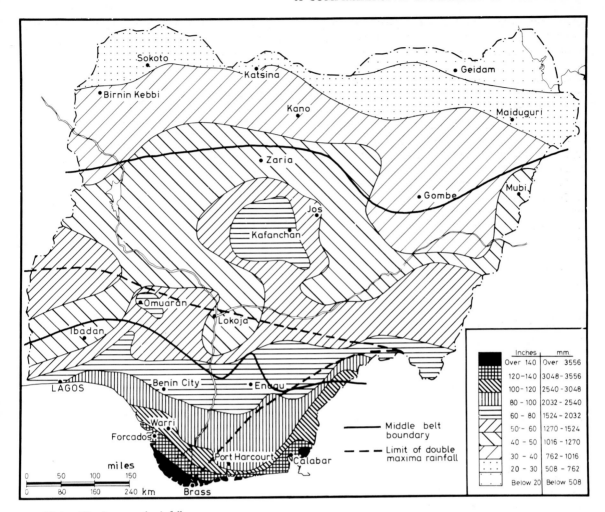

Inches	mm.
Over 140	Over 3556
120 - 140	3048 - 3556
100 - 120	2540 - 3048
80 - 100	2032 - 2540
60 - 80	1524 - 2032
50 - 60	1270 - 1524
40 - 50	1016 - 1270
30 - 40	762 - 1016
20 - 30	508 - 762
Below 20	Below 508

———— Middle belt boundary

− − − − Limit of double maxima rainfall

FIG. 27.4—Nigeria: annual rainfall

are essentially causeways across extensive *firki* swamps and in the region of Lake Chad, the terrain is so flat that such rivers as the Yedseram and the Alo disappear into *firki* swamps instead of flowing into the lake.

Fixed dunes occur in central Bornu and along the Bornu and Kamen shores of the lake. The dunes, which were formed during a drier period which preceded the formation of the lake, support an abundant growth of trees. The lake itself has been considerably reduced in area during the last 100 years and presently covers an area which varies from 10,400— 25,900 sq.km (4,000 to 10,000 sq. miles) according to the season of the year.

12. The eastern mountains

The eastern borderlands of Nigeria consist of a chain of low mountain ranges of which the best known are the Mandara Mountains in the north (1,200—

1,500m; 3,940—4,920 ft), the Atlantika Mountains (1,200m; 3,940ft) and the Shebsi Mountains (1,800m; 5,900ft). The whole region is heavily dissected by numerous fast-flowing streams which flow into the Benue and the Cross Rivers. The chain is breached by the upper Benue Valley between Garua and Yola. In some areas the highlands occur as plateau surfaces but in other areas the surfaces are so dissected that only isolated residuals can be identified. Many large areas are covered with volcanic lava which is very common all over the region. The varied topography of deeply incised river gorges and grass-covered peaks contrasts markedly with the monotonous plains found in other parts of the country.

CLIMATE AND WATER RESOURCES

Nigeria has a tropical climate which is hot and wet all through the year in the south-east but has a

231

marked dry season in the west and north. As a rule, the length of the dry season increases inland from the coast.

Two air-masses, the Equatorial Maritime air-mass and the Tropical Continental air-mass dominate the climate of the country. The former is associated with the rain-bearing south-west winds from the Atlantic Ocean while the latter is associated with the dry and dusty harmattan from the Sahara Desert. There are two major seasons, the rainy season and the dry season. The length of the rainy season decreases from about nine months in the south (March to November) to only four and a half months (mid-May to September) in the far north. This pattern is modified in the south which has a double-maxima regime with a short August break in the rains. Four seasons are therefore recognized in the south. These are the long rainy season (March to early August), the short dry season (August), the short rainy season (September to early November) and the long dry season (mid-November to February. (See Fig. 27.4, p. 231.)

The annual total rainfall map (Fig. 27.4) shows that the rainfall is heaviest in the south-east which has more than 3,050mm (120in.) a year, as compared with about 1,780mm (70in.) along the west coast. There is a general decrease away from the coast, such that the far north has about 510mm (20in.) of rain a year. Other aspects of the rainfall characteristics are noted in Chapter 2.

Temperature conditions and the relative humidity remain fairly constant throughout the year in the south, but the north experiences considerable seasonal change as well as a wide diurnal range. The mean monthly maximum temperature remains steady throughout the year at 35°C and 30°C (95°F and 85°F) at Lagos and Port Harcourt respectively, while the mean monthly minimum hovers around 21°C (70°F) for Lagos and 22°C (73°F) for Port Harcourt. In the far northern city of Maiduguri, the mean monthly maximum temperature may exceed 38°C (100°F) during the hottest months of April and May when the mean monthly minimum is below 22°C (72°F).

During the harmattan, which blows for over three months in the north but rarely more than two weeks along the coast, there is a considerable fall in the relative humidity. Bush fires which often destroy vegetation and on several occasions some villages, are very common during the harmattan.

The main source of water for agriculture is rainwater while the source of domestic water for the vast majority of the people is still from streams and springs. The northern peoples also rely on the use of water from deep wells during the dry season. The reliability of the rainfall is therefore very important

for successful agriculture, while delays in rains and occasional droughts have been responsible for crop failures and famine. Rudimentary irrigation is practised in parts of the middle Niger Valley and in the Chad Basin, but this is largely restricted to river floodplains. Modern irrigated agriculture is practised in the middle Niger Valley at Bacita, Bida and Badeggi as well as in the far northern districts of the Chad Basin and the Sokoto-Rima Basin where the need for irrigation is greatest.

Southern Nigeria is well served by perennial streams which can be used for irrigation so as to prevent crop failures when there is a delay in the rains as well as to permit multiple cropping. Unfortunately, the drier far north has very few permanent streams, although parts of the Chad Basin and the Sokoto-Rima Basin have adequate ground-water resources which are being tapped for irrigation purposes.

VEGETATION

The vegetation map (Fig. 27.5) should be compared with the map showing the total annual rainfall (Fig. 27.4). The great influence of rainfall on the vegetation of Nigeria is unquestionable. The human factor should also be noted since some areas which would normally support forest vegetation have been replaced with wooded savanna owing to periodic clearing of the forest for the purpose of cultivation. The oil palm bush of south-eastern Nigeria, for example, is a derived vegetation in an area which was formerly covered with dense rain forest. In much of the Ondo, Ogun and Bendel States, large areas of natural forests have since been replaced by man-made forests of cocoa and rubber trees. Remnants of the original vegetation, however, exist all over the country. Other information on the vegetation of Nigeria is given in Chapter 3 to which reference should be made.

SOILS AND SOIL EROSION

The importance of climate as a factor of soil formation is obvious from the fact that the four major soil groups almost correspond with the climatic zones. The four soil groups are the alluvial and swampy soils of the coastal region, the rain-forest soils, lateritic soils of the savanna areas and the sandy soils of the far north. A wide variety of parent materials and topography have combined to produce different soil sub-groups in each of the major four groups. Parent materials are also largely responsible for the physical characteristics and natural fertility of the soils. Within the tropical rain-forest climatic belt for example,

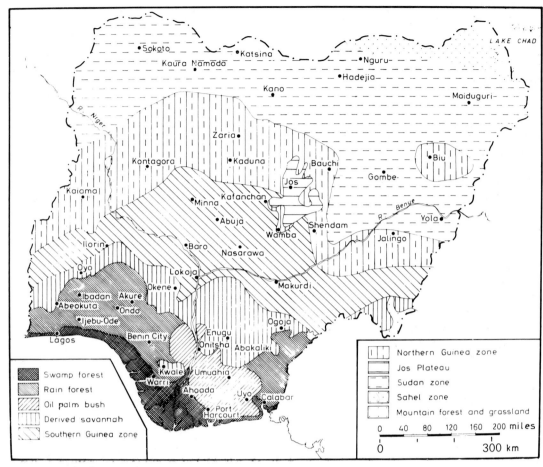

FIG. 27.5—*Nigeria: vegetation*

soils derived from old hard rocks of the Basement Complex are generally more fertile than soils from sedimentary rocks.

Along the coast, the soils are either sandy or swampy and like the soils of the equally rainy forest belt, are heavily leached. The fertility of the forest soils is generally concentrated in a thin top layer and is readily lost after cultivation. The acids sands which are the most common soil group in the scarplands and the eastern coastal plains are developed on sandstones and are rather porous, structurally unstable and relatively infertile compared with the forest soils of western Nigeria. The various plateau surfaces and plains have considerable areas under lateritic soils which form primarily along gentle slopes in areas which experience a marked dry season. Lateritic soils are rich in iron compounds and may become so hard as to appear as rock. They are often difficult to cultivate and are commonly used for making roads.

Serious cases of soil erosion occur in the very densely populated areas of the northern and eastern States, where over-cultivation and over-grazing have impoverished the soils and made them more liable to soil erosion by wind and running water. The worst affected areas are the steep slopes of the scarplands of south-central Nigeria, the Jos Plateau, Katsina and parts of Sokoto provinces. Large areas of land at Agulu, Nanka and Nsudde in the central Iboland have been completely destroyed by erosion gullies. Similar but smaller gullies feature along hill slopes in the Sokoto-Rima Basin and in the foothills of the Jos Plateau. In the far north sheet erosion by wind is particularly serious towards the end of the dry season when the storms preceding the onset of the rains blow off much soil.

Efforts to check soil erosion include the introduction of new methods of cultivation involving crop rotations, planting of cover crops and green manuring. Farmers have been advised to cultivate on ridges running across slopes rather than on mounds. In the badly eroded areas of the central Iboland, fast-growing trees like the cashew tree have been planted in an effort to reclaim the land.

233

Chapter 28—Nigeria:
II. Population and Economy

The population of Nigeria in 1963 was 56 million and in 1975 the official estimate put the population at 71.02 million.* Nigeria is therefore the most populous country in Africa and well over two-thirds of the people of West Africa live in this country. The breakdown of the population on the basis of the nineteen states created in 1976 is given in Table 36. The main demographic characteristics of the population include high birth and death rates, a high but declining rate of infant mortality, a gradual increase in life expectancy and a high illiteracy rate. There are over 200 ethnic groups in the country, the largest concentration of small ethnic groups being in the Middle Belt provinces. The largest and best known groups are the Hausas (6 million in 1963), the Fulanis (5 million), the Yorubas (10 million) and the Ibos (7 million). Other prominent but smaller groups include the Edos of Benin, the Ibibio of the southeast, the Tivs and Nupes of the Middle Belt and the Kanuris of the Chad Basin. (See Fig. 28.1.)

DISTRIBUTION OF THE POPULATION

The rural population density, based on the 1963 census, is shown in Fig. 28.2 (p. 236). It is quite clear from the map that the main concentrations of people are in the eastern states, the cocoa belt and the Lagos metropolitan district of the western states and the Kano and Sokoto regions of the northern states. In parts of Iboland and Ibibioland in the eastern states, the population density exceeds 580 persons per sq.km (1,500 persons per sq. mile), which may be compared with the national average of only 60 persons per sq.km (156 persons per sq. mile). This is the most densely populated area in Africa south of the Sahara. It is curious that this concentration of agricultural people occurs in areas with heavily leached and impoverished soils.

*The provisional figure for the 1973 census was 79.76 million, but the census was cancelled by the government in 1975.

Smaller pockets of dense population occur in the Jos Plateau, southern Tivland and Okene district. The remaining and by far the greater part of the country is, however, very sparsely populated. Indeed, vast areas of the Cross River district, the Niger Delta, the Chad Basin and parts of the Middle Belt are virtually uninhabited. The sparse population of the Middle Belt has been largely attributed to slave raids during the nineteenth century as well as to the ravages of sleeping sickness. There are however, some areas in the Middle Belt such as the Great Muri Plain of the middle Benue valley which like the Niger Delta, have never been densely populated owing to difficult environmental conditions.

RECENT MIGRATIONS

Population movements since the end of the Second World War have featured the large-scale migration of people from rural areas to the growing industrial and administrative urban centres although more than 50 per cent of migrants originating from rural areas also settle in other rural areas. There is also increasing movement of people from the smaller to the bigger towns which offer greater employment opportunities. Recent migration studies in the country have clearly established that economic considerations, that is, the desire to better oneself in material respects, constitute the most important factor inducing migration. Most of the migrants, both in the towns and rural areas are either self-employed or earn wages in the private sector of the economy.

The greatest number of migrants into the cities as well as to rural areas go to the three western states of Lagos, Ogun, Ondo, Oyo and Bendel States. This is by far the most urbanized and best-developed part of the country. A wide range of industries at Lagos, Ibadan, Benin and Warri provide employment opportunities which attract migrants. Most of the universities and other higher institutions and federal research centres are located in these five states. A large number of seasonal agricultural labourers also migrates into the

Table 36—Size and population of Nigerian states 1952/3 and 1963

State	Capital	Area sq.km	Area sq. mile	Population 1952/3	Population 1963	% increase 1953—63	Major Ethnic Group
Anambra	Enugu	17,360	6,701	2.24	3.57	59	Ibo
Bauchi	Bauchi	67,282	25,971	1.40	2.43	74	Hausa
Bendel	Benin	38,653	14,920	1.49	2.53	69	Edo
Benue	Makurdi	48,096	18,565	1.69	3.04	80	Tiv
Bornu	Maiduguri	107,508	41,498	1.56	2.95	89	Kanuri
Cross River	Calabar	35,570	13,730	1.76	3.62	105	Ibibio
Gongola	Yola	96,909	37,407	1.36	2.65	95	Mixed
Imo	Owerri	12,557	4,847	2.32	3.66	58	Ibo
Kaduna	Kaduna	70,233	27,110	2.40	4.09	70	Hausa/Fulani
Kano	Kano	43,083	16,630	3.40	5.77	69	Hausa
Kwara	Ilorin	61,373	23,690	0.83	1.72	107	Yoruba
Lagos	Ikeja	3,575	1,380	0.50	1.43	186	Yoruba
Niger	Minna	66,233	25,566	0.06	1.19	98	Nupe
Ogun	Abeokuta	17,414	6,722	0.98	1.55	58	Yoruba
Ondo	Akure	21,145	8,162	0.95	2.73	187	Yoruba
Oyo	Ibadan	36,829	14,216	2.43	5.21	114	Yoruba
Plateau	Jos	53,971	20,833	0.85	1.41	66	Mixed
Rivers	Port Harcourt	18,160	7,010	0.73	1.54	110	Ijaw
Sokoto	Sokoto	102,531	39,577	2.80	4.54	62	Hausa/Fulani

Source: Federal Office of Statistics, Lagos.

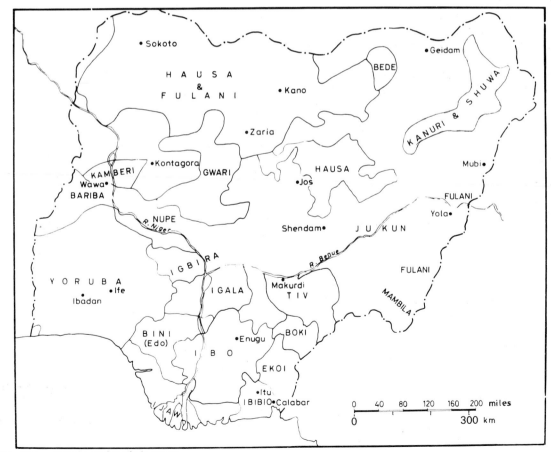

FIG. 28.1—Nigeria: major ethnic groups

235

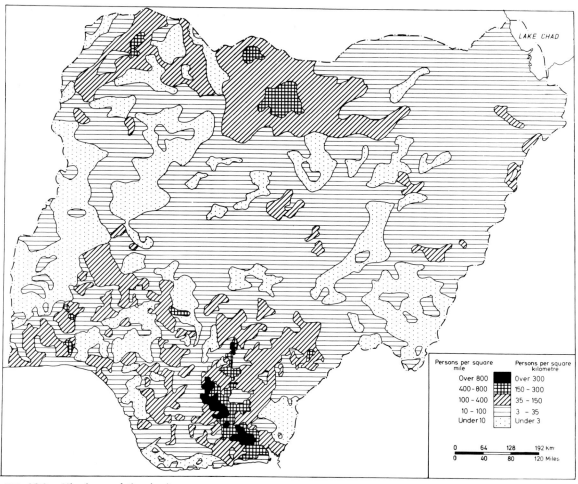

FIG. 28.2—Nigeria: population density

cocoa and rubber farms of the region to work for wages. In recent years an increasing number of these rural-rural migrants have settled permanently as self-employed tenant farmers who cultivate food crops for sale to the urban centres as well as to specialist cocoa farmers.

As may be expected, the main source regions of rural-rural migrants are the very densely populated rural areas shown in Fig. 28.2. In the heavily populated areas of the eastern states, the shortage of farmland and poor crop yields resulting from over-cultivation are largely responsible for the migration of people in search of farmland in other parts of the country.

URBANIZATION AND MAJOR TOWNS

The largest concentration of traditional or pre-European towns in Africa is found in the areas occupied by the Hausas and Yorubas of Nigeria. These pre-colonial towns were largely administrative, religious and in some cases educational centres. Agriculture, trade and crafts formed the main basis of their economy, although Yoruba towns were occupied by predominantly agricultural populations. Another set of traditional towns grew up along the coast where the trade in slaves and palm oil became the main source of income for the people of Lagos, Warri, Forcados, Burutu, Bonny, Opobo town and Calabar. These coastal port-towns had a more cosmopolitan population as compared with the interior towns. They were, however much smaller in size and with the exception of Lagos, Warri and Calabar, these coastal port-towns have suffered permanent decline since about the end of the Second World War.

A third group of towns emerged during the colonial period when some new towns were established and when many existing village settlements were functionally transformed. The colonial-period new towns

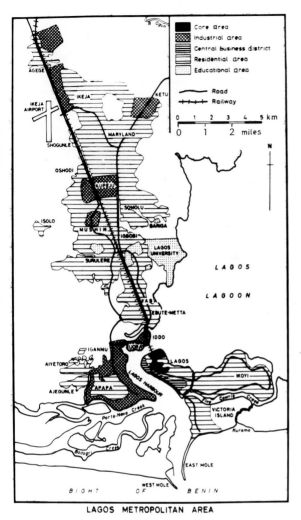

LAGOS METROPOLITAN AREA

FIG. 28.3—Nigeria: Lagos

include the port-towns of Port Harcourt, Sapele and Koko as well as the mining and administrative new towns of Jos, Enugu and Kaduna. The selection of existing villages such as Ikot Ekpene, Umuahia and Abak as district headquarters, which were served by a hospital, police station, prisons, post offices, schools and courts, soon elevated them to urban centres.

Since about 1956, there has been a growing emphasis on industrialization, and since these industries have been located in the major port-towns and the large interior cities, more and more people have continued to migrate into these urban centres. The increase in the population of towns like Enugu, Lagos, Port Harcourt and Kaduna is still predominantly through immigration and is likely to continue to remain so for several decades. It is also important to observe that the creation of new states in 1967 and again in 1976, has brought about the rapid growth

in population of the state capitals, some of which like Calabar, Sokoto and Benin, are pre-colonial cities. The sudden upgrading of fifteen of the nineteen state capitals from provincial headquarters to state capitals with all the necessary civil service ministries and departments has created job opportunities which have attracted large numbers of citizens from rural areas.

It is important to realize, however, that the vast majority of Nigerians (over 80 per cent) still live in rural areas. Rural settlements in most parts of the country consist of nucleated or compact villages some of which were walled round during the pre-colonial period. The Tivs, Ibibios and some Ibo people, however, live in homesteads which are scattered all over the village territory.

Lagos (900,970 in 1971)

Lagos is the federal capital of Nigeria and was until 1976 the capital of Lagos State. It is also the major port and by far the largest industrial centre in the country. Its growth in recent years has been phenomenal and in 1963 the population of Greater Lagos was over 1 million as compared with about 330,000 in 1952.

The island city of Lagos or Eko was founded more than 300 years ago by a Yoruba sub-group, the Aworis. By 1800, the small fishing and farming settlement had grown to become one of the leading slave ports in West Africa. The population of the island was about 5,000 in 1800 but by 1850, Lagos Island together with Iddo and Ebute Metta had a population of over 20,000. Since 1900, the growth in population has been primarily through immigration from other parts of the country.

The oldest residential areas are located on Lagos Island where the Oba's palace is also located. Housing conditions are very poor in this part of the city, which is one of the worst slums in Nigeria. Newer and equally low-grade residential areas characterized by narrow streets with open gutters include Shomolu, Mushin and Ajegunle. The middle-grade residential areas of Ebute Metta, Yaba and Surulere house most of the wage-earning population while top civil servants and company executives live in the high-grade residential areas of Ikoyi, Victoria Island and Ikeja.

The most impressive part of Lagos is the Central Business District (CBD) which covers the southern part of Lagos Island. This district is characterized by many skyscrapers rising to over twenty-five floors and a great intensity of land use. Important functions of the CBD include wholesaling, financing, administration and retailing. The main industrial

PLATE 87 — Lagos Island

estates, which include Ikeja, Apapa and Ilupeju, like the university campus and the teaching hospital are all located in the mainland districts.

Lagos Island is linked to the rest of the country by only two bridges, and since the bulk of the workers lives in the mainland districts, the rush-hour traffic is one of utter confusion thanks to the recklessness of Lagos drivers. Attempts to ease the traffic congestion on Lagos roads include the construction of flyovers from Lagos Island and the main port of Apapa to the mainland districts. (See Fig. 28.3 and Plate 87.)

Ibadan (758,330 in 1971)

The old walled city of Ibadan started as a military camp and was built on a hilly and defensible site. Most of the early settlers came from Old Oyo which was destroyed early in the nineteenth century during the Fulani Jihad. Later, the town attracted a large number of people from all over Yorubaland and by 1851 the population was estimated to be between 60,000 and 100,000. The town was then surrounded by a wall about 16km (10 miles) in circumference and the people who were predominantly farmers

lived in large traditional compounds, only a few of which remain today.

The old city is notorious for its lack of planning, narrow and winding lanes and is essentially one continuous slum. The new residential districts of Ekotedo, Sabo, Mokola and Molete are located outside the old city walls and have a predominantly migrant population. The night clubs and other places of entertainment are concentrated in these migrant surburbs. The range of hills which runs through the heart of the city is the most prominent feature of the physical landscape. These hills have provided sites for such landmarks as Mapo Hall, Bower Tower and the Premier Hotel. Other prominent buildings include the twenty-seven storey Cocoa House and the ten-storey Co-operative building.

As the capital of Oyo State, Ibadan is essentially an administrative centre although it is best known as the seat of Nigeria's premier university which had a student population of 6,000 in 1975. Other important educational and research institutions include the International Institute of Tropical Agriculture, the University College Teaching Hospital, Ibadan Polytechnic, the Federal School of Forestry and the Federal Agricultural Research Centre at Moor Plantation.

There are also a number of large modern manufacturing establishments in the city the most important of which include the Nigerian Tobacco Company's cigarette factory, a plastics factory and the Pepsi Cola factory.

Benin City (121,700 in 1971)

The fortified ancient city of Benin was founded in the tenth century AD as the capital of the famous Kingdom of Benin. During the fifteenth century Benin started trading with Portugal, the main trade goods consisting of guns, gunpowder and other manufactured goods from Portugal in exchange for slaves, elephant tusks, leopard skins and pepper from Benin. The city was conquered by the British in 1897 when much of it was destroyed and when many bronze works of art for which Benin is famous were looted and taken to Europe.

When the Mid-western State now Bendel State, was created in 1963, Benin became the capital city and since then there has been a rapid growth in population and manufacturing. Industrial products made in Benin include carpets, beer and high quality furniture. There is also a car assembly plant and several rubber-processing factories.

The University of Benin with its modern teaching hospital was opened in 1970 and there are many other institutions which attract students from all over Nigeria. The traditional wood carving of ebony figurines has received a new lease of life thanks to the great demand by tourists and the Nigerian élite.

Enugu (167,340 in 1971)

Enugu owes its origin and early growth to coal mining, which started in 1915. It is essentially a new town and is much better planned compared with the traditional cities of Ibadan or Zaria. Its growth has been very rapid since 1950, but particularly after the civil war in 1970. Today the city is important largely because it is the capital of Anambra State and a growing industrial area. Large-scale factory industries include the steel-rolling mill at Emene and a furniture factory. A campus of the University of Nigeria and the University Teaching Hospital have contributed to the importance of the town as an educational centre.

The main medium-grade residential areas are Ogbete, Uwani, Asata and Ogui. A large open space which is occupied by the sports stadium and the railway yard separates the oldest residential areas of Ogui and Asata from the Central Business District and the high grade residential area formerly reserved for British colonial officers.

Kano (357,100 in 1971)

Kano was founded in the eleventh century A.D. as a small iron-smelting settlement at the foot of Dala Hill, which is still a major landmark in the old city. It later grew up to become one of the most important trading centres in the Western Sudan during the days of the trans-Saharan caravan trade. The ancient walled city where the mosque and the Emir's palace are located remains conservative in architecture and way of life. By contrast the new residential areas of Sabon Gari, Fagge, and Nassarawa which are located outside the city walls are modern towns with well-laid streets and modern houses. (See Plate 88.)

As the primary city and capital of Kano State, Kano is the major focus of economic activities and educational institutions. It is the most industrialized interior city in West Africa and almost all its factories at the Bompai Industrial Estate depend very much on agricultural raw materials from the rich farmlands of the Kano region. The most important factory products include groundnut oil, corned beef, textiles, shoes and soft drinks.

Kano has Nigeria's second largest international airport and is an important religious and educational centre. The main post-secondary institutions are the Ado Bayero College of Education, the School of Basic Studies and the School of Arabic Studies.

Kaduna (181,200 in 1971)

The new town of Kaduna was established in 1917 as the administrative capital of the former Northern Region of Nigeria. Today it is the capital of Kaduna State and a growing industrial centre. It is built on a very attractive and readily accessible site which is located 912km (570 miles) by rail from Lagos. The location of Kaduna in the heart of the cotton belt has contributed to the establishment of several textile factories including Kaduna Textiles Ltd, Arewa Textiles Ltd, and Norspin Ltd. Other factory products include beer and soft drinks, bicycle assembly, ammunition and shoes.

Kaduna is an important military training centre for recruits and officers of the Nigerian army as well as of the police force and the air force. Important landmarks in the city include the ultra-modern Hamdala and Durbur Hotels, the ₦2 million Olympic-style Ahmadu Bello Stadium and Lugar Hall.

Zaria (200,850 in 1971)

The walled city of Zaria is one of the oldest urban centres in the country. It was founded in the fourteenth century and like ancient Kano it is occupied

PLATE 88—Kano, Nigeria

almost exclusively by the Local Hausa and Fulani population. Nigerian strangers and foreigners live outside the city walls in the newer residential areas of Tudun Wada, Sabon Gari and the former European reservation. Important institutions such as the main campus of the Ahmadu Bello University, the Samaru Agricultural Research Institute, hospitals and secondary schools are also located outside the old city walls.

Zaria has a few industrial establishments which include the Nigerian Tobacco Company's cigarette factory, Zaria Oil Mills Ltd, a cosmetics factory and a bicycle assembly plant.

Jos (100,000 in 1971)

The Plateau State's capital city of Jos owes its origin and growth to tin-mining in the Jos Plateau, which started in 1905. Apart from Lagos, it is the most cosmopolitan city in the country and before independence it had the second largest European population in the country (after Lagos). The cool climate of this well-planned city which is located at a height of about 1,200m (4,000ft) above sea level has made it a major holiday resort for expatriates working in Nigeria.

Jos is an important road centre and the Middle Belt terminus of the railway from Port Harcourt. It has a regular air service from Lagos and Kaduna. Important educational and research establishments include the veterinary research station at Vom and the University of Jos.

Port Harcourt (217,000 in 1971)

Port Harcourt is the second largest sea port in Nigeria and is located on the Bonny River, about 64km (40 miles) from the sea. It was founded in 1912 as a coal port but later became a major port for the exporting of palm produce, tin and groundnuts. The port, which is equipped with modern facilities for loading and unloading goods, is linked by road and railway to its vast hinterland which includes the four eastern States, Benue Plateau, Kano, Gongola and Bornu States. Before 1967, the tonnage of exports (not the value) through Port Harcourt was greater than that through Lagos but in 1970 and 1971 the value of exports through the port was also greater than that through Lagos. Lagos has, however, always been the leading port for imports into Nigeria.

Port Harcourt is one of the leading industrial centres in the country. The main industries include the oil refinery at Eleme, glassmaking, aluminium wares, paints, motor tyres, pressed concrete, tiles and cigarettes.

Onitsha (197,100 in 1971)

The important market town of Onitsha is one of the oldest urban centres in Nigeria. The modern ₦1.06 million market built in 1955 is the largest market in West Africa. This market was destroyed during the civil war but was completely rebuilt in 1975. Before 1967, the value of goods handled at Onitsha per annum was estimated to be about ₦20 million.

Apart from the great variety of manufactured goods sold at Onitsha, this river port-town is the most important collecting and distributing centre for food-stuffs throughout the country. Beans, dried fish, shea-butter, onions, rice and yams arrive at Onitsha daily from the northern states and Abakaliki while the supply of fruits, cassava and new yams come from the nearby districts of Asaba, Anambra and Awka. Most of the foodstuffs thus collected (about 90 per cent) are exported by road to the major urban centres of Lagos, Benin, Ibadan, Enugu, Port Harcourt and Aba.

Calabar (120,000 in 1974)

The Cross River State capital of Calabar was founded more than 300 years ago. It is located on the Calabar River at a point about 65km (42 miles) from the sea. Before the colonial period, Calabar was an important port of export for slaves and palm oil. In 1901—6 the town served as the capital of the British Protectorate of Southern Nigeria and was for many years the lead-ing educational centre in the eastern states of Nigeria. The town, however, suffered a marked decline after the founding of Port Harcourt and the selection of Enugu as the capital of the former Eastern Region of Nigeria.

The creation of states in 1967 brought a new lease of life to Calabar with an influx of people including civil servants and businessmen. The establishment in 1972 of a College of Technology and the University of Calabar added greatly to the educational impor-tance of the town. There are only a few industries, of which the most important are a cement factory and a plywood mill.

ECONOMIC ACTIVITIES

Although crude oil is now by far the most important source of government revenue, about 70 per cent of the labour force is still employed in agriculture. In-deed the low *per capita* income of less than ₦100 per annum reflects both the continuing reliance of most Nigerians on traditional agriculture and the low productivity of agriculture in the country. An increas-ing number of people is now employed in manufactur-ing, while a much larger proportion obtains meagre income from petty trading. This section gives a brief account of the major economic activities in the country.

AGRICULTURE

Most Nigerians are still peasant farmers producing their own food crops and deriving income from one or more cash crops as well as from the sale of surplus food crops. The main food crops grown in the south and the Middle Belt are yams, cassava, rice and maize while the main subsistence crops of the far north are guinea corn, millet, cassava and hungry rice.

Mixed cropping on fields which rarely exceed 0.4 hectares (1 acre) in the south or 1.2 hectares (3 acres) in the north and extreme dispersal of holdings are characteristic features of farming in the country. Small-scale traditional irrigation is practised along the floodplains of the major rivers in the north, although large-scale modern irrigation schemes are becoming important in the Middle Belt and the far north. Important irrigation projects for sugarcane, rice and other crops include the Bacita sugar estate near Jebba, the Edozhigi and Badeggi rice schemes (near Bida), the Jere Bowl rice scheme in the Chad Basin and the Sokoto-Rima irrigation schemes for producing rice, sugar-cane and cotton. Market gardening is important around the major towns where the increasing number of educated Nigerians has created a great demand for crops like tomatoes, lettuce, carrots and cucumbers. The establishment of large modern poultry farms in the outskirts of the major towns is a relatively recent development in Nigerian agriculture.

The most developed parts of rural Nigeria have been those districts which cultivate crops such as the oil palm, cocoa, groundnuts, rubber and cotton, which are commonly called export crops although an increasing proportion of these crops is now used for local manufacturing. The geographical conditions suitable for the production of these crops and the pro-cesses of marketing them have already been discussed in Chapter 8, to which reference should be made. The areas where these crops are produced in Nigeria are shown in Fig. 28.4 (p. 242).

There are, however, a few facts about the changing character of Nigerian agricultural production which should be noted at this point. These facts include:

1. The gradual displacement of yams by cassava in the eastern and parts of the western states. Cas-sava, which was formerly considered to be a poor man's food is now consumed in the form of garri by even well-to-do Nigerian families. It is less expensive to cultivate in terms of initial capital and labour and is more tolerant of impoverished soil than yams.

2. The growing emphasis on rice cultivation. Before 1946 almost all the rice consumed in the country was imported. Today the country is almost self-sufficient in rice production. The major rice fields are in the rainfed swamps of Abakaliki, the *fada-mas* of the Middle Niger Valley and those of the Sokoto-Rima Valley.

3. The rapid expansion of tree-crop plantations

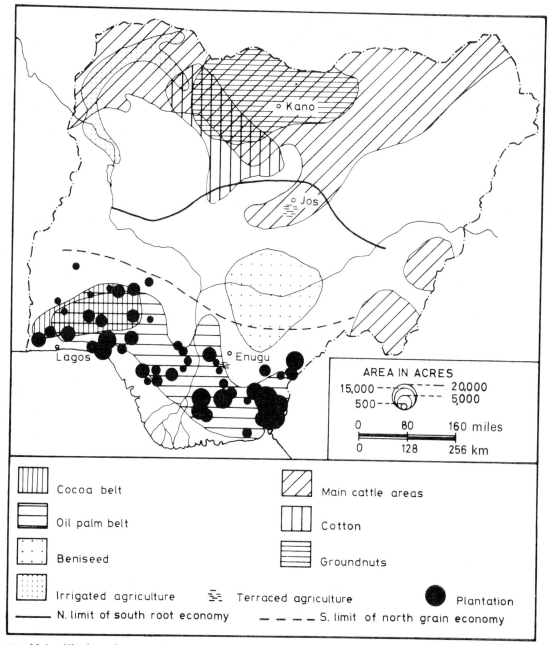

FIG. 28.4—*Nigeria: major crop regions*

since 1951. Before this date the government did not approve of plantation agriculture which is capital-intensive, largely because the government argued that it did not wish to transform Nigerians from being peasant farmers to wage-earners, who would suffer when the plantations folded up when world prices became too low.

Despite the huge investments in plantation agriculture, however, the plantation contributed very little to the export trade in Nigerian palm produce (3.5 per cent), rubber (5 per cent) and cocoa (about 3 per cent) during the decade ending in 1970.

4. The decline in the export of palm produce and cotton following increasing consumption of these crops in local factories. In July 1974 for example a government decree authorized for the first time the import of duty-free palm oil into the country. It is indeed significant that Nigeria, which until 1936 was the world's largest exporter

PLATE 89—Ripe cotton on farm in northern Nigeria

of palm oil and remained one of the largest exporters till 1966, is now a net importer of palm oil. The situation with cotton lint has become equally serious since local supplies do not appear to meet the demands of local textile factories. Export of groundnuts was banned in 1973/4 because of the disastrous drought which resulted in very poor crop yields. The expected yield of only 300,000 tons was considered to be inadequate to meet the needs of local crushing mills. Export figures for the main agricultural exports are given in Table 37 below. (See plate 89.)

5. The establishment of farm settlements in the nine southern states of Nigeria after independence in 1960. The farm settlements, which varied in size from 800 to 4,800 hectares (2,000–12,000 acres) were originally meant for settling young school-leavers who had been trained in modern techniques of farming. Each settler was settled at a cost of about ₦4,000 and was allocated about 4–8 hectares (10–20 acres) which was never to be fragmented. Most of the original settlers have since left the settlements to take up jobs in the towns.

6. Attempts to increase the output of 'export crops' in recent years. This has taken the form of rehabilitation schemes for rubber, cocoa and oil palms, whereby farmers are paid some money to compensate them for cutting off old trees and replanting the land with improved young seedlings. Higher producer prices are now paid to farmers following the abolition in 1974 of produce tax on cocoa, groundnuts, rubber, cotton and palm produce.

LIVESTOCK

The livestock population, which is concentrated in the north of Nigeria, consists of cattle (12 million), goats (21 million) sheep (7.2 million) pigs (0.8 million), camels (16,000), donkeys (2 million), horses (431,000) and poultry (80 million). The cattle, which are mostly short-horned zebus, are found mainly in the northern States, where they are under the care of nomadic Fulani cattlemen. The tsetse fly prevents the keeping of cattle in the forest belt where only the resistant dwarf Muturu breed is kept. Shortage of grazing and water during the dry season is largely responsible for the nomadic way of life led by the Cattle Fulani. This situation has made it difficult to integrate cattle-rearing with arable farming as is done in the more developed countries of the world.

Goats and sheep are a major source of meat all over the country and are slaughtered more often than cattle, particularly during the Mohammedan festi-

Table 37—Agricultural exports of Nigeria ('000 tons)

	1938	1948	1958	1960	1962	1964	1966	1967	1968	1970	1972
Cocoa			87	303	421	382	190	244	206	193	228
Groundnuts	180	245	513	332	530	544	573	540	638	287	106
Groundnut oil			39.6	46.6	62.9	80	104	71	109	89	
Groundnut cake			58.3	53.3	88	139.3	133	131	171	160	
Raw cotton			33.7	27	23.2	25.3	14.9	33	14	27.8	
Palm kernels	312	327	445	422	358	401	394	162	159	182	212
Palm oil	110	139	184	189	130	148	143	16	3	7	2
Rubber			41.1	58.5	59.1	72.1	70.3	48	52	58.3	41.2

vals. The long-legged Fulani and Sokoto goats are usually left to fend for themselves and are not very popular in the south where the short-legged dwarf goats are kept in the backyard of most rural homes. Both the goat and the sheep populations are concentrated in the north. There are, however, more pigs in the south since the predominantly Muslim population of the north do not eat pork because their religion prohibits it.

Camels and horses are found mainly in the far north, and particularly in the Chad Basin, where they are used as pack animals. Camels also provide milk and skins for the local leather cottage industry. Donkeys are used as beasts of burden throughout the grassland areas of the north and the Middle Belt.

The most widespread livestock in the country is the local poultry which is normally small in size. Since these birds are left to fend for themselves, they grow very slowly but provide a more tasty meat, which most Nigerians prefer to that of the exotic poultry breeds introduced from Europe. An increasing number of élite farmers have, however, concentrated on the exotic breeds, which are being reared in the outskirts of major towns.

FORESTRY

There are two main types of forest in Nigeria, namely the southern closed forest zone and the more extensive woodlands of the savanna zone. In 1970, about 360,100 sq.km (139,000 square miles) or just over one-third of the total area of the country was under forest. The permanent forest estates or forest reserves, however, occupy only 93,300 sq.km (36,100 sq.miles) or 10 per cent of the total land area. These reserves are made up of 19,380 sq.km (7,480 sq. miles) of high forest in the south about 220 sq.km (85 sq. miles) of mangrove swamp, and 73,930 sq.km (28,536 sq.miles) of savanna woodland in the north.

The high forests of the Ondo, Ogun, Bendel and Cross River States account for 90 per cent of the total industrial wood exports (timber and sawn logs) of the country. The savanna zone yields very little timber but provides poles for building, the major savanna wood products being firewood and charcoal. Uncontrolled grazing and annual bush fires have combined to restrict the area under forest cover in the north.

In the high forest zone of the south, a considerable proportion of the timber products still comes from the open forests, which consist of forest areas not under reserve. Timber-felling in the reserves is controlled and it is estimated that only 30 out of the more than 100 useful tree species in these forests are at present exploited. The main problem limiting timber extraction in the high forest zone is inadequate transportation.

A number of forest plantations of teak and *gmelina* as well as of some indigenous tree species have been established outside the major cities, including Ibadan, Lagos, Enugu and Benin, to provide poles and firewood. Smaller forest plantations are common in the tobacco-growing grassland areas of Oyo province where there is a great demand for wood for curing the tobacco leaves.

In addition to timber, poles and firewood, the forests of Nigeria are a major source of twines and ropes used in local crafts industry. Leaves for wrapping cooked food and for preserving kola nuts as well as edible leaves and snails are an important source of income to farmers during the slack season in the farming calendar.

FISHING

The demand for fish in Nigeria is estimated to be over one million tons of fish a year compared with an estimated annual catch of only 150,000 tons. Since fish has a high content of protein and since there is a high protein deficiency in Nigerian diets, there is a great need to step up local fish production. Fortunately it can be greatly increased through a fuller exploitation of the fish resources of Lake Chad, Kainji Lake, inland rivers, the coastal creeks and lagoons as well as from the open sea and from fish ponds.

Full-time fishermen exist mainly along the coast and consist mainly of Ijaws, Efiks, Ibenos and Ilaje Yorubas as well as migrant fishermen from Benin and Ghana. There are also some full-time fishermen in the Lake Chad region and along the Niger-Benue Valley. The vast majority of Nigerian fishermen are, however, essentially part-time fishermen who also engage in farming or petty trading. This is particularly true of those engaged in freshwater fishing.

Before the civil war, the value of annual fish imports consisting largely of stockfish amounted to about ₦14 million. Large quantities of canned fish are also imported but presently attempts are being made to step up domestic supplies, which are derived from three main sources, namely industrial fisheries, canoe fisheries and freshwater fisheries.

Industrial shrimp fishery and Nigerian deep water trawling started in 1965. The State governments, the Aiyetoro community in Okitipupa division and the Ibru Fish Company are amongst the increasing number of establishments which take part in sea fishing. Local and migrant fishermen along the lagoons and creeks also supply large quantities of both fresh and smoked fish to southern parts of the country. Freshwater fish comes mainly from the Niger-Benue system and Lake Chad as well as from local streams and fish ponds. The use of refrigerated cars has made it possible for firms and traders to distribute frozen fish to the major inland towns.

MINING

Nigeria is rich in mineral resources and is currently one of the leading world producers of crude petroleum, tin, columbite and zircon, all of which are produced mainly for export. Minerals which are produced largely for the domestic market include coal, limestone, marble and clay. The sizeable deposits of iron ore, lead and zinc have not yet been exploited.

The first minerals to be exploited during the early years of the colonial period were coal and tin. It was, however, not until the rapid increase in the export tonnage of mineral oil in the late 1960s that mining became the dominant sector of the Nigerian economy. In 1970, for example, mining contributed over 27 per cent of the total Federal Government current revenue and 44 per cent of the export earnings. The contribution of crude petroleum to the national income continues to increase such that in 1974 oil exports earned ₦ 5.50 billion which was over 90 per cent of the total export earnings. The strategic importance of mining to the national economy has been largely responsible for the setting up by government of a National Prospecting and Mining Company for solid minerals and the Nigerian National Oil Corporation for the prospecting and mining of crude petroleum. The major centres of production of the most important minerals discussed below are shown in Fig. 28.5 (p. 246). (See Table 38, p. 247.)

Tin

Tin is obtained from alluvial deposits in the Jos Plateau, where mining started in 1904. The ore is extracted by the open-cast method and in the early days, mining was by hand, the tin-bearing sands being transported by head-pans to sluice-boxes where the mineral was extracted. The use of large hydro-turbine gravel pumps has since replaced manual labour, which was rather inefficient. Since the installation of a tin-smelting plant in 1962, the metal has been exported mostly in its pure form as tin ingots.

Production has been on the decline since the wartime peak period of 1941–5 when annual exports averaged about 17,000 tons of ore. The price of tin has, however, fluctuated very much since then, so

much so that the total export of 12,000 tons in 1953 was valued at ₦17 million while the total export of 9,800 tons in 1963 was valued at ₦18 million. Production since 1968 has averaged less than 12,000 tons valued at ₦13 million.

Columbite

In the Jos Plateau, columbite occurs in close association with tin as alluvial deposits and in the early days of tin mining, columbite was discarded as waste material. The mineral was first extracted in 1933 when three tons were produced, increasing to over 800 tons in 1943. After a peak of over 2,000 tons in 1944, production increased again during the late 1950s and since 1960 it has averaged about 2,000 tons per annum. Nigeria produces over 70 per cent of the world output of columbite, which is used largely in the manufacture of stainless steel as well as in alloys of a high degree of heat resistance. Most of the mineral is exported to the United States of America.

Coal

Nigeria is the only country in West Africa producing coal. Mining started in 1915, about six years after the mineral was first discovered in the Enugu area of Anambra State. Production is still concentrated in the Enugu area which has an estimated reserve of 72 million tons. The much more extensive coal reserves of over 170 million tons in Kwara, Benue and Plateau States are still largely undeveloped except for a small mine opened in 1968 when the Enugu field was temporarily closed down as a result of the civil war.

Nigerian coal is of sub-bituminous grade and occurs in seams of which five have been identified in the Enugu area. The thickest seam varies from 1–2m (4–6ft) and mining is by the adit method whereby tunnels are driven into the hillsides. Unlike tin and petroleum which are mined by private companies, Nigerian coal has always been mined under direct government control. The Nigerian railways and the Electricity Corporation were the main consumers of Nigerian coal but the demand for coal has since declined greatly following railway's changeover to diesel in 1954 and the commissioning of the Kainji hydro-electric power station in 1969. The use of gas and petroleum for generating power has also had an adverse effect on the demand for coal.

Production since 1960 has averaged about 600,000 tons per annum. This is expected to increase considerably when the iron and steel industry at Ajaokuta near Lokoja is commissioned. Unfortunately, Nigerian coal is of a non-coking variety, which

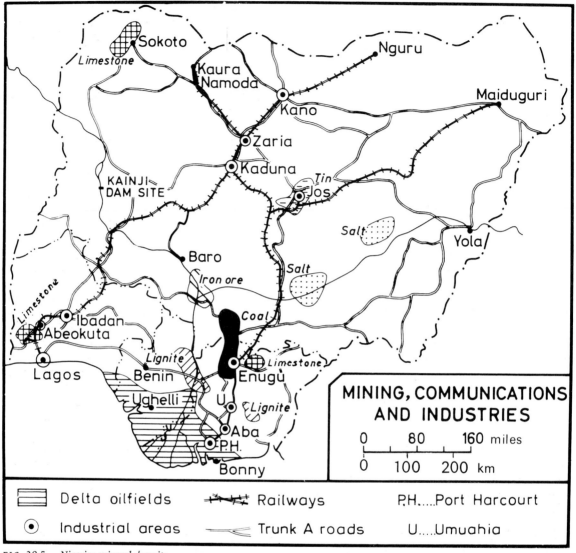

FIG. 28.5—Nigeria: mineral deposits

makes it unusable in blast furnaces. There is however a process known as the Krupp-Kenn process whereby pig-iron is produced without the use of coke. The proposed iron and steel mill may decide to use this process, although it may be more economical to import coking coal.

Petroleum

Crude petroleum or mineral oil is by far the most important mineral mined in Nigeria today in terms of its direct contribution to the country's economy. Oil prospecting started in 1937, but it was not until 1956 that oil was found in commercial quantities at Oloibiri in the Niger Delta. One year later, more promising discoveries were made at Afam and Bomu and in 1958 the country exported 9,000 tons of crude oil.

Production rose to 20.7 million tons in 1966, the year before the civil war, when production was disrupted. The war ended in January 1970 and at the end of that year the production figure stood at 53 million tons as compared with 7 million tons in 1968.

In 1961 a crude oil terminal was opened at Bonny and in 1966 the storage capacity of the terminal was increased from 330,000 to 3.5 million barrels. A new terminal to serve the western delta oil wells was commissioned in 1976. There is only one oil refinery near Port Harcourt but it supplies less than half of the refined petroleum product needs of the country. Two new refineries, one at Warri and another at Kaduna, are, however, expected to go into production in 1978.

Crude petroleum export has been the main source of revenue for Nigeria since 1970.

Table 38—Production of principal minerals in Nigeria (000 tons)

Mineral	1960	1964	1966	1968	1969	1970	1971	1972
Crude petroleum	837	5,859	20,929	7,127	27,002	54,203	76,378	90,918
Coal	562	688	640	4	20	61	194	341
Tin ore & metal	10.4	11.8	12.6	13	12	10	10	9
Columbite	2.1	2.3	2.3	1.1	1.6	1.6	1.4	1.4
Natural gas (million cu.ft)	5,095	3,633	101,582	51,628		284,930		

Iron ore

There are many shallow deposits of medium- to low-grade oxidized ores all over the country, but no large deposits of rich ore similar to those of Liberia, Guinea, or Sierra Leone have been discovered. The most promising ore deposits which are likely to be mined to feed the proposed iron and steel mill at Ajaokuta include the Agbaja Plateau deposits near Lokoja and the rich lateritic ore near Nsude village on the Udi Plateau. The Agbaja area has estimated reserves of 206 million tons of ore with about 45 per cent iron while the Nsude area has reserves of about 40 million tons of ore with about 33 per cent iron.

MANUFACTURING INDUSTRIES

Early industrial projects in Nigeria, as in other West African countries, were concerned primarily with semi-processing of crops and mineral ores for export. This was in keeping with the colonial economic policy which considered the colonies as a source of raw materials for the factories of the metropolitan countries. It was not until 1960 when Nigeria became independent that the government came to see industrialization as a crucial factor in the pace and pattern of the general economic development of the country. The growing emphasis on industrialization during the early years of self-rule is obvious from the fact that industrial investment rose to ₦60 million in 1964 as compared with less than ₦10 million per annum during the period 1950 to 1960. Since 1965 the manufacturing sector has grown faster than any other sector of the economy, except for the mining sector, which has become the dominant sector, owing to the crude oil boom which started about 1965.

It is misleading to talk of industrial zones in Nigeria since there are no such zones, with the possible exception of Greater Lagos. Rather what we have are a few industrialized urban centres which, with the exception of Aba, Umuahia, Onitsha, Warri and Shagamu, are state capitals. It is important to notice that almost all the important manufacturing centres are located on the railway and that most of them are located in the south.

Greater Lagos is by far the most important manufacturing centre. Up to 1970 about one-third of the industrial capacity of the country, both in terms of the number of establishments and the number of employees as well as in terms of the gross output, was concentrated in Greater Lagos. This situation has come about largely as a result of the good port facilities of Lagos as well as the large consumer market provided by a predominantly wage-earning population. Government incentive through establishment of such industrial estates as Apapa, Ijora, Ikeja, Mushin and Ilupeju has also played an important part in attracting industrialists. Lagos is, however, rather overcrowded and it appears that the larger inland cities of Ibadan, Kaduna, Kano and Aba will attract more attention than Lagos in future.

The most important industrial products include cement, textiles, plastics, shoes, food and drinks, metal products, soaps and detergents, pharmaceutical products and cigarettes. There are also many vehicle and radio assembly plants.

Small-scale modern industries, which are defined as establishments which employ less than fifty people and with investment capitals of about ₦60,000, are much more widespread. Such industries include corn-milling, cabinet-making, bakeries and printing. Traditional crafts industries, which are essentially cottage industries, constitute the third category of industrial production. Weaving, pottery and wood-carving are the most widespread and are all based on local raw materials.

TRANSPORT

In the early years of the colonial period, rivers and the coastal creeks provided the only means of modern transport in the country. The most important waterways were the Niger, the Benue and the Cross Rivers, all of which still carry substantial quantities of goods. The navigability of these rivers is, however, limited to

Table 39—Composition of domestic exports from Nigeria, selected years 1900–70 (per cent of value)

Commodity	1900	1929	1946	1950	1954	1962	1964	1966	1968	1971	1973
Cocoa	—	13	16	22	27	20	19	10	25	12	5.6
Groundnuts (nuts, oil, cake)	—	14	24	17	23	24	22	20	25	3	3.8
Palm produce	82	46	26	33	16	16	15	14	7	2	0.8
Cotton (lint & seed)	—	3	2	3	5	4	4	3	3	0.9	0.2
Rubber	10	1	6	3	2	7	6	4	3	0.9	0.8
Sub-total	92	77	74	78	73	71	66	51	63	18.8	11.2
Petroleum	—	—	—	—	—	10	15	33	18	74.4	83.4
Other Exports	8	23	26	22	27	19	19	16	19	6.8	5.4
Total	100	100	100	100	100	100	100	100	100	100	100

the rainy season when the water level is high enough to permit the use of large vessels.

The first railway was built in 1898 to link Lagos with Abeokuta and was later extended to Ibadan in 1901. The progress of railway construction is shown in Fig. 28.6. In 1964, when the Bornu extension was opened to traffic, the total route coverage was 3,560km (2,180 miles) of 1.166m (3ft 6in.) single track. There are two main lines, the eastern line from Port Harcourt to Maiduguri and the western line from Lagos to Kano. In 1955, the Nigeria Railway which was run as a government department, was constituted into a corporation, with the view to making it a commercial enterprise. The railway has, however, found it difficult to pay its way, largely owing to loss of traffic to road transport, which is faster and more flexible, and to general inefficiency.

Since about 1955, the road has emerged as the most important means of transport in the country. Large trailers from Kano, Maiduguri, Jos and Sokoto to Lagos are a common sight on the roads and most of these vehicles carry goods which were formerly carried exclusively by the Nigeria Railway. Road development has received great attention from both the Federal and State governments since 1960 and today all Federal or trunk A roads and most state or trunk B roads are tarred.

The development of rail and road transport brought about the decline of pre-colonial seaports like Forcados, Burutu, Abonnema, Bonny and Calabar, which had no direct link by land to the hinterland. The ports of Lagos and Port Harcourt which have both road and rail links to the rest of the country grew rapidly and by 1970 these two ports handled more than 70 per cent of the imports and exports of Nigeria.

Kano and Lagos are the two main international airports in the country. The other international airports are Calabar and Maiduguri and there are plans to extend this status to the new airports planned for Enugu and Ibadan. Each state capital is served by an airport. Numerous landing strips also exist for private and international flights. Nigeria Airways has a monopoly over all internal flights.

TRADE

Domestic trade

There is a great deal of internal trade in foodstuffs, crafts and imported as well as local factory products. Large quantities of beans, onions, rice, dried fish and yams are sent by rail or road from the north and Middle Belt to the major urban centres in the south. The kola trade valued at ₦ 12.20 million in 1964 and the cattle trade valued at ₦ 17.30 million in the same year deserve special attention. The trade in these two commodities is essentially between the north and the south and often the money obtained from sales of cattle is invested in buying kola nuts for sale in the northern cities. The larger market centres of Onitsha, Kano, and Ibadan are major collecting and distribution centres for foodstuffs as well as for manufactured consumer goods.

Foreign trade

From the end of the Second World War to 1954, Nigeria's foreign trade showed an export surplus. This trend was reversed between 1955 and 1965 partly because export prices fell and partly as a result of increases in public expenditure to finance development plans. Since 1966, however, there has been a favourable balance of trade (see Table 40), thanks to the remarkable growth in petroleum exports, which contributed 90 per cent of the export earnings of ₦ 5.50 billion in 1974 as compared with 1.7 per cent of the total export earnings of ₦ 271.6 million in 1959.

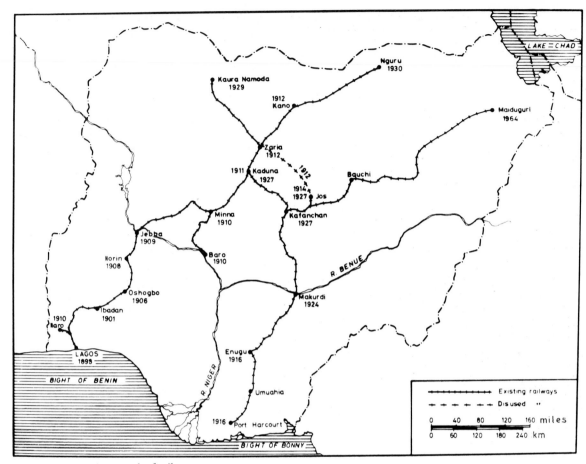

FIG. 28.6—Nigeria: growth of railways

The growth in petroleum exports has resulted in a significant change in the structure of exports. In 1959, for example, the four traditional commodities, namely cocoa, palm oil, palm kernel and groundnuts (including groundnut oil and cake) contributed about 70 per cent of the total export earnings, while petroleum contributed only 1.7 per cent. In 1974 however, the share of crude petroleum had risen to 90 per cent. The principal exports, which consist of crops and minerals, are listed in Tables 38–9.

Textiles (including cotton cloth), motor vehicles, iron and steel goods and petroleum products are some of the main imports into Nigeria. The rapid expansion of manufacturing has resulted in marked changes in the structure of imports. The share of

consumer goods (durable and non-durable), for example, fell from 51 per cent of the total import bill of N 358.8 million in 1959 to 31 per cent of the total import bill of N 497.4 million in 1969. During the same period the value of capital goods rose from 46 per cent to 68.2 per cent.

Britain remains the chief trading partner of Nigeria, although the United States, France, Japan, West Germany and recently the Soviet Union are also important. Trade with the Soviet Union grew considerably during the Nigerian civil war when most countries in the West, including the United States of America and France, unlike the Soviet Union, failed to support the Nigerian government against secessionist Biafra.

Table 40—Trade balance of Nigeria 1964–73 (N million)

	1964	1965	1966	1967	1968	1969	1970	1971	1972	1973
Imports	507.8	550.4	512.6	447.2	386.4	497.4	772.8	1,079.0	990.6	1,224.8
Exports	421.0	536.6	566.2	483.6	422.2	636.2	886.0	1,293.2	1,434.2	2,278.4
Balance	−86.8	−13.8	+53.6	+36.4	+35.8	+138.9	+113.2	+214.2	+443.6	+1,053.6

Chapter 29—Senegal

PLATE 90—Dakar, Senegal

The first French forts were established in the Senegal in the middle of the seventeenth century when the ports of St Louis and Dakar served as important slave ports. It was from Senegal that French influence spread into the western part of West Africa and until 1958, Dakar, the capital of Senegal, remained the administrative centre of French West Africa. In 1958, after the referendum in which Guinea decided not to remain in the French West African community, the rest of French West Africa broke up and the following year, Mali (formerly French Sudan) and Senegal agreed to form the Mali Federation. Internal disputes led to the collapse of the Federation in August 1960 when Senegal really started to function as a separate independent country.

Senegal has an area of about 196,200 sq.km (76,000 sq. miles) and a population of about 4.2 million (1973). Much of it is semi-desert and in most

parts of the country water for crops and domestic use is very scarce. The economy is still largely dependent on one crop, groundnuts, which in 1970 provided more than 80 per cent of Senegal's export earnings.* Production has been on the decline since the peak year of 1965/6 when 1,011,000 tons were produced, falling to a disaster level of 449,000 tons in 1972/3. Senegal is however still one of the leading world producers of groundnuts and groundnut oil. Over-dependence on this single crop constitutes a major economic problem for the country. Unfortunately the country is poor in basic raw materials and minerals, as compared with Guinea and the Ivory Coast for example. Additionally the small size of

---

*The unusually low contribution of groundnuts to the export by value in 1973 of 35 per cent was caused largely by the severe drought that affected the Sahel belt of West Africa from 1972 to 1974.

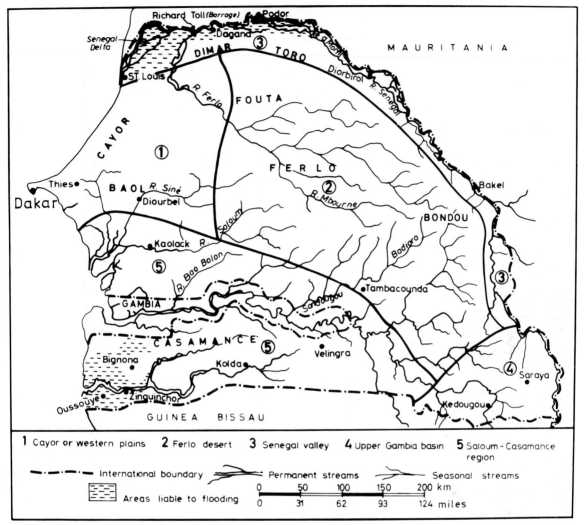

FIG. 29.1 —Senegal: drainage and physical regions

the market area served by the Dakar industrial region since the break-up of French West Africa in 1958, has not encouraged large-scale manufacturing which could have helped to diversify the economy.

PHYSICAL REGIONS, RELIEF AND DRAINAGE

The main physical regions of Senegal are (Fig. 29.1): 1) Cayor or the western plains, 2) the Ferlo Desert, 3) the Senegal Valley, 4) the Upper Gambia Basin, 5) The Saloum-Casamance region.

1. Cayor or the western plains

This region has a remarkably smooth coastline behind which lies a dune belt which extends inland for about 24km (15 miles). Sand dunes which may rise to over 40m (130ft) are the characteristic landforms and in the northern part, these dunes are separated by marshy freshwater depressions called *naiyes*. In this relatively dry coastal area, water for the *naiyes* comes from dews and intermittent streams. In the southern part of the coast extending down to Cape Verde, the depressions, which are frequently inundated by the sea, contain saline water.

Around Thies, there is a small upland called the Thies Plateau with a bold western scarp which is about 60m (200ft) high. The relief effect of the scarp results in Thies having 70mm (3in.) of rain more than the coastal port-town of Dakar. A few extinct offshore volcanoes occur in the region of Dakar and have since been joined to the mainland by sandy beaches.

Away from the coast the region consists of an undulating sandstone plain which is slightly more than 30m (100ft) above sea level. Numerous old dunes which lie in a north-east to south-west direction appear in many places. It is a rather dry region (250–400mm or 10–16 in. of rain p.a.) which supports only Sahel grassland vegetation. There are no perennial streams and water is in short supply for most of the year.

2. The Ferlo Desert

This region is similar in appearance to the western plains but it is a bit higher in elevation and is much drier. Most of it is uninhabited because of lack of surface water, but there are numerous dry valleys along which water may be found near the surface, but elsewhere water is obtained from deep borings of 45–75m (148–203ft) deep. Most villages are located close to these dry valleys. But wherever water is available from deep wells, the interfluves are cultivated with groundnuts.

Along the eastern end of this desert region the land rises abruptly in the area of the Faleme Valley to mark the beginning of an upland region which forms the upper Gambia Basin. The two important rivers draining the region are the upper Ferlo and upper Sine, both of which are seasonal streams.

3. The Senegal Valley

From the source of the River Senegal in the Futa Jallon Highlands right down to the upstream end of the Ile a Morfil (Fig. 29.1), the Senegal Valley consists of a narrow belt along both sides of the river. At the point where the river divides to enclose the Ile a Morfil, which measures 480km (300 miles) long and has an average width of 13km (8 miles), it flows through a rather open valley which often suffers from extensive annual floods. Throughout this stretch the river is characterized by braided channels, most of which remain dry except during the annual flood season.

Richard Toll is the head of the Senegal Delta, below which the river breaks up into several tributaries especially when in flood. The Delta is usually referred to as the Oualo region and is characterized by innumerable abandoned or dry river courses, swamps and old sand dunes. Along the coast the swamps are saline and provide a major source of salt for which the town of Gandiole is noted. Much of the floodplain areas of the Oualo and the Ile a Morfil have been irrigated for rice and millet cultivation.

The Senegal Estuary at St Louis has since been blocked by the Langue de Barbarie, a long sandspit which extends southwards for about 32km (20 miles) below St Louis. This sandspit is a major factor in the decline of the ancient port-town of St Louis.

In the early days of French penetration, the Senegal River was the original route into the hinterland, but its importance has since diminished following the construction of the railway from St Louis to Kayes. Podor is now the head of all-season navigation for river steamers from St Louis but above Podor navigation is possible only during the high-water season (mid-August to late September) when large river steamers can go up to Kayes.

4. The Upper Gambia Basin

The highest land area in Senegal appears in this region which has a general elevation of over 90m (300ft), with some peaks rising over 360m (1,200ft). As the northern extension of the Futa Jallon Highlands of Guinea, the region is characterized by extensive patches of lateritic soils which support a poor vegetation of savanna woodland. This is a small and sparsely settled region with rather poor soils except along the river valleys and hill slopes which support denser vegetation.

5. The Saloum-Casamance region

This is a low-lying region which is drained by three important rivers—the Saloum, the Gambia and the Casamance. The small independent state of Gambia (see Chapter 18) forms a small part of this region of southern rivers, which are characterized by broad, flat floodplains. This region marks the beginning of the *ria* (drowned valley) coast which continues south into Sierra Leone. The Saloum Estuary is the first important *ria* and consists of an old drowned river valley. The estuary has been silting rapidly with the result that the river now enters the sea through many channels which enclose salt flats called *tannes*, which are now being desalted to provide good rice lands.

The Gambia Valley is discussed in a separate chapter, but is similar in many ways to the drowned valley of the Casamance which is the wettest part of Senegal. The lower part of the valley consists of low marshy areas which support a dense growth of mangroves but the upper reaches of the river consist of more rugged country in which steep-sided valleys separate large areas of bare lateritic surfaces (*bowal*), similar to those in the Futa Jallon Highlands of Guinea.

CLIMATE

The wettest part of the country is along the coast of the Saloum-Casamance region which has a monsoon-type climate with a rainfall of about 1,620mm (64in.) per annum at Ziguinchor, and this may be compared

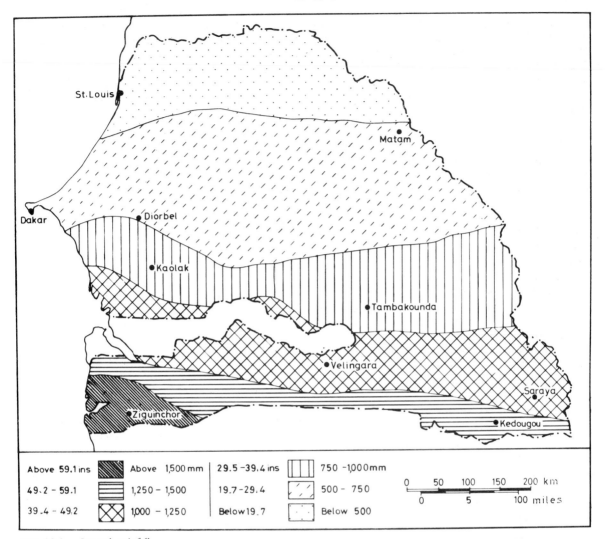

Above 59.1 ins	◤ Above 1,500 mm	29.5 - 39.4 ins	‖‖ 750 - 1,000 mm
49.2 - 59.1	≡ 1,250 - 1,500	19.7 - 29.4	⫽ 500 - 750
39.4 - 49.2	⊠ 1,000 - 1,250	Below 19.7	⬚ Below 500

0   50   100   150   200 km
0   5   100 miles

FIG. 29.2—Senegal: rainfall

with only 580mm (23in.) for Dakar, which is located in a much drier coastal area. In general the rainfall decreases northwards, St Louis having only 380mm (15in.) of rain per annum, but Tambacounda, which is an inland town in the south-east of the country, receives as much as 1,010mm (40in.) of rain.

In the south the rainy season is much longer (May-October) and the rains start much earlier. August is everywhere the rainiest month when as much as half the annual rainfall of Dakar, St Louis and many other stations are recorded. There is no break in the rains and so the country has a one-maximum rainfall regime even along the coast. Usually the rain falls in heavy showers during the afternoon, but along the coast much of the rain comes at night.

Senegal suffers from extreme variability in the onset of the rainy season and the amount of rainfall per annum. St Louis, for example, had only 125mm

(5in.) of rain in 1903 and 660mm (26in.) in 1912. Often this extreme variability leads to crop failures and severe famines. (See Fig. 29.2.)

Temperatures remain high throughout the year but the coast is much cooler, more equable and more pleasant than the interior. Dakar has a mean daily maximum of 29°C (85°F) and a daily minimum of 22°C (71°F) as compared with 36°C (96°F) and 20°C (68°F) respectively for the interior town of Tambacounda. Irregular variations in the temperature are rare and occur only during sudden thunderstorms. The relative humidity is highest in the west and south, that is, nearest to the coast.

VEGETATION

Except for the Casamance coastal area which has a dense forest vegetation similar to the rain forest, the

253

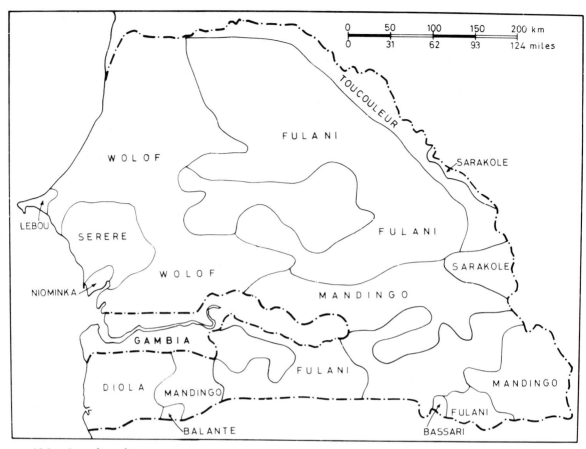

FIG. 29.3—Senegal: peoples

rest of the country has grass-woodland vegetation in the south, and thorn scrub in the north. The higher rainfall of the Casamance coast supports a forest vegetation much of which has been destroyed by man in the course of preparing farmland. The oil palm is a common tree in the area, which also has considerable stands of the African teak and the silk cotton tree, both of which grow to well over 18m (60ft) in height. The estuary of the Casamance and the immediate coastland supports mangrove swamp-forest, large areas of which have been cleared and reclaimed for cultivating swamp rice.

Grass-woodland vegetation covers the southern half of the country, with a northward bend in the west due to oceanic influence. Grassland is continuous over the area but here and there are to be found tree clumps or large trees standing individually. The most common species are the African locust bean, (*Acacia sieberiana*) the borassus palm and the gingerbread plum or pomme du Cayor (*Parinari macrophylla*). Most of the trees shed their leaves during the dry season when bush fires also destroy the patched grass vegetation.

The area lying north of the line joining Kayar (north of Dakar) to Kidira is covered by thorn bush, which supports various species of *acacia* some of which yield gum Arabic. Annual bush fires and over-grazing have greatly modified the natural vegetation of this belt, which is now characterized by tufted grass in the more open areas.

Aspects of the population

Senegal has a population of about 4.2 million occupying an area of 196,200 sq.km (76,000 sq. miles). The most numerous tribal group consists of the Wolofs (1,103,000) who occupy the Cayor plains. Almost all Wolofs are Muslims and amongst them are to be found the most prosperous merchants, contractors and groundnut farmers in the country. The Serers, who number over 600,000, live in western Senegal and are related in many ways to the Wolofs. The striking thing about the Serers is the fact that they are a settled farming group who also breed livestock, and are therefore in a position to practise mixed farming. The northern peoples include the Fulanis

(400,000), the Malinkes (84,000) and the Moors (30,000). (See Fig. 29.3.)

Most of the people live in rural villages and the main areas of population concentration are the lower Casamance Basin and the southern part of the western plains. The Senegal Delta, the Ferlo Desert and the upper Gambia Basin are very sparsely settled with an average density of fewer than 8 persons per sq. km (20 per sq. mile) (Fig. 29.4).

The seasonal migration of groundnut farmers into the country from Mali and Guinea is now an important feature of the population of Senegal. These migrant farmers settle to work as labourers or to grow groundnuts on land leased to them by the local people. It is estimated that in some years, the number of migrants may exceed 60,000 and that about 40 per cent of these originate from Mali, 35 per cent from Guinea and the rest from other parts of Senegal.

AGRICULTURE

Food-crop production and export agriculture

Agriculture, that is, farming and animal rearing, provides employment for more than 85 per cent of the working population. As in other parts of West Africa, it is possible to distinguish an export-based agriculture from agricultural production for internal exchange. In Senegal, however, export agriculture is synonymous with groundnut production which is often carried out at the expense of producing enough food for internal consumption. There is a considerable diversity in the staple food crops but although there has been a considerable increase in the output of the various staple foods, the country still spends much money on the import of foodstuffs like rice which is also produced locally.

Food-crop production

The most important staple foods are millet, rice, guinea corn and cassava which are all produced in small farms owned and operated by local peasants. Groundnuts, which are the main export crop are also an important source of food for the people, but millet is by far the most important foodstuff. It is usually grown in rotation with groundnuts. In the wetter south, guinea corn is more important than

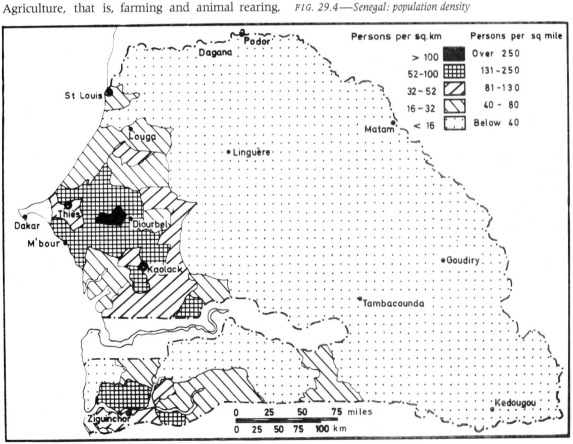

FIG. 29.4—*Senegal: population density*

millet and in the Casamance area the dominant food crop is rice, of which both the upland and swamp varieties are grown. In addition to these main staples, most farmers also grow vegetables on their compound lands.

Over-dependence on the monoculture of groundnuts has been a major source of concern to the government whose fears were justified between 1966 and 1969 when there were three poor harvests in a row owing to bad weather conditions. Production fell from 1,011,000 tons in 1965/6 to 786,000 tons in 1966/7, 834,000 tons in 1967/8 and as low as 623,000 tons in 1968/9. Crop failure during this period was accompanied by declining producer prices and in consequence many farmers returned to the production of food crops. The result was a record production of staple food crops so that in 1968 the country produced 86,000 tons of maize as compared with 28,000 tons ten years earlier while the corresponding output of rice during the period increased from 63,000 tons to 137,000 tons. But despite the great increase in rice production, Senegal was still the largest importer of rice in West Africa in 1974. The country is, however, aiming to be self-sufficient in rice by 1978.

Groundnuts and other export crops

In 1970, groundnuts still accounted for more than 80 per cent of the export earnings of Senegal, which is the fourth largest world-producer of the crop after India, China and Nigeria (see Fig. 29.5). The soil and climate are good for the crops but as indicated earlier unfavourable weather conditions may result in very poor harvests while over-cultivation has resulted in impoverished soils in the older areas of cultivation (between St Louis and Dakar).

The first groundnut exports date back to 1840 when the crop was in great demand by French soap manufacturers. As in Nigeria the improvement of transportation resulted in rapid expansion of the crop; this time it was the opening in 1885 of the St Louis-Dakar railway and much later of feeder roads. Today the most important producing area is the Kaolack district which produces about 50 per cent of the country's output.

Production is controlled by peasant farmers cultivating small family holdings but mechanical cultivation has been tried in a few areas, including the Sefa district and the sparsely settled area around Boulel. Most of the labour used in cultivating and harvesting the crop in the Kaolack district are seasonal migrants from the Republic of Guinea.

The recent decline in groundnut production has been due partly to unfavourable climatic conditions but largely to the decline by up to 20 per cent in the producer prices paid between the 1966/7 and the 1969/70 season. The consequent switch to food production by many farmers may appear to be a welcome development but the government is worried about the loss of revenue resulting from the decline in the production of the country's main source of external exchange earnings. The government therefore decided to try to remedy the situation as from 1970 by cutting the price of fertilizers and by increasing the producer prices.

All groundnuts produced were exported with shells up till the early years of the Second World War when the crop was shelled in order to save cargo space. Later, small oil-extracting mills were established at Kaolack, Diourbel, Ziguinchor and Lounga in addition to the earlier mill established at Dakar in 1924.

In recent years the production of cotton and sugar for export has been stepped up but climatic conditions have not been very favourable.

The Richard Toll irrigation scheme

The Richard Toll project, which is sometimes called the Delta Irrigation Scheme, was initially intended to be used for producing cotton on a commercial scale. Shortage of imported rice during the Second World War, however, prompted the government to direct that the area be used for rice cultivation. The scheme, which was completed at a cost of about ₦ 11.00 million, consists of a barrage built in 1948 at a point near Richard Toll to impound flood waters and to prevent the penetration upstream of salt water from the delta into the tributaries of the Senegal River. The water impounded behind the barrage is used for irrigating about 5,600 hectares (14,000 acres) of land from which some 16,000 tons of rice is produced, mostly through mechanized farming. Production averages just over two tons per hectare and is considered to be low for an irrigating scheme.

Livestock rearing

The cattle population of Senegal is about 2.7 million while the combined sheep and goat population is about 2.8 million. There are also about 190,000 donkeys and 202,000 horses. The greatest concentration of cattle is in the area around Kaolack where the Serer cattle-rearers are also settled groundnut farmers, not nomads as in many other parts of West Africa. In the northern parts of Senegal, the cattle population is controlled by the nomadic Cattle Fulani.

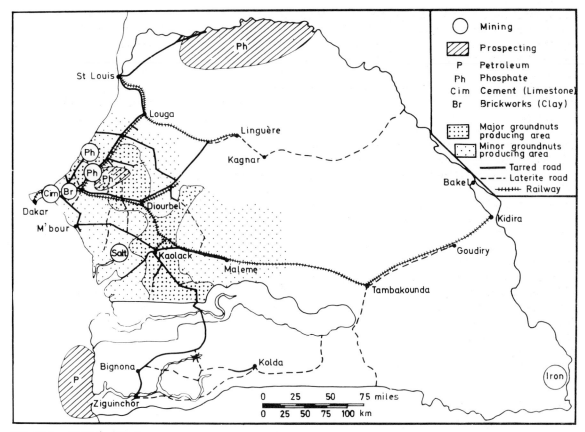

FIG. 29.5—Senegal: economy

MINERALS AND MINING

Senegal is not rich in minerals. Limestone is worked near Rufisque where it is manufactured into cement. Phosphate is the most important mineral and is worked near Thies where the annual output exceeds 700,000 tons. Other minerals worked include basalt and laterite which are quarried for road-making and titanium-ilmenite (see Fig. 29.5).

INDUSTRIAL DEVELOPMENT

Until the late 1960s when Nigeria became the leading industrial country in West Africa, Senegal was the most highly industrialized country in the area. This situation was made possible by the fact that the Dakar industrial area catered for the needs of all of French-speaking West Africa (20 million), of which Dakar was the political capital until 1958. The break up of former French West Africa into small independent countries has meant a loss of much of the market hinterland of Dakar and other industrial areas in Senegal. Large-scale industrial development has been greatly slowed down for this reason.

Some of the more important industrial establishments include food and drink, that is, the manufacture of beer and soft drinks, human and animal foods from groundnuts, and fish products. The extraction and refining of groundnut oil is a major industrial enterprise and almost the entire Senegal crop is fed into local mills and refineries which also produce valuable fuel from the shell waste. Most of the oil is exported to France, while a considerable amount is manufactured into soap and detergents.

Other important industries include an oil refinery near Dakar, textiles at Dakar and Richard Toll, a steel mill using scrap-iron and a chemical fertilizer plant using locally quarried phosphate rocks. Some farm machinery is produced locally and so are paper products. Shoes, cigarettes, furniture and plastic wares are also made in Dakar, which also undertakes ship repairs.

TRANSPORT

As in Nigeria, the earliest means of penetration into the interior was by river, but today the road and the railway have become by far the most important

257

PLATE 91 —St Louis Bridge in Senegal with Wolof woman at centre

means of transport in the country (see Fig. 29.5). The 260km (164 miles) St Louis-Dakar railway built in 1885 was the first in West Africa and was an important factor in the expansion of groundnut cultivation in the Cayor region. The 1,290km (804 miles) Dakar-Niger line connecting Dakar with Bamako and Koulikoro in Mali Republic has since replaced the Senegal River as the main means of export of produce from the hinterland. It serves the groundnut areas of western and south-central Senegal and has since halted the diversion of groundnut exports through the Gambia River to Banjul.

No more than 800km (500 miles) out of the existing 11,200km (7,000 miles) of roads have been tarred. Traffic on the roads is often delayed by the poor condition of the laterite surfaced roads, which may become impassable during the rainy season.

Senegal has thirteen airports of which Dakar is the only international airport. St Louis and Ziguinchor have relatively large airports of the class B grade; but the remaining ten airfields are only suitable for use by small planes.

SETTLEMENT

The capital and industrial city of Dakar

Dakar, the capital of Senegal, and formerly of all French West Africa has a population of over 580,000. Its importance as a great seaport started with the opening in 1885 of the Dakar-St Louis railway and its strategic location at the most westerly point of Africa (nearest to South America) has been an important factor in the large volume of ships and aircraft passing through its ports. Today Dakar has the largest and most modern seaport in West Africa. About 33 ships can be accommodated in the port, which has 4.8km (3 miles) of quays and 225 hectares (555 acres) of protected waters. The port is largely artificial and is enclosed by concrete breakwaters which provide effective shelter from local winds. (See Fig. 29.6.)

Its strategic location has made it an important naval point and its international airport at Yoff is one of the three largest in West Africa. The railway terminal is kept busy by the large volume of passenger and cargo arriving daily by air and sea. The city itself is well-planned and neat and appears more like a French city than an African town. Unlike in Lagos and Accra where Europeans come and go, the French live permanently in Dakar, thanks to the climate which they consider to be good. Multi-racial schools are common and Frenchmen own and operate shops, hotels and restaurants.

In addition to its administrative and commercial functions, Dakar is an important industrial centre. As in Lagos, the main industrial estate is located near the port and rail terminus. Some of the major industrial works include three large groundnut oil refineries, factories producing soap, shoes, beer and soft drinks, a textile mill and cigarette factories. There is a large shipyard for repairing both naval and mercantile ships. The chief exports of the port of Dakar are groundnuts and groundnut oil. (See plate 90.)

Other towns

The other import towns of Senegal include St Louis, Rufisque, Kaolack, and Thies.

St Louis (81,000) was formerly the main port and capital of Senegal and served as the base of French colonization of West Africa. It was a major slave trade port and later handled the bulk of the interior trade before the coming of the railways. In recent years, the trade of the port has declined to no more than 2,755 tons (1962) as compared with 100,000

tons in 1920. The town remains the most important West African collecting and distributing centre for fish, now a major resource for sustaining the town. Like Dakar, its urban landscape is like a small European town in an African setting (plate 91).

Rufisque (50,000) is an old town near Dakar. It was formerly the main port of export for groundnuts until Dakar and Kaolack replaced it during the Second World War, when the port suffered a marked decline. Today the economy has been revived following the establishment of several industries, including a cement factory, a tannery and shoe factory, groundnut oil refineries and pharmaceutical works.

Kaolack (96,000) is now the main groundnut port

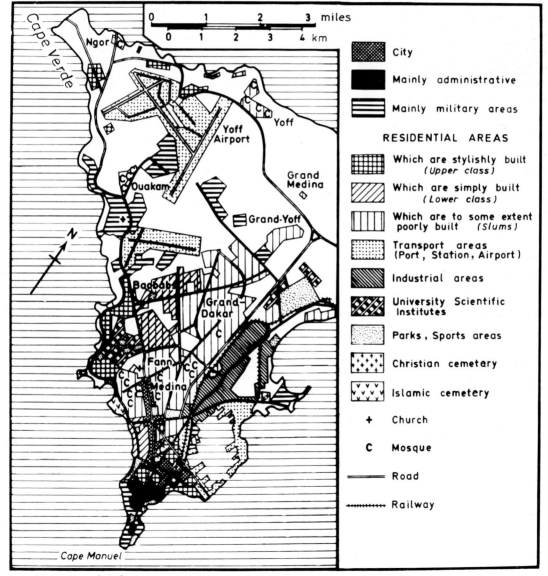

FIG. 29.6—Senegal: Dakar

Table 41—Trade balance of Senegal (million francs CFA)

	1960	1965	1966	1967	1968	1969	1970	1971	1972	1973
Imports	42,500	39,600	38,300	38,900	44,500	51,300	53,600	60,600	70,300	79,800
Exports	27,900	31,700	36,800	33,900	37,400	31,900	42,200	34,700	54,400	43,240
Balance	−14,600	−7,900	−1,500	−5,000	−7,100	−19,400	−11,400	−25,900	−15,900	−36,560

Note: 1,000 francs CFA = ₦ 3.00

of the country, owing to its proximity by road and rail to the new producing centres of the western plains. It has a large groundnut oil processing factory and the largest salt works in West Africa.

Thies (91,000) is the main town of the western plains and is linked to Dakar by a double-track railway. It is an important groundnut market and a growing industrial centre.

EXTERNAL TRADE

Groundnuts and groundnut oil dominate the export trade of Senegal, and practically all the shipments (85 per cent) go to France, which is also the main source of her imports. Other exports include phosphates and titanium concentrates, while the main imports are wheat, rice, sugar, petroleum products, machinery, textiles and motor vehicles and spares. About one-third by value of her imports consists of food, drink and tobacco, a rather undesirable situation for a country which has an unfavourable balance of trade as shown in Table 41. Government efforts to expand agricultural production and import-substitution industries are aimed at improving the unfavourable balance of payments.

Senegal imports various manufactured goods from West Germany, Italy, the Netherlands and the United States of America, as well as from France. Trade with other countries in West Africa remains insignificant, the value of exports to Nigeria being only 15 million francs CFA in 1968 as compared with 24,769 million to France and 1,600 million to the Netherlands.

Chapter 30—Sierra Leone

PLATE 92—*Clouds near Bunumbu, Sierra Leone, on the forest savanna margin*

The name Sierra Leone, which means Lion Mountains, was originally given to the mountains of the Freetown Peninsula, which is the only area of coastal mountains in West Africa west of the Cameroon Mountains. Later, the name was extended to the whole country, which came under British rule in 1896. British interest in the country, however, dates back to 1792 when a settlement for freed slaves was established at Freetown. In 1808, Britain proclaimed the whole Sierra Leone Peninsula together with Tasso Island, the Banana Islands, York Island and Bonthe a crown colony. Freetown itself became a major naval base for tracking down slave ships and became the main settlement for those liberated slaves whose homeland could not be traced. The mixed population of this peninsula remains distinct from the hinterland people who, for many years, were very hostile and suspicious of the descendants of ex-slaves, who are called creoles.

In 1896, Britain established the Protectorate of Sierra Leone with an area of about 72,000 sq.km (27,669 sq. miles) as compared with only 660 sq.km (256 sq. miles) for the crown colony. Later both territories were united to form the Colony and Protectorate of Sierra Leone which became independent of British rule in April 1961. The first decade of independence proved to be very trying and featured three military coups. In 1970, however, constitutional government was restored and in 1971, Sierra Leone became a republic within the British Commonwealth of nations.

Sierra Leone is a small country with an area of

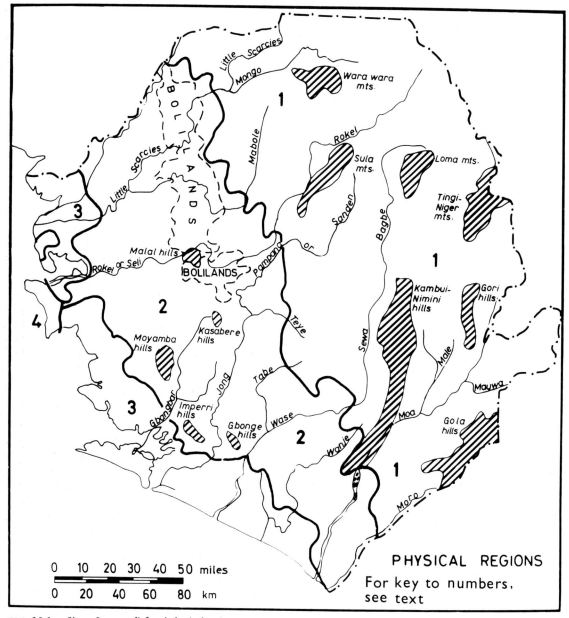

FIG. 30.1—Sierra Leone: relief and physical regions

about 72,000 sq.km (27,669 sq. miles), which is a bit smaller than the Kwara State of Nigeria. Its population of about 2.9 million in 1973 is about the same as that of Kwara State (2.4 million in 1963). Like other West African countries, Sierra Leone is inhabited by people from many ethnic groups. The country has since adopted a new currency, the leone which is equivalent to fifty pence sterling, in place of the old colonial currency based on the British pound, shillings and pence. However, English remains the official language.

The country is located on the south-west coast of West Africa between latitudes 6°55'N. and 10°N. and between 10°16'W. and 13°18'W. As a former British-administered territory, it has greater economic, social and cultural ties with distant Ghana and Nigeria than with the neighbouring countries of Guinea, Ivory Coast, Mali and Liberia.

PHYSICAL REGIONS

There are four distinct physical regions in the country

(Fig. 30.1). These are: 1) the interior plateaux and mountains, 2) the central plains, 3) the coast and coastal swamps, 4) Freetown or Colony Peninsula.

1. The interior plateaux and mountains

The greater part of this region consists of a plateau lying between 425–610m (1,400–2,000ft) above sea level. The entire area, which is covered with granitic rocks, is an extension of the Guinea Highlands. Important rivers which rise from this region include the Mongo, Rockel, Baffi and Bagbe, all of which have cut very deep valleys through the plateau surface. Inselberg landscape is characteristic of the plateau, much of which is covered with lateritic crust. A number of hill masses called mountains rise above the general level of the plateau, the most prominent being the Loma Mountains, the Wara Wara Mountains, the Sula Mountains and the Gingi-Niger Mountains. The Sula Mountains contain large reserves of iron ore which are as yet untapped.

2. The central plains

The land surface varies in elevation from 30–215m (100–700ft) in elevation, although some residual hills rise to heights of well over 305m (1,000ft) above sea level. The river valleys are deeply incised with little development of floodplains, although their terraces are quite extensive. With the exception of a few high hills which rise abruptly above the plains, the interfluves are rather flat and extensive. Some of the more prominent hills include the Malal Hills, the Kasabere Hills and the Gbonge Hills. An elongated area of grassland swamps occurs in the northern part of this region, in the area lying between Kukuna and the Malal Hills. These swamps, which are called *bolilands* also occur between the Malal Hills and the Kasabere Hills. They consist of old river channels which are dry except during the rainy season when they become flooded.

3. The coast and coastal swamps

The coastal swamps cover an area with an average width of 32km (20 miles) from the coastline and are usually flooded during the rainy season. The region is an area of young sedimentary rocks and is much cut up by tidal creeks and river estuaries, the banks of which are colonized by dense stands of mangrove forests. The coastline itself shows clear evidence of submergence and is very much indented except along the beach bar east of Sherbro Island.

In several places, beach bars form the actual coast and in some places such bars enclose a lagoon, the longest of which lies immediately east of the River Jong estuary.

Evidence of uplift is also available in the raised beaches of the Bullom Peninsula and the Freetown Peninsula. It appears that in the distant past, the entire coastal area of Sierra Leone was under the sea with the exception of the coastal mountains of the Freetown Peninsula. At a later date the entire coastline was uplifted, giving rise to raised beaches in the highland areas. This uplift was later followed by a slight lowering of the land when the low-lying parts of the coast became submerged, giving rise to the many river estuaries which characterize the coastline of Sierra Leone. In the Sierra Leone Peninsula, the raised beaches lie at an elevation of 15–60m (50–197ft) above the present sea level and are well represented in the Kissy Flats behind Freetown harbour and in the area east of Kent.

4. Freetown or Colony Peninsula

This unique region of coastal mountains is the only one of its type in West Africa. The peninsula is about 40km (25 miles) long and has a width which varies from 16 to 20km (10–12 miles). It is built on very resistant rocks and rises very steeply from the sea as can be seen at Freetown. The highest peaks include Picket Hill (875m or 2,872ft), Leicester Peak (585m or 1,920ft) and Sugar Loaf (75m or 245ft). A number of raised beaches which provide sites for settlements like Freetown, Kissy and Kosso Town appear at the base of the coastal cliffs. The mountain range is highly dissected by numerous fast-flowing streams which have cut very deep and steep-sided valleys. Level land for settlement is highly restricted and much of the inaccessible uplands is given over to forest reserves.

Drainage characteristics

There are nine main river systems, all of which drain directly into the Atlantic Ocean in a north-east to south-west direction. The main rivers are the Great Scarcies, the Little Scarcies, the Rockel, the Jong, the Sewa and the Moa. The drainage basins are all small, the largest being the Sewa (14,150 sq.km or 5,460 sq. miles) followed by the Little Scarcies (12,880 sq.km or 4,970 sq. miles) and the Rockel (10,620 sq. km or 4,100 sq. miles).

In their upper and middle courses, the rivers have deeply incised valleys and almost all of them swing westward as they leave the interior plateau to enter the central plains. Submergence of the coast has caused the drowned estuaries of all rivers north of the Sherbro Island while the deeply incised valleys are due to a subsequent uplift of the coast. There is

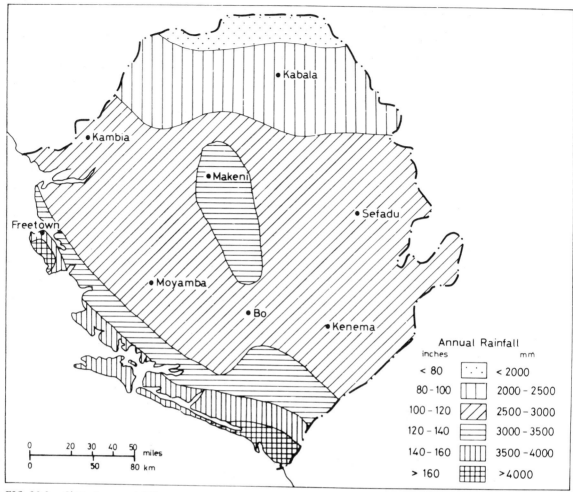

FIG. 30.2—Sierra Leone: rainfall

also a marked seasonal fluctuation in the water level of the upper courses, which are usually very shallow during the dry season. The drowned lower courses experience a tidal range of 2–4m (7–12ft) and are usually flooded during the rainy season.

As with other rivers in Africa, the upper courses of Sierra Leone rivers are characterized by rapids and waterfalls which, together with the seasonal fluctuation in volume, restrict navigability to the lower courses. Fortunately, navigation of the lower courses is assisted by tides.

CLIMATE AND VEGETATION

Climate

Sierra Leone has a tropical climate with a marked dry season (November–April) and a rainy season (May–October). The highest rainfall occurs in the Freetown or Colony Peninsula where the coastal

mountains lie at right angles to the direction of the South-west Monsoon winds which bring most of the rains to the country. Freetown, which is located at the foot of these mountains receives 3,500mm (138in.) a year, while Regent which is located 300m (1,000ft) above sea level receives 5,210mm (205in.). The remaining parts of the coastal areas receive a high annual rainfall of over 3,560mm (140in.) rising to over 4,060mm (160in.) in the Sulima district which is located in the extreme south-east of the country.

In general, the total annual rainfall decreases with distance away from the coast (Fig. 30.2), except that the highest plateau areas such as Tonkolili have a much higher rainfall than the surrounding plains. The eastern part of the interior plateaux receives the lowest rainfall which is usually not much less than 2,160mm (85in.). Kaballa, which is located in the far north receives 2,240mm (88in.) a year and this may be compared with 1,830mm (72in.) for Lagos.

Violent tornadoes and storms herald the onset and end of the rainy season. July is the wettest month along the coast, but in the far north, the rainiest month is September. The two-maxima regime which is characteristic of southern Nigeria is only obvious in the south-east where Sulima has a short dry season in August.

There is very little rain during the dry season, which is under the influence of the dry harmattan wind. Temperatures are relatively cooler when the harmattan blows, but the coolest months are the rainy season months of May to October. In contrast the highest temperatures are recorded just before the onset of the rains when the weather is rather unpleasant. The daily maximum temperature for Freetown hovers around 27°C (80°F) throughout the year, the annual range being 2.8°C (5°F) as compared with 5.8°C (10.3°F) at Yengema, near Sefadu.

Vegetation

There are three main types of vegetation in Sierra Leone (Fig. 30.3). These are: 1) swamp (coastal and inland), 2) tropical forest, 3) savanna or tropical grassland. The most extensive areas of swamp occur along the coast where there are two classes of swamp, namely the mangrove swamp and the freshwater swamp. Mangrove swamps occur mainly along the river estuaries, the broadest areas being those of the Scarcies the Rockel and the Sherbro Rivers. In many areas, but particularly along the estuaries of the Scarcies, these swamps have been cleared for rice cultivation.

Freshwater swamps occur immediately behind the saline mangrove swamps. The vegetation here consists of grass since the area suffers from alternate flooding and drought. Like the mangrove

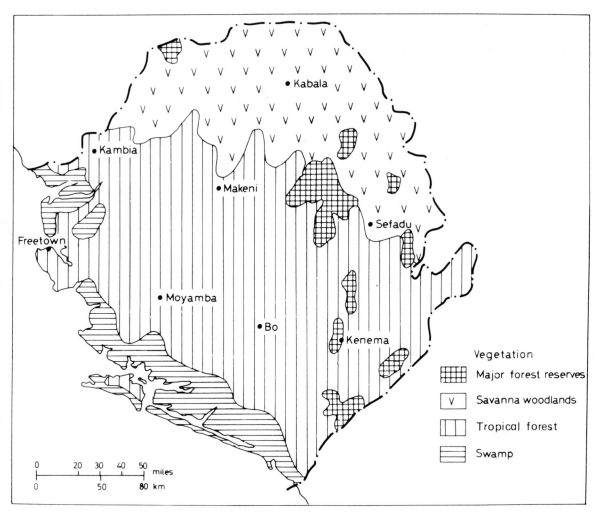

FIG. 30.3—Sierra Leone: vegetation

swamp, these freshwater swamps have been developed as rice fields. The third class of swamps are the *bolilands* or inland swamps which usually occur along the banks of rivers. These inland swamps are caused by river floods and may remain for several months before drying out towards the end of January. The typical vegetation is parkland type with short grass and scattered trees.

Away from the coastal swamps, the vegetation consists of forest and secondary bush. The small area of high forest which covers less than 5 per cent of the country and of secondary forest (20 per cent of the land area) is strange in view of the high annual rainfall of over 2,160mm (85in.) all over the country. Human interference in the course of clearing the forest for farmland is thought to be mainly responsible for the small area of forest vegetation. Today the small areas of high forest are restricted to the forest reserves on the eastern ridges and in the southeast.

About one-third of the country is covered with savanna vegetation which is still encroaching on existing areas of secondary forest. The most extensive areas of grassland occur in the far north in the region of the interior plateau. (See plate 92.)

AGRICULTURE

Farming is by far the most important occupation of the people of Sierra Leone, and fortunately the rainfall is everywhere adequate to permit farming without irrigation. The farm year begins in March when the bush is cleared and burnt. The swamps are hoed and weeded in March and April when rice is also sown in nurseries. In May and June, rice is transplanted to the swamps while upland farmers cultivate crops like ginger, groundnuts and millet. The harvest season begins in late July when early rice, millet and groundnuts are harvested but the main harvest season on upland farms begins in October and continues till January.

Farming practices in the northern, southern and eastern provinces are very similar while those in the western provinces are strikingly different. In the first three groups of provinces, farmers cultivate both for internal exchange and for the export market. There are two distinct types of farmland. These are the upland farms on which crops like upland rice, millet, groundnuts, cassava and vegetables are grown under the system of the rotation of bush fallow; and swampland cultivation in which swamp rice is the chief crop. On upland farms, upland rice is the main crop; but is usually inter-cropped with other crops including cassava, maize, cotton and beans.

Tree crops such as oil palms, cocoa, coffee and kola are also grown on upland farms, Piassava is the only other crop produced along with swamp rice on the swamps. In the western provinces, agriculture is restricted to the river valleys of the interior plateaux and here, cassava is by far the most important crop.

Both food crops and export crops are produced on small-sized holdings operated by local peasants. Mechanized farming is highly restricted and is largely associated with swamp rice cultivation.

Staple food crops

About 60 per cent by value of the total agricultural output of Sierra Leone is accounted for by staple food crops, of which rice is by far the most important. The other major food crops are cassava, millet and groundnuts, all of which are usually cultivated in small peasant holdings. (See Fig. 30.4.)

Rice is cultivated almost throughout the country, and in 1969 about 384,000 tons of which two-thirds were swamp rice, were produced. The other third was upland rice which is grown as a first crop on cleared farms before the land is cropped with other crops like millet, groundnuts and cassava. Upland rice has been grown for many centuries and is still widely grown in the interior provinces. The present policy of the government's Department of Agriculture is to discourage the cultivation of upland rice which has already caused much deforestation and soil erosion in the country.

Swamp rice was first cultivated on the mangrove swamps of the Scarcies during the last decade of the nineteenth century. It gives higher yields per hectare (about 990–1,680kg per hectare as compared with about 568kg for upland rice), and its expansion means the addition of more cultivable land through the reclamation and use of more swamps which were formerly uncultivated. It is estimated that there are still about 200,000 hectares (500,000 acres) of suitable swamps, including 120,000 hectares (300,000 acres) of seasonal flooded grasslands, awaiting developing.

Large-scale cultivation of swamp rice under government supervision started before the Second World War and by 1950 rice cultivation had been extended to all the areas of mangrove swamp along the coast. The area under upland rice decreased by as much as 20 per cent between 1947 and 1957 following the introduction of the mechanical rice scheme in 1949. There are now zones in which tractor units operate and farmers may hire tractors to plough and harrow swamps at 12 leones and 2 leones per hectare respectively (1 leone = 1 naira).

The most extensive areas of reclaimed mangrove swamps for rice cultivation are in the estuaries of the

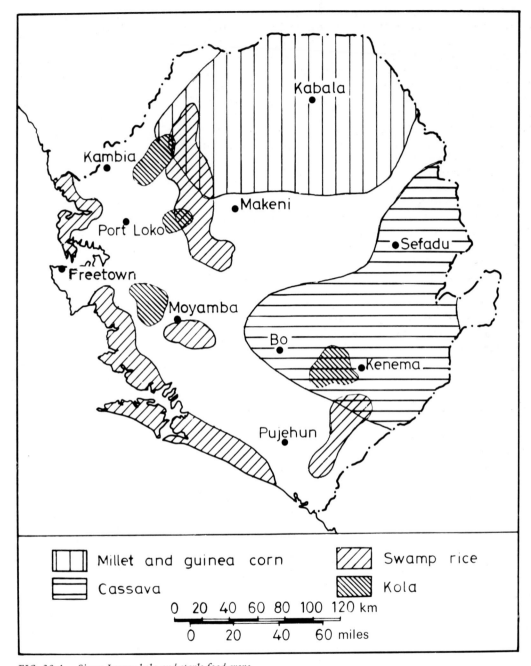

FIG. 30.4—Sierra Leone: kola and staple food crops

Great and Little Scarcies and the Port Loko district. But initial clearing of the coastal swamps is a very difficult job as compared with that of preparing the inland swamps or *bolilands*. The result is that there are now more extensive areas under swamp rice in the inland districts of Makeni, Bo, Kenema and Kailahun than in the mangrove swamp areas along the coast. The coastal swamps are, however, much more fertile and give much higher yields per hectare than the inland freshwater swamps. On average, the size of rice farms in the country is about 1.5 hectares.

Most of the rice crop is milled in small local mills although the government has now established a number of large mills. There are also many buying and selling stations as well as storage facilities for pro-

267

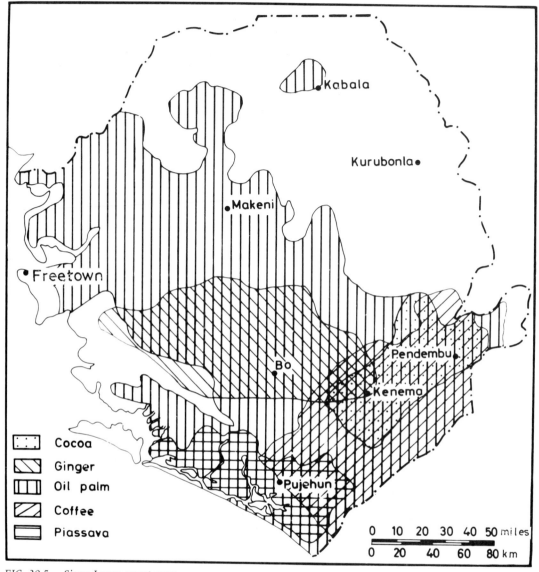

FIG. 30.5—Sierra Leone: export crops

cessed rice. Unfortunately, although there are vast areas of suitable rice lands awaiting development, Sierra Leone still imports a considerable quantity of rice, the figure for 1963 being 28,960 tons. The reason for this is that the rice farming population has decreased considerably as a result of the diversion of labour to the mining of diamond and lately of iron ore.

Cassava is grown throughout the country, as in Nigeria, although the most important areas of cultivation are in the central plains. The crop is usually planted on land which has already been cropped with rice and when the crop is harvested, the land is normally left under fallow for a few years.

Millet is the crop of the north. It is grown either in areas that are too dry for upland rice or as a second crop on land which has already been cropped with rice. In the far north, millet is the major food crop and is usually grown in rotation with groundnuts.

Groundnuts are produced mainly in the Kambia, Bombali and Koinadugu districts of the north and the Kailahun district of eastern Sierra Leone. There is very little for export since the crop is an important item of food for the people of the northern districts.

Export crops

The crops discussed in the last section are grown both for home consumption and for internal exchange, although a small amount of groundnuts are also exported. The oil palm is considered in this section because although palm oil is no longer exported, owing to increasing local demand, almost all the palm kernels are exported. (See Fig. 30.5.)

Oil palm kernels remained the most important export for many years, often accounting for as much as 90 per cent by value of all exports until 1953 when this proportion was greatly reduced following the diamond boom and the increase in iron-ore production. Production declined from 76,000 tons in 1952 to 47,000 tons in 1972, a trend which has been attributed to the loss of labour to mining and other crops. Foreign exchange earnings from palm kernels are however still considerable, amounting to over Le.4 million every year, and the government has embarked on new planting projects on plantations while local farmers are encouraged to plant new improved seedlings, about 100,000 of which are distributed every year.

The oil palm grows almost all over the country, except in the far north, the north-eastern districts and the mangrove swamps. The main oil palm areas are shown in Fig. 30.5. Peasant farmers produce almost all the crop but there is a large government oil palm plantation at Masanki and a few smaller private plantations owned mostly by clan chiefs. New large-scale plantations have been established by the government at Sahn, Kangah and Mange Bureh, but as in Nigeria, it appears that the peasant producer will continue to dominate the scene for very many years.

Raffia palm is the source of piassava, which is an important export commodity. The palm grows in swamps, and production is largely confined to the south-east coastlands, particularly in the Bonthe and Pujehun districts. Piassava is used in the manufacture of brooms and brushes. The leaves of the raffia palm are used in making roofing mats but palm wine which is the most valuable product of the raffia palm in south-eastern Nigeria is not very popular in Sierra Leone.

Cocoa production is limited to the south-east and is largely in the hands of peasant farmers whose cocoa farms rarely exceed 1.5 hectares. Unlike the situation in the Nigerian and Ghanaian cocoa belts, cocoa is a secondary crop in Sierra Leone where farmers in the cocoa-producing areas are more concerned with food-crop cultivation. Annual exports from 1960 to 1970 varied between 3,000 and 5,000 tons (rising to 6,600 tons in 1972), which is insignificant when compared with 470,000 tons for Ghana in 1972 and over 241,000 tons for Nigeria in 1972.

Coffee, like cocoa, is grown in the south-eastern districts. Production increased from 132 tons in 1946 to over 9,500 tons in 1966, declining to 7,500 tons in 1972. The most popular variety is *Robusta* coffee which has virtually replaced the indigenous *Liberica* variety.

Kola nuts, like cocoa and coffee, is a crop of the forest belt and in Sierra Leone the main centres of production are in Moyamba and southern Kono districts. A considerable proportion of the nuts is exported to Gambia and Mali. Kola nuts are also an important item of internal trade between the south where the crop is produced and the north where kola nuts are in great demand by the Fulanis and other northern peoples.

Ginger is mainly produced in Moyamba district, followed by southern Kono and the Freetown Peninsula. The first export was in 1890 and since 1960 the average production has varied between 2,500 and 3,500 tons, making Sierra Leone the largest world producer of this crop. Ginger is used medicinally as well as for making ginger ale, some perfumes and as a spice.

Livestock

Cattle rearing is largely restricted to the northern districts of Bombali and Koinadugu where there are about 200,000 Ndama cattle. Most of the cattle are owned by Fulani herdsmen who lead a semi-nomadic life, migrating in search of grazing and water during the dry season, but settling down to cultivate groundnuts, millet and cassava during the rainy season. Extensive areas of good grassland exist in the central districts of the country, but the inhabitants of these areas are not interested in cattle rearing and it appears that the quickest way to increase the cattle population is to encourage the Fulanis to settle in such areas. At present the country imports much of her meat supply from Guinea.

Sheep, goats and local poultry are kept in almost every part of the country while pigs are found mainly in the western districts.

MINING

Mining is now the leading sector of the economy of Sierra Leone, a situation which started in the mid-1950s when mineral exports became more important than agricultural exports. About 31,100 sq.km (12,000 square miles), or almost half of the country, is covered by mining leases, and mining is by far the most important occupation in terms of employment. The rapid decline in agricultural labour which has affected rice production in particular is caused by the loss of labour to mining. Mining has brought with it the problem of smuggling (of diamonds) which is of major concern to the government and there is also the question of loss of agricultural land to mining in

269

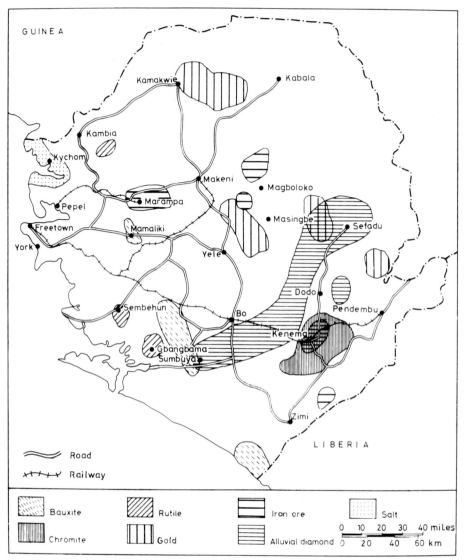

FIG. 30.6—*Sierra Leone: mineral resources*

Table 42—Mineral exports from Sierra Leone

	Quantity Exported ('000 tons) (Diamonds in '000 carats)					Value in '000 Leones				
	1968	1969	1970	1971	1972	1968	1969	1970	1971	1972
Diamonds	1,683	2,020	1,955	1,934	1,846	46,900	61,900	51,000	50,000	5,670
Bauxite	470	420	392	552	682	1,500	1,300	1,500	2,500	3,300
Iron Ore	2,535	2,427	2,427	2,569	2,283	10,500	9,900	10,500	11,400	1,020
Rutile	6	28	44	11	13	n.a*	n.a	n.a	n.a	n.a

*n.a. = not available

some districts. In 1963 mineral exports represented two-thirds by value of the total exports of about Le. 60 million while an additional Le.5 million was paid to the government in the form of mining royalties, taxes and fees. Ten years later, in 1973, mineral exports represented over 74 per cent by value of the total export earnings of Le.106.7 million.

The two most important minerals are diamond and iron ore (see Table 42), and in 1973 these minerals accounted for 60 per cent and 10 per cent respectively of the country's exports by value. Figure 30.6 shows the distribution of the mineral resources of the country.

Diamonds

Diamonds were first discovered in 1930 in the Kono district which is still one of the main producing areas. Production has increased greatly since 1950 and since 1963 Sierra Leone has been the fourth most important world producer of industrial diamonds (producing 5 per cent of the world output in 1970). All the diamonds come from alluvial deposits and about 33,000 people are employed in the diamond industry.

Highly mechanized mining goes on side by side with primitive hand-digging and hand-panning. The Sierra Leone Selection Trust formed in 1935 is the largest mining company, but there is also a large number of private companies. As a result of widespread illicit mining, the government set up in 1956 the Alluvial Diamond Mining Scheme to permit small-scale mining by indigenous people who operate in small groups of about four miners. Most of these small-scale miners work under the tributor system in which they work for a portion of the diamonds won. The recovery rate of tributors is low and much diamond is wasted by this system. A government company, the Diamond Exploration Company, formed in 1960 has been investigating the possibility of reworking some of the areas already exploited by these small-scale miners.

Iron ore

Large deposits of iron ore occur in the Marampa and Tonkolili districts but mining is confined to the Marampa area which is linked by rail to the special iron-ore port of Pepel. Mining is by open-cast methods using large mechanical shovels. The ore contains about 47 per cent iron but is concentrated to about 65 per cent at Marampa before being exported through Pepel. The entire mining operation is controlled by the Sierra Leone Development Company Ltd which also owns the private railway from the mines to the port of Pepel, which is provided with special facilities for loading iron ore.

About 2,800 workers are employed by the company, which exports about 2 million tons of concentrated ore every year. Untapped reserves of iron ore in the country are estimated to be about 100 million tons.

Bauxite

Mining started in 1964 when more than 150,000 tons were produced. Production is at present restricted to the Mokanji Hills deposits which are linked by a good access road to the newly built port of Point Sam (on the Bargu Creek). Mining is by open-cast methods involving the use of mechanical shovels.

Other minerals

The minor minerals of Sierra Leone include chrome ore and rutile. Chrome ore was important between 1937 and 1964, when mining ceased with the closure of the mines. The main producing centre was the Hanga area (near Kenema) and mining was by open-cast as well as by adit methods.

Rutile, the source of titanium, used in aircraft and missiles, is mined near Gbangbama which is located about 24km (15 miles) southwest of the Mokanji Hills bauxite deposits. Production started in 1966 and is controlled by the Sierra Leone Ore and Metal Company, which also owns the bauxite mines at Mokanji Hills.

MANUFACTURING INDUSTRIES

Manufacturing is not yet an important sector of the economy although the government has made considerable efforts to attract private foreign investment in industry so as to reduce expenditure on imported goods. Sierra Leone is rich in industrial raw materials but in addition to lack of capital, the small size of her population does not provide an adequate home market for large-scale manufacturing.

The number and range of manufacturing industries, is, however, increasing and most of the factories are located in the Freetown area where the government has established an industrial zone stretching from Kissy to Wellington. The first factories built just before independence in 1961 included a cigarette factory, a nail factory, a brewery and distillery, an oxygen-producing plant, a paints factory and a fish-canning plant. Industries established since independence include a palm-kernel crushing mill, soap factories, a textile mill, a shoe factory and cement works.

There is very little industrial activity outside Freetown although rice mills and oil palm mills are widespread. There is also an integrated sawmill and

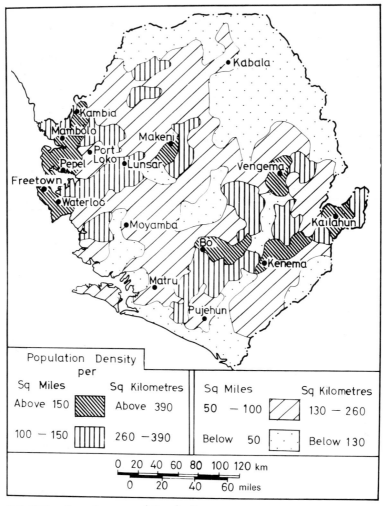

FIG. 30.7—*Sierra Leone: population density*

furniture factory at Kenema and a palm kernel crushing mill and soap factory at Bo.

POPULATION AND SETTLEMENT

With an estimated population of 2.9 million in 1973 and an area of 72,000 sq.km (27,669 sq. miles), Sierra Leone has an average population density of 30 persons per sq.km (78 per sq. mile). The main concentration of people is in the Colony Peninsula with over 95 persons per sq.km (250 persons per sq. mile), parts of Port Loko, and Kambia districts in the west with about 77 persons per sq.km (200 persons per sq. mile) and the chiefdoms of Bombali, Mimi Koro, Luawa, Kukua-Baoma and Nongowa with over 58 persons per sq.km (150 persons per sq. mile). The last four areas of higher density are also the areas of diamond mining in the eastern parts of the country. Amongst the very sparsely settled areas are the coastal

swamps lying east of Sherbro Island and the northern districts which have a density of less than 20 and less than 10 persons per sq.km (51 and 26 per sq. mile) respectively.

It is important to stress that the high density of over 95 persons per sq.km for the Colony Peninsula is caused by the presence of Freetown which contains two-thirds of the population of the area. The rest of the peninsula, particularly the hilly interior is very sparsely populated. (See Fig. 30.7.)

Ethnic groups

Although the creoles, who are descendants of ex-slaves, are politically, educationally and economically the most advanced group in Sierra Leone, they number only 42,000 (about 2 per cent). The great majority of them live in the Peninsula. The most numerous groups are the Mende (672,830 or 31 per

PLATE 93—Market in Freetown, Sierra Leone

PLATE 94—Original building of Fourah Bay College, Freetown Sierra Leone

cent and the Temne (648,930 or 30 per cent). The main concentration of the Mende is in the south and south-east, that is, in the area lying south of the Freetown-Pendembu railway. Temne territory lies immediately north of Mende territory and extends westwards to embrace the entire western coastlands of Sierra Leone, including the Colony Peninsula. The creoles therefore occupy land which the British Government acquired from the Temne people.

The rest of the population is made up of very small ethnic groups of which the best known are the Fulanis (67,000), of the north and central districts, the Kono (104,570), the Koranko (80,730), the Susu (67,290) the Loko (64,460) and the Mandingo (51,000). (See Fig. 30.8, p. 274.)

Rural settlements

About 75 per cent of the people live in rural settlements which have a population of less than 1,000. The forms and sizes of settlements vary considerably from one part of the country to another. The main factors influencing the forms of settlement are historical reasons, cultural habits and road construction. In the north and north-eastern grassland districts which were exposed to mounted Fulani warriors, defence

was a major consideration in the selection of settlement sites. Closely nucleated villages on interfluves, encircled by a wall of woodland were common in the north where the Koranko and Limba peoples live. The Mende village of Kokohun is a typical defensive village in the forest belt, while Betaya is a stockaded siege town in the northern grassland area inhabited by the Yalunka.

During the last fifty years, road building has brought about marked changes in traditional settlement forms. Some hill villages have since been re-located on the surrounding plains which are more accessible, while many villages by-passed by the new roads have been re-located to form street villages. The walls of woodland which surrounded some villages remain intact but in some cases these woodlands have been destroyed and built on to accommodate the increasing population.

Urbanization and towns

The urban population of Sierra Leone in 1963 was just over half a million, that is about 25 per cent of the population of the country in that year. This apparent high degree of urbanization derives from the fact that all settlements with 1,000 people or more

273

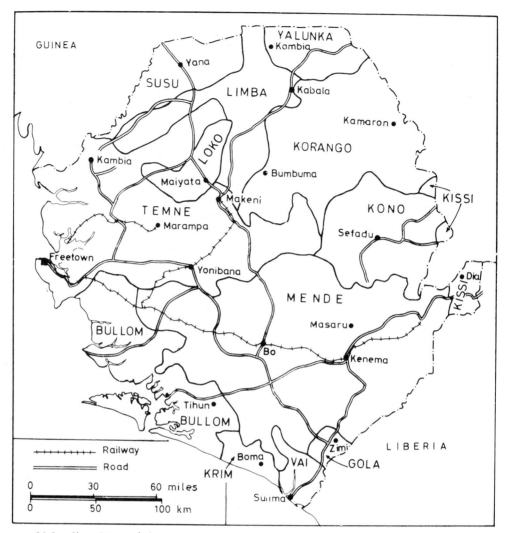

FIG. 30.8—Sierra Leone: ethnic groups

have been classified as towns (the comparable figure in Nigeria is 5,000 people), although many of them are essentially large villages. A large number of Sierra Leone towns have, however, grown from pre-colonial villages and may be distinguished from the planned towns of the coastal districts which date from the colonial period.

The construction of railways encouraged the foundation of towns like Bo, Makeru, and Kenema while mining and road development in the rice farming districts have been the main factors of urban growth in recent years. The settlement of Koidu had a population of 96 in 1923 increasing to 11,706 in 1963 when it had become the centre of a diamond-mining district. In 1970, its population was estimated to be over 90,000. It appears that the population will drop suddenly if the diamonds are exhausted unless alterna-

tive employment opportunities are created by the establishment of manufacturing industries.

Freetown (128,000) is the capital city and premier port and was founded in 1792 for the settlement of freed slaves. It has the best natural harbour in West Africa, but the hilly landscape immediately behind the coast has very much restricted the area available for expanding the city. Freetown is linked by road and railway to the interior. As the major growth point in the country, its population has doubled during the last twenty years although its growth rate is much less than that of Lagos, Accra or Abidjan, which are also capital cities and major ports. The creole population, which dominates the commerce and politics of Sierra Leone is concentrated at Freetown, which is also the main industrial and educational centre in the country. (See plates 93, 94.)

In 1954 the port of Freetown was greatly improved by the construction of the Queen Elizabeth II Quay which can take two vessels at a time. Further development has been planned to enable the port to take four additional vessels. All the imports of Sierra Leone pass through this port, which is also the major port of export for palm kernels, cocoa, coffee and ginger.

TRANSPORT

Railways

The main-line railway, which was closed down by the government in 1972, played a major part in the development of the economy and towns of Sierra Leone for about seventy-five years. It was built between 1895 and 1916 and consisted of 500km (310 miles) of narrow gauge 0.7m single track. Traffic was slow and even after the lines had been re-laid (1953–61) and diesel engines introduced (1962) the railway continued to run at a deficit of about Le.1 million a year. Hence the decision to close down the line on which all the provincial capitals and six district headquarters were located and which made it possible to transport coffee, cocoa and timber to the port of export at a time when roads were very few.

A 90km (56 mile) mineral line was built in 1933 to carry iron ore from Marampa to the port of export at Pepel. This line continues to operate and has a wider gauge of 1.05m.

Roads

The only tarred road runs from Freetown to Taiama, with a branch line to Lunsar. All the other main roads are unsurfaced as are all the secondary roads. The greatest concentration of roads is in the south-east. Generally, road transport is not well developed and even the major roads may become impassable during the rainy season. Many of the bridges are poor and to avoid as many rivers as possible, the roads usually follow a circuitous route along the watersheds.

Waterways

Inland waterways were important in the past but declined considerably following the opening of roads and railways. Most of the rivers are navigable by small craft, particularly during the rainy season. Traffic on the rivers, however, consists largely of canoes. There is also a considerable coastal traffic along the sea and lagoons of the south-east. Small vessels link up Freetown with Bonthe while canoe traffic is important along the south-east coast.

EXTERNAL TRADE

Sierra Leone has experienced a marked rise in external trade since 1960 as can be seen in Table 43. The number of ships using her ports has increased greatly and so have earnings from customs duties on imports and exports which constitute about half the total revenue of the country. In 1963, for example, earnings from import duties was Le.12.4 million while earnings from export tax amounted to Le.1.2 million. Her balance of trade has, however, always shown a deficit except for 1960 and 1968 and this trend may continue for some years if the present decrease in palm kernel tonnage continues. It is therefore very necessary to step up food production so as to reduce the large expenditure on food imports, valued at Le.12.5 million in 1967 and Le.16.8 million in 1972.

Exports still consist largely of primary products of which the most important are diamonds, iron ore and palm kernels. Other exports include coffee, cocoa, piassava and ginger. Most of the exports go to Britain, the Netherlands, West Germany and Japan. Nearly all the kola nut exports go to Gambia. The main suppliers of manufactured goods are Britain, Japan, West Germany, the Netherlands and Hong Kong. In addition Sierra Leone imports rice from Burma, wheat and flour from Canada, meat and dairy products from New Zealand and jute bags and sacks from Pakistan.

Table 43—Trade balance of Sierra Leone (million leones)

	1960	1963	1964	1965	1966	1967	1968	1969	1970	1971	1972	1973*
Imports	52.6	59.6	71.0	76.9	71.6	65.3	75.5	93.0	97.3	94.3	93.3	127.2
Exports	53.2	57.8	68.0	63.2	59.2	50.5	79.7	90.8	85.6	83.4	91.6	106.7
Balance	+0.6	−1.8	−3.0	−13.7	−12.4	−14.8	+4.2	−2.2	−11.7	−10.9	−1.7	−20.5

Note: Le. 1.00 = N1.00
*Provisional Figures.

Chapter 31—The Republic of Togo

PLATE 95—Lomé, Togo

Togo means 'behind the sea' in Ewe language and was the name given by the local inhabitants to the area around Lake Togo, but was later adopted as the name of the territory which is now the Republic of Togo. It is one of the smallest countries in West Africa, its population being about 2.2 million (1974) while the land area is only 56,600 sq.km. (21.620 sq. miles), about the size of the Plateau State of Nigeria. Between 1884 and 1914, Togo was a German colony but after the First World War, the territory which today constitutes Togo Republic came under a French mandate. The western part of German Togo was administered by Britain until 1957 when it became a part of the Republic of Ghana.

PHYSICAL REGIONS

Taking into consideration the nature of the parent rocks, the height of the land and the general aspect of the landscape, it is possible to recognize four relief regions in Togo (Fig. 31.1). These are: 1) the coast and coastal lowlands, 2) the eastern high plains, 3) the Togo-Atakora Highlands, 4) the Mango Basin.

1. The coast and coastal lowlands

The 56km (35 miles) coast of Togo is rather smooth and unindented, and has a sandy shore which rarely exceeds a few hundred metres in width. Lagoons and marshes, similar to those in Ghana and Nigeria, occur immediately behind the shore. The northern part of this region consists of a low clay plateau, called the Terre de Barre, which extends eastwards into southern Benin. Soils in the Terre de Barre district are fairly fertile and the area is extensively cultivated with maize, cassava, yams and oil palm trees. Several rivers including the Chio, the Lili and the Joto flow through the coastal lowlands into the longest lagoon which is called Lake Togo. The volume of water in these rivers, like the depth of the lagoons, fluctuates considerably with the seasons.

2. The eastern high plains

Extensive plains similar to those in Upper Volta extend eastwards from the base of the Togo-Atakora Highlands through Benin into western Nigeria. They are developed on very old hard rocks of the Basement Complex and consist of two surfaces: a lower plain of about 300m (1,000ft) and a higher plain of about 600m (2,000ft). Like other plains developed on crystalline rocks, this region is characterized by several dome-shaped inselbergs at various stages of disintegration. Much of this region is still so sparsely settled that fallow periods of more than eight years are common. Since 1926, however, many new villages have been established in the region which is an important cotton-growing area. Maize, yams and upland rice are grown in the interfluves while swamp rice is cultivated along the Mono River floodplains.

3. The Togo-Atakora Highlands

The Togo Highlands form the central and highest part of a range of mountains which begins from south-east Ghana and ends in northern Benin. The highlands are very much dissected in several areas and are characterized by steep-sided, forested valleys. Both the Togo Highlands and the Atakora Highlands further north, are developed on resistant sandstone and quartzites, the same type of rocks which form the range of hills passing through Ibadan City in Nigeria. Several peaks in the Togo-Atakora Highlands exceed 900m (3,000ft) above sea level. The Togo Highlands are heavily forested and provided the main centre for plantation agriculture during the period of German rule when cocoa, rubber and coffee plantations were established. Cocoa is still grown on plantations, but production on small farms is now more important. Upland rice, maize and millet are the main food crops. In the Atakora Highlands millet is the dominant food crop, the main cash crops being groundnuts and tobacco.

4. The Mango Basin

Sansanne Mango is an important route centre in this region and the term Mango Basin is used in the same sense as for the Paris Basin in France. The Mango Basin consists of low plains developed on sandstones through which the River Oti has cut a wide flat valley which is given to extensive floods. West of the Bogou-Ouagadougou road, the land becomes very hilly as

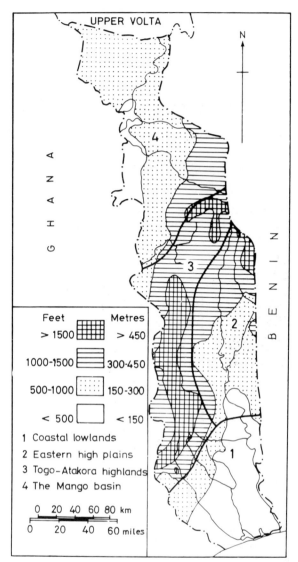

FIG. 31.1—*Togo: relief and physical regions*

one approaches the Gambaga Plateau of north-east Ghana. This area has relatively infertile soils and is very sparsely populated. Many people migrate from this region to the richer areas in the south. Groundnuts and millet are the main crops cultivated.

CLIMATE, VEGETATION AND SOILS

Togo lies between latitude 6°N. and 11°N., the southern part being exposed to the full influence of the sea. These two factors: latitudinal extent and distance from the sea bring about marked differences between the climates and vegetations of the south

277

and north, as is the case in Ghana and Nigeria. Some of the differences can be discovered by studying the climatic data given in Table 44. The south, for example, has four seasons made up of two rainy seasons and two dry seasons while the area north of latitude 7°N. has two seasons, one dry and one wet.

It is important to note that although the rain-bearing wind comes from the south, Sokodé, which is in the Middle Belt, has more rainfall than Lomé which is located along the coast. One explanation for this is that Lomé is in that stretch of the coast which forms part of the Accra dry belt. Another factor is that Sokodé is located on a higher elevation. Indeed, the Togo Highlands in the west have more rain than the lowlands further south. Altitude is therefore an important factor in the climate of Togo.

Togo is a grassland country. Poor grassland with sparse woody vegetation covers the dry coastlands. Fringing forests found along rivers in this coastal grassland have trees such as the oil palm, bamboo, mahogany and teak, which are usually found in the rainforests of West Africa. Further north and up to latitude 10°N. the country becomes more wooded. This is the guinea savanna belt which is characterized by isolated remnants of forest vegetation. The far north is in the sudan savanna zone which is more open in aspect. Important trees of this belt include acacias, the shea-butter tree and the silk-cotton tree.

The present-day vegetation of all Togo is largely a product of human interference through cultivation and grazing. In the uplands, for example, the slopes are still covered with forest remnants while the forests which formerly grew on the plateau surfaces

have been cut down and replaced by coffee or cocoa plantations.

Soils in Togo are generally poor, especially in the grassland areas, the most fertile soils occurring in the south, where the denser tree vegetation provides adequate humus. The clay region of the Terre de Barre has relatively fertile soils of clayey sands which support a dense population. The use of night-soil has made it possible for soils in the region to be cropped continuously. Along the coast the soils are rather sandy and not very suitable for farming.

ECONOMIC HISTORY

The period of German rule was one of marked economic progress during which Togo recorded the highest level of educational development in Africa. Like Ghana, Togo had a viable economy from the early years of colonial rule, thanks to the rapid development of plantation agriculture in the south. In 1914, there were about 13,000 hectares (about 32,100 acres) of German-owned tree-crop plantations and a much larger area of native-owned estates. During the 1914—18 war, indigenous Togolese took over the German estates and thereby prevented their seizure by the French and British as was the case in Cameroon.

Togo witnessed a period of economic stagnation during the first twenty years of French colonial administration (1920—40). Indeed by 1949 (that is, after 30 years of French rule), the volume of exports was about the same as it was during the period of

Table 44—Climatic data for selected stations in Togo

R = rainfall (mm), D = rain days, T_1 = mean maximum temperature (°C), T_2 = mean minimum temperature (°C)

Station			Jan.	Feb.	Mar.	Apr.	May	June	July	Aug.	Sept.	Oct.	Nov.	Dec.	Year
Sansanne Mango	R		4.0	2.0	5.0	58.0	73.8	143.8	162.5	295.3	223.5	69.0	2.0	7.0	1,045.9
	D		0.2	0.5	2.0	5.0	9.0	9.0	11.0	17.0	19.0	8.0	0.4	0.1	81.2
	T_1		34	37	38	37	35	32	30	29	30	33	36	35	34
	T_2		18	21	24	26	24	23	22	22	22	22	19	18	22
Sokodé	R		2.0	10.8	51.3	91.5	158.5	147.8	193.0	259.8	245.0	125.0	10.8	7.0	1,302.5
	D		0.5	1.0	5.0	9.0	11.0	13.0	17.0	19.0	18.0	11.0	2.0	1.0	107.5
	T_1		33	35	34	33	32	31	28	27	28	31	33	33	32
	T_2		19	22	22	22	22	21	21	21	21	21	19	18	21
Lomé	R		15.0	22.5	45.0	115.0	142.5	220.0	70.0	7.5	35.0	60.0	27.5	10.0	770.0
	D		1.0	2.0	4.0	6.0	9.0	12.0	7.0	3.0	7.0	6.0	3.0	1.0	61.0
	T_1		29	31	31	30	30	28	27	26	27	28	30	29	29
	T_2		22	23	23	23	23	23	22	22	22	22	23	22	23

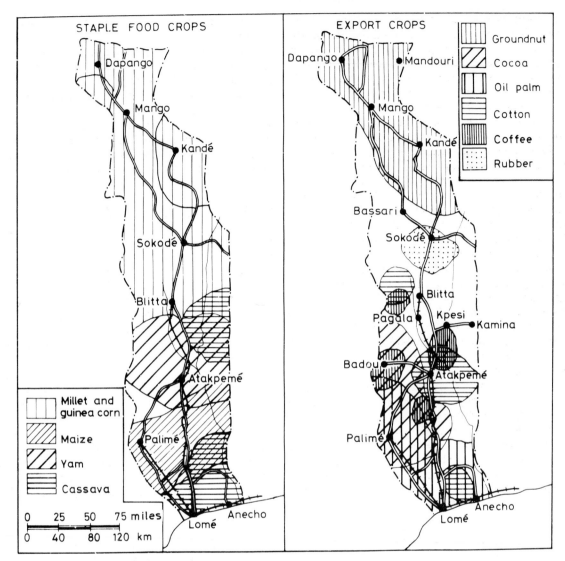

FIG. 31.2—Togo: staple food crops and export crops

German rule. There was, however, a marked growth in the economy between 1950 and 1960 when the average annual growth rate for exports was 7 per cent as compared with less than 1 per cent per annum between 1920 and 1950. The recent phase of Togo's economic growth has been characterized by a rapid increase in the population and the growth of urban centres. The population increased from 700,000 in 1920 to only 1,420,000 in 1960, and much more rapidly to 2,166,000 in 1974.

Agriculture is still the dominant sector of the economy although phosphate is now a major source of foreign exchange earnings. Since 1956, Togo has had a negative balance of trade and has increasingly depended on foreign aid to balance its national accounts.

ECONOMIC ACTIVITIES

As in other West African countries, farming is the most important occupation, except for along the coast, where fishing is the main occupation. In 1970, 741,000 people were employed in agriculture, 43 per cent of whom participated in the production of coffee, cocoa and palm produce. There were only 25,000 wage earners, mostly in the civil service and in mining (phosphates). The vast majority of the people are therefore self-employed, mostly in farming, fishing and trading.

Farming

Apart from the far north, which lies in the grain-producing zone, the rest of the country is in the root-

279

crop producing zone. Farming practices in both zones are similar to those in other parts of West Africa. Most of the land is still held by the community, which may be the extended family, clan and occasionally the tribe. Farm-holdings are small but there are a few large plantations which date back to the period of German rule. (See Fig. 31.2, p. 279.)

In the south, the main food crops are yams, cassava and maize. Groundnuts are also important because climatic conditions make it possible to grow this crop for local consumption as well as for export. Pigeon pea (*Cajanus cajan*), which is a shrub often used to protect young coconut palms from direct rays of the sun, is a common item of food. Export crops from the south include the oil palm which grows as far north as latitude 8°N., but is mainly concentrated in Atakpamé province, coffee which is grown in the hills around Palime, and cocoa. Southern Togo is a food surplus region exporting such food crops as maize and cassava.

Millet and maize are the main food crops in the north. Hungry rice (*Digitaria exilis*) is important in Mango Province while the borassus palm, like beans and groundnuts, is common in many parts of the country. Like the oil palm the borassus palm has many uses. The sap is made into palm wine, the fruit pulp is eaten raw or cooked and the trunk used for fuel and as pillars for building houses.

Cotton and tobacco are common crops grown for export as well as for local industries. Cotton is commonly interplanted with yams just as groundnuts are to be found growing between oil palm trees. The reader should take note of these crop combinations—crops of the far north growing side by side with crops of the forest belt. As in Nigeria, tobacco is put to several local uses. The leaf is smoked in pipes or made into 'bookies' while much of the crop is used as insecticide for sheep-dips.

Animal rearing

Togolese farmers, like most West African farmers, base their farming on crop production, the keeping of livestock being very restricted. The tsetse fly prevents the keeping of cattle even though most of the country is grassland, and the few thousand zebu cattle found in the country are raised in the far north. Sheep, goats and chickens are more numerous and are to be found all over the country. The animals provide much of the household manure which is applied on compound lands. Neither the goat nor the sheep is milked, their only use being for meat and skin. Fresh milk is therefore scarce and restricted to the north. Pigs are common in the southern and central provinces. Some

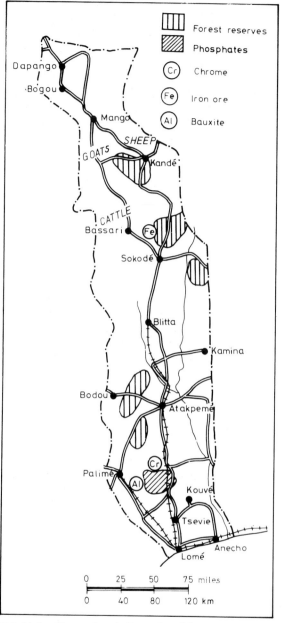

FIG. 31.3—*Togo: minerals, livestock and forest reserves*

villagers in the south also keep the small lagoon cattle which may be found grazing under coconut palms.

Fishing

Fish is an important article of internal trade and provides, along with crops, the main source of income for the coastal people. Villagers along the coast engage in both sea and lagoon fishing. A small proportion of the fish is sold fresh to inhabitants of the coastal towns but the rest is cut up and

PLATE 96 — Phosphate export wharf at Kpémé, Togo

dried in the sun before being transported to inland markets.

Nets are the main fishing gear used by those who go out to sea, but in the lagoons, both nets and several other traps are used. Lagoon fishermen usually live in huts erected on stilts, since much of the area is wet and liable to flooding.

Trading

There is a considerable internal trade in local foodstuffs and dried fish as well as in imported consumer goods. Local foodstuffs are also exported to the food-deficit Accra plains of Ghana. The smuggling of goods like brandy and wines into Ghana is made easier by the fact that the Ewes live on both sides of the border and can readily travel across the border without passing through established customs posts.

Mining

Togo is not rich in minerals, but it has one of the largest phosphate deposits in the world (about 50 million tons) in the area near Anecho. Mining started in 1961 and four years later, the output of 982,000 tons had already exceeded that of the older phosphate-

producing country of Senegal. The ore is transported by rail to Porto Seguro where it is processed and exported. (See Fig. 31.3 and plate 96.)

Other minerals which occur but have not yet been worked include bauxite (Mt Agou) and chromite (Mt Ahite). The charcoal-iron industry which was based on local iron ore mined near Bassari has since been discontinued.

POPULATION AND SETTLEMENT

Population

In 1974, the population of Togo was estimated to be 2.2 million, about 47 per cent of which were under the age of fifteen. The vast majority of the people are still illiterate, as is the case in most West African countries. This situation is likely to continue for many years, since only 42 per cent of the school-age population in 1972 was actually enrolled in schools.

Although the average population density for the country is only about 27 persons per sq.km (75 persons per sq. mile), Togo has the highest population density in French-speaking West Africa. The main concentration of people is in the coastal lowlands,

281

THE REPUBLIC OF TOGO

particularly in the Ewe territorial area where the average density exceeds 75 persons per sq.km (200 persons per sq. mile). A smaller but much more densely populated area occurs in the Lama Kara district of the Atakora Highlands where the Cabrais and Losso peoples live. In this area of rugged terrain, but relatively fertile soils, the average density exceeds 154 persons per sq.km (400 persons per sq. mile). The hillsides are terraced and intensively cultivated by the Cabrais and Losso who also irrigate and manure their farmlands. Smaller pockets of population concentrations occur in the Dapango area of the far north, around Sokodé, and in the Palime-Atakpamé region.

The rest of the country is rather empty. The Mango district which has rather infertile soils and is subject to periodic flooding, is the most sparsely settled area followed by the Middle Belt area lying between Atakpamé and Sokodé.

There is a considerable and increasing migration of people from the north and central districts into the growing towns of Lomé and Palime. In 1960, for example, about 55 per cent of the people in Lomé and 50 per cent of those in Palime were born outside these towns, both of which are located in the rich maritime region of Togo. As the capital, chief port and the main industrial centre, Lomé attracts the largest number of rural-urban migrants. Rural-rural migrants go mainly to the cocoa- and coffee-producing districts of the Togo Highlands and the main oil palm producing areas of the south. This group of migrants works mainly as agricultural labourers in the commercial plantations as well as in small peasant farms. The main source regions for migrant labour are the Lama Kara high-density zone and the highly impoverished, sparsely populated savanna region of the Mango Basin.

Despite its small size, Togo is inhabited by several ethnic groups speaking different languages. The Ewes (185,000) are the best known people in Togo, although only 40 per cent of the people are Togolese citizens, the remaining 60 per cent being of Ghanaian nationality. Ewes are considered to be very industrious and are to be found working as migrant labourers in the plantations and mines of southern Ghana, Togo and Ivory Coast. Other important groups include the Quatchi (152,000) of the southeast and the Cabrais (236,000) of the Lama Kara district.

Rural settlement and urbanization

The vast majority of the people live in small rural villages, some of which grew up to become important administrative and market centres during the colonial period. During the period of French rule several new villages were established in the sparsely settled areas between Sokode and Tsevie. The main reasons for the creation of these new villages were to ensure the better maintenance of the railway line from Lomé to Blitta, which passed through a largely uninhabited region, and to redistribute population so as to ease congestion in the Lama Kara district.

Since independence, the rate of urbanization has increased considerably and since 1966 the government has placed great emphasis on rural development in the hope that it will slow down the exodus to the towns. Amongst other things the government has established the Young Agricultural Pioneers Corps which seeks to make agricultural life attractive and profitable to young people, who are trained in agricultural experimental stations staffed by Israeli experts.

Lomé (140,000) is the capital and main port of Togo. Before the time of the German administration, Lomé was a small Ewe fishing village, but today it is a well-planned town with paved roads, squares and magnificent buildings. It is the terminus of the three rail routes linking the capital to Palime (118km, 73 miles), Blitta (272km, 169 miles) and Anecho (43km, 27 miles). Industrial establishments associated with transportation include railway workshops and car assembly plants. The town is also served by West African and inter-continental air services. (See plate 95.)

Lomé is a growing industrial town with a newly-built and enlarged port. The industrial zone is located near the port in the eastern part of the town while the main residential areas are in the north and west. Lome handles considerable road traffic between Nigeria and Ghana and is an important collecting point for dried fish and garri, which is exported to Ghana.

Sokodé (20,000) is the second largest town in Togo. It is a provincial capital and the main centre of trade in central Togo. The location of Sokodé at the southern end of the road and footpaths through the Atakora Highlands has made it of great strategic importance. It is the main collecting centre for kapok, which is gathered locally, tobacco and groundnuts.

Anecho (15,000) or Petit Popo is located near the Benin border. It is a provincial headquarters and the terminus of the coastal railway from Lomé. It was formerly an important slave port but today its trade is rather insignificant, consisting mainly of cassava and dried fish. Anecho was the capital of Togo from 1884–7 and again from 1914–20.

THE DEVELOPMENT OF TRANSPORTATION

The Germans and later the French realized that a good transport network was necessary for trade, agricultural development and effective administration. To facilitate external trade, a jetty was built at Lomé in 1900 to provide berthing facilities for large ships. This was followed by the first railway line built between Lomé port and Anecho (Petit Popo) in 1904. The second line, called the 'Cocoa-line' because it was built to tap the rich cocoa (and oil palm) areas of Kpalime was opened in 1907. A few years later the longest line linking Lomé to Atakpamé was built to serve the cotton-growing areas of southern Togo.

Road development was carried out in co-operation with trading firms and plantation owners. During the period of German rule, the roads were all constructed by the use of forced labour. Only a few of these roads have been tarred, and one of the best roads in West Africa is the coastal road linking Lome with Cotonou in Benin.

Lagoon transport is still important along the coastal areas where canoes and flat-bottomed barges are used to evacuate produce. Air transport is limited to the capital city of Lome which has regular services to Paris and some West African countries.

EXTERNAL TRADE

The main agricultural exports of Togo have always been cocoa, palm kernels, copra and coffee. Phosphate was added to the export list in 1961 and soon became so important that by 1966 it was already contributing up to 42 per cent of the total export by value. Table 45 shows the principal exports by value.

In 1965 the total exports were valued at ₦21.00 million (£10.5 million) while the total imports for the same year were valued at ₦32 million (£16 million). The visible trade gap for that year was therefore ₦11 million (or £5.5 million). Unfortunately, the unfavourable balance of trade recorded for 1966 is a common feature of the country's economy (see Table 46). It started in 1956 and until independence in 1960, Togo depended on French financial assistance to balance its budget.

Imported goods consist mainly of machinery and transport equipment including cars and bicycles (20 per cent by value in 1973), manufactured goods including textiles (26 per cent), beverages (3 per cent) and chemicals (9 per cent). About one-third of the country's imports come from France, the rest coming from other EEC countries and Japan. Almost all the exports go to France (about a third in 1973) and other EEC countries.

Table 45—Principal exports from Togo (by value) (million francs CFA)

Exports	1960	1967	1968	1969	1970	1971	1972	1973
Cocoa	1,382	2,349	2,314	4,063	6,336	4,246	3,719	3,556
Coffee	636	838	1,602	1,748	2,657	2,435	2,599	1,801
Cotton & seeds	411	415	379	162	351	311	385	310
Palm kernel	487	427	573	481	656	517	191	210
Phosphate	—	3,032	3,237	3,356	3,720	4,787	4,794	6,267

Note: 668 francs CFA = £1 = ₦ 200.

Table 46—Trade balance of Togo (million francs CFA)

	1960	1965	1966	1967	1968	1969	1970	1971	1972	1973
Export	3,588	6,626	8,872	7,894	9,549	11,477	15,176	13,626	12,542	13,755
Import	6,452	11,100	11,688	11,133	11,623	14,572	17,928	19,455	21,381	22,388
Balance	−2,864	−4,474	−2,796	−3,239	−2,074	−3,095	−2,752	−5,829	−8,839	−8,633

Note: 668 francs CFA = £1. = ₦2.00.

Chapter 32—The Republic of Upper Volta

PLATE 97—Landscape in Upper Volta

The Republic of Upper Volta takes its name from the Volta River system and is drained by all the three main streams that make up the Volta system, namely the Black Volta, the Red Volta and the White Volta Rivers. Its total area is 724,000 sq.km (106,000 sq. miles), about one-third the size of Nigeria, and its population in 1973 was estimated to be 5.7 million. Upper Volta is one of the landlocked and poorest French-speaking states of West Africa. More than 800,000 people have migrated to settle temporarily or permanently to work in the farms, timber concessions and mines of Ivory Coast and Ghana. But while the Voltaic labour force has contributed to the rapid growth of the Ivory Coast economy, it has also tended to reinforce the economic stagnation of Upper Volta. Government has in recent years undertaken various projects aimed at overcoming the exceptional poverty of this country which was one of the West African countries affected by the severe Sahelian droughts of 1973. The more recent economic projects include the Kou Valley Rice Scheme and the exploitation of mineral deposits. (See plate 97.)

RELIEF AND DRAINAGE

Apart from the Sikasso Plateau in the west and the northern highlands of Mossi and Koudougou, the country consists of an extensive high plain about 300m (1,000ft) above sea level, broken into several plateaux by the valleys of the Black Volta, the Red Volta and the White Volta. The main physical regions are (Fig. 32.1): 1) the Sikasso Plateau, 2) the Volta high plains, 3) the Mossi-Koudougou Highlands.

1. The Sikasso Plateau

This area of porous sandstone has an elevation of over 600m (2,000ft), but several hills on the surface attain heights of 750m (2,500ft) above sea level. The slope of the plateau is particularly marked in the south and east where the local relief exceeds 120m (400ft). Like the Jos Plateau of Nigeria, the Sikasso Plateau is the source of several streams, the more important of which include the headwaters of the Black Volta and the Comos Rivers. The course of the upper Black Volta, which flows in a north-easterly direction, suggests that it formerly flowed into the River Niger before it was captured near Dedugu and diverted southwards.

During the dry season, the smaller streams dry up completely while the main rivers are reduced to disconnected pools. In the second month of the rainy season the streams begin to flow normally. The dryness of the surface of the plateau, much of which is covered with lateritic soils, is due largely to the porosity of the sandstone and the great depth of the water table. These physical attributes of the plateau and the fact that it is densely populated, although not a fertile agricultural district, compare with conditions on the Nsukka Plateau of Nigeria.

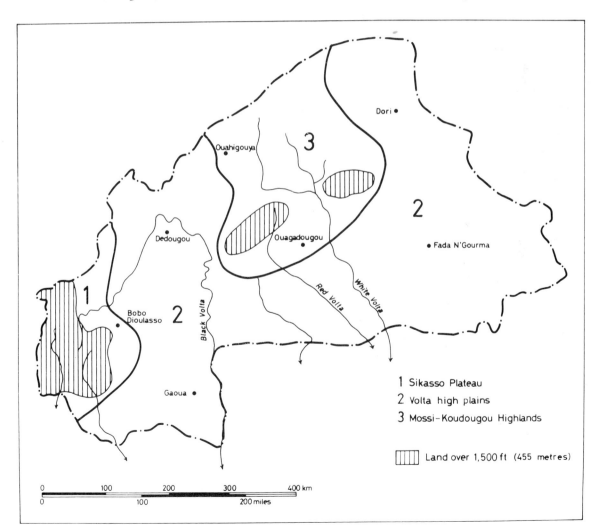

1 Sikasso Plateau
2 Volta high plains
3 Mossi-Koudougou Highlands

Land over 1,500 ft (455 metres)

FIG. 32.1—Upper Volta: relief and physical regions

2. The Volta high plains

Most of Upper Volta consists of high plains which like the high plains of Hausaland in Nigeria, are developed on old hard rocks of the Basement Complex. The monotony of this extensive grassland area is broken occasionally by granitic domes or inselbergs which are to be found in various stages of disintegration. Shallow but broad water courses are characteristic. These valleys become flooded towards the middle of the rainy season but as soon as the dry season sets in, the rivers dry up. Lateritic soils are common but the plains are intensively cultivated and support, in some districts, very large population densities.

3. The Mossi-Koudougou Highlands

Unlike the sandstone plateau of Sikasso, these highlands are of old crystalline rocks on which the Volta High Plains are built. They may be compared with the Idanre Hills of Yorubaland. This is particularly true of the Mossi Highlands which, like the Idanre Hills, served as a refugee settlement outpost during the period of the slave trade. The highlands are relatively low, being about 600m (2,000ft) above sea level and are so remote from the coast that they have no noticeable effect on the local climate.

CLIMATE AND VEGETATION

Climate

Some of the important aspects of the climate can be obtained by studying the climatic figures for Ouaga-dougou (north) and Bobo Dioulasso (south) presented in Table 47. (See Fig. 32.2.)

As in other parts of the western Sudan, there are two seasons, the wet and dry seasons. The wet season lasts for just over four months in the north and about seven months in the south. The wettest month is August when most waterways become flooded and the temperature shows a marked drop while the relative humidity reaches its highest figure. Other deductions may be made from Table 47 by the reader. The rainfall is brought by the south-west winds while the harmattan prevails during the dry season.

Upper Volta was one of the countries worst affected by the 1973 drought which caused great losses in crops and cattle throughout the sahelian belt of West Africa. Although the drought was particularly severe in 1973, it was not unexpected in Upper Volta, which has been declared a drought area by the FAO since 1967.

Vegetation

Two of the main vegetation types of West Africa occur in Upper Volta. These are the Sahel or thornland in the north-east and the Sudan savanna which covers the rest of the country. The vegetation in both belts has been considerably modified by long periods of intensive cultivation, particularly in the densely settled Mossi area around Ouagadougou. Close woodland thrives along water channels but the floodplains of the wider valleys support a grass vegetation.

The rapid absorption of rainwater by the porous sands of the Sikasso Plateau results in dry soil conditions, such that the predominant vegetation cover is

Table 47—Climatic data for Ouagadougou and Bobo Dioulasso

R = Rainfall (mm); D = Number of rainy days; H_1 & H_2 = Relative humidity at 8 a.m. & 6 p.m.; T_1 & T_2 = Maximum and Minimum Temperature (°C)

Station		Jan.	Feb.	Mar.	Apr.	May	June	July	Aug.	Sept.	Oct.	Nov.	Dec.	Year
Ouagadougou	R	0	0	1.5	7.8	64.5	103.8	139.8	218	128	14.8	3.0	0	681.2
	D	1.0	0.1	0.6	1.9	4.9	8.2	10.5	13.4	10.6	2.2	0.5	0	52.97
	H_1	42	39	39	50	64	72	81	87	83	70	49	51	61
	H_2	22	18	19	28	42	50	64	73	71	52	36	29	42
	T_1	36	39	41	41	34	36	34	32	33	38	39	37	37
	T_2	14	16	21	24	25	23	22	21	21	22	19	16	21
Bobo Dioulasso	R	2.0	4.0	27	52.3	114.5	118.8	246	300	213.5	62.8	18.5	0	1,159.4
	D	0.1	0.5	1.6	3.8	6.4	9.4	10.4	16.0	11.6	6.7	1.6	0	68.1
	H_1	45	46	54	64	74	81	88	91	89	79	65	54	69
	H_2	23	25	27	37	50	61	73	81	79	66	46	29	49
	T_1	34	37	38	38	36	33	31	29	31	34	35	35	34
	T_2	16	17	21	22	22	22	21	21	21	21	19	17	20

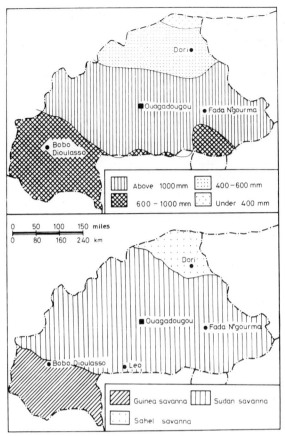

FIG. 32.2—Upper Volta: rainfall
FIG. 32.3—Upper Volta: vegetation

grass. Adjacent low-lying areas of the high plains support a denser vegetation. (See Fig. 32.3.)

ECONOMIC ACTIVITIES

The chief occupations of the people are farming, cattle rearing, hunting and collecting and trading. Most of the 2.8 million working population are self-employed in agriculture, commerce, and crafts industries. The wage-earning population in 1967 was about 43,000, most of whom were in the civil service.

Farming

Farming practices consist of the bush fallow rotation system characteristic of the grasslands of West Africa and in which grains constitute the basis of the farming economy. Guinea corn, millet, maize, beans and groundnuts are grown on upland farms while the smaller farms on river floodplains are usually reserved for rice, onions, tobacco and, in the south, yarms. In 1972 the country produced about 258,000 tonnes of millet, 477,000 tonnes of guinea corn, 55,000 tonnes of maize and 37,000 tonnes of rice.

In the densely settled Mossi territory around Ouagadougou, a more intensive form of cultivation similar to that around Kano City in Nigeria is practised. The soils in this area are as poor as in other parts of Upper Volta, but through hard work and the use of household manure, the land has been made to support a dense population of over 190 persons per sq.km (500 per sq. mile). Although Mossi farmers do not produce enough food to feed the local population, the hunger period which features in most parts of West Africa between April and June, when the crops have all been planted, rarely occurs in the Mossi country. This is because the crops listed above are harvested at different periods during the year. In August, for example, when the millet stocks are almost exhausted, the maize crop is ready to be harvested. There is therefore no period of marked food shortage, but it also means that the Mossi farmer is very busy during the short farming season which starts with bush-clearing in April. Millet, maize, guinea corn and rice are planted as soon as the first rains come in late May or early June. Cotton is cultivated in August. (See Fig. 32.4, p. 286.)

Most farmers in Upper Volta still produce for subsistence. Attempts to increase farm incomes through the policy of 'modernization' by encouraging the use of draught animals have made little progress. Draught ploughing requires more land and more labour. The Mossi territory has the labour but not enough land and it is only in the less densely populated Bobo and Senuofo regions of the west that some good results have been achieved.

Although the colonial government resorted to compulsory cultivation of cotton as a means of increasing earnings from agricultural exports, the production of export crops is still not well developed. Since 1960, the production of cotton and groundnuts has increased, thanks to the efforts of some French organizations towards rural improvement. In 1972 for example, the quantity of groundnuts (in shell) produced was estimated to be 60,000 tons, as compared with 3,000 in 1960; the corresponding figures for cotton being 12,000 tons in 1972 and 5,000 in 1960. Sesame is another principal export crop, but the production figure of 15,000 tons per annum is, like those of cotton and groundnuts, insignificant on a world scale. Land shortage and soil erosion in some areas, poor roads and the great distance to the sea from land-locked Upper Volta, are the main features which limit production for export.

Recent agricultural development projects

Since 1960, when Upper Volta gained political independence from France, the government has sought

287

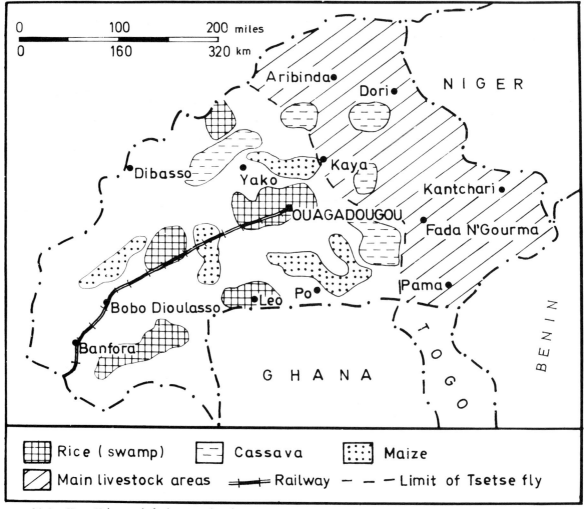

FIG. 32.4—*Upper Volta: staple food crops and cattle*

aid from various sources to help develop agriculture in the country. One of the projects supported by foreign aid is the Kou Valley Rice Scheme which is financed and administered by Chinese (Taiwan) capital and managerial staff. The scheme was completed in 1970 and is currently the largest single development project in the country. It is designed to irrigate about 1,800 hectares (4,500 acres) near Bobo Dioulasso with the view to producing about 4 tons of rice per hectare plus 3 tons of guinea corn as an intercrop. Building costs are high, but the project will support about 9,000 farmers and their families settled in five model villages. The cost of the scheme was put at ₦2.5 million.

Another important agricultural project is the Martoukou Project which is financed and administered by the Food and Agricultural Organization (FAO) arm of the United Nations. It consists of a training centre for graduates in agriculture and a centre for training extension workers and farmers, who are encouraged to cultivate cash crops. At present the large number of subsistence farmers in the country (about 95 per cent of the working population) constitutes a major problem to economic growth, hence the need to increase the number of farmers producing crops that can be sold for cash. The current plan is to encourage cotton cultivation and considerable progress has been made so far. The output of cotton increased from 17,274 tons in 1967/8 to 32,200 tons in 1969/70 and it is hoped that production will exceed 100,000 tons by 1978. The amount of ₦3 million paid to cotton farmers in 1968/9 added considerably to the purchasing power of the people.

Stock rearing

The greatest concentration of the cattle population, estimated to be 2.9 million in 1973, is in the sparsely settled areas of the north and east, which are also relatively free from tsetse fly (Fig. 32.4). In the south, which is infested with tsetse fly, only the small Ndama and Lobi cattle may be found. Goats and sheep are kept all over the country but particularly in areas occupied by Tuaregs and Fulanis. The goat and sheep population was estimated to be 4.1 million in 1973.

Live animals have always been the most important export from Upper Volta. Of the total export earnings of 5,288 million CFA francs in 1968, live animals accounted for 2,525 million CFA francs (that is almost 50 per cent). An average of 30,000 heads is exported annually to Ghana and the Ivory Coast. The nomadic Fulani and Tuareg cattle-herders who control the cattle economy of Upper Volta are therefore a very important force in the export trade of that country, even though they form only 3 per cent of the population of Upper Volta. (See Fig. 32.5.)

The rather shaky economy of Upper Volta is therefore based mainly on livestock raising. It is for this reason that the effects of the severe droughts of 1972/3 in the Sahelian zone of West Africa has assumed catastrophic proportions in Upper Volta

where 35 per cent of the animal population were considered to be in danger of death through thirst and hunger.

Mining

A reserve of about 10 million tons of manganese ore valued at about N240 million has been discovered in the Trere region of north-eastern Upper Volta. Up till 1973, their development was held up by lack of good transport facilities and water. Gold and bauxite have also been found in commercial quantities, but have not yet been mined. (See Fig. 32.6, p. 290.)

Development of manufacturing industries

Modern industrial activity is still not well developed owing partly to the poor state of the infrastructure (roads, water supply, communications and power supply) and partly to the small size of the internal market. The cost of electricity which is produced by a few thermal power stations is rather high since the oil and coal used for generating power has to be im-

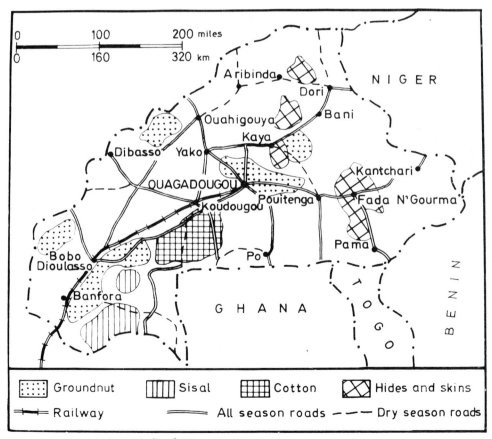

FIG. 32.5—Upper Volta: agricultural export

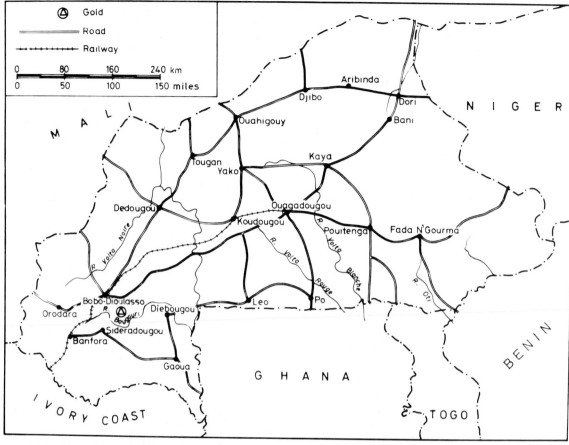

FIG. 32.6—Upper Volta: minerals, road transport

ported at high cost to locations in a landlocked country. Local raw materials for manufacturing are few and the quantity produced can only support small plants, which often do not operate at a profit.

The list of industries published by the Chamber of Commerce shows that manufacturing in Upper Volta consists largely of the processing of agricultural products for export as well as for local consumption and a few import-substitution industries, including textiles, shoes and drinks. Almost all the industries are located in Bobo Dioulasso and Ouagadougou. Important industries at Bobo Dioulasso include a combined groundnut-oil mill and soap factory, a candy factory, a brewery and a soft drink bottling plant, a cigarette factory, a cotton ginnery, an inner-tube factory and an assembly plant for bicycles and motor-bikes. In the capital city of Ouagadougou, the main industries include assembly plants for shoes and farm implements, a clothing factory, a paint factory and a match factory. The tannery (capacity 175,000 skins), the brick factory and facilities for cotton-ginning at Ouagadougou are all based on local raw materials.

Outside the two main industrial cities, the only

important factories are the new textile mill opened in 1970 at Koudougou and a flour mill at Ranfora, which also has a sugar-refining factory for processing locally grown sugarcane.

POPULATION – DISTRIBUTION AND MIGRATION

Upper Volta is best known both as the poorest of the Sahelian countries of West Africa and as the main source of labour for the miraculous high growth of the economy of Ivory Coast. In 1973, there were about 5.7 million people in the country, about 3 per cent of which were nomadic cattle-rearers. The settled population was mostly unevenly distributed, some parts of the country being virtually uninhabited. Along sections of the three Volta Rivers, there are some uninhabited areas which extend for about 16km (10 miles) on either side of each river. This is caused largely by annual floods as well as by the high incidence of sleeping sickness along the wooded riverine floodplains. The large swampy area of the Fada N'Gourma district is also virtually uninhabited.

The most densely populated areas of Upper Volta are located in Mossi tribal territory. Unfortunately, Mossi territory has relatively infertile soils, with the result that the district does not produce enough food to feed its predominantly agricultural population. This, indeed, is the main reason why the Mossi people migrate to work in other parts of West Africa, notably Ghana and Ivory Coast. It is estimated that about 100,000 Mossi workers migrate every year to work in Ghana while another 40,000 go to work in the cocoa and coffee plantations of Ivory Coast. Most of these are temporary migrants while some stay on for many years. The number of Upper Volta people in these countries at any given time is therefore much higher than is suggested by these figures. In 1965 for example there were 200,000 Upper Voltaian migrants in Ivory Coast and in 1969, the number of Upper Voltaians expelled from Ghana was estimated to be 250,000. Most of these migrants are between the ages of sixteen and thirty and while Ivory Coast and Ghana have benefited greatly from the labour of these young migrants, the economy of Upper Volta has continued to remain stagnant. (See Fig. 32.7.)

It is important to stress that Mossi migration is predominantly seasonal and that, like the Sokoto Hausa migrants to the Nigerian cocoa belt, Mossi migrants always cultivate their farms at home before going to Ghana or Ivory Coast. They usually leave Upper Volta in November and December (that is, after local crops have been harvested) and return in early

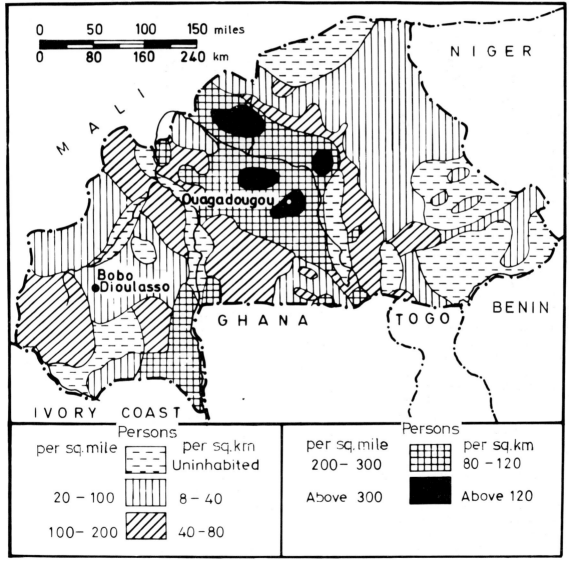

FIG. 32.7—Upper Volta: population density

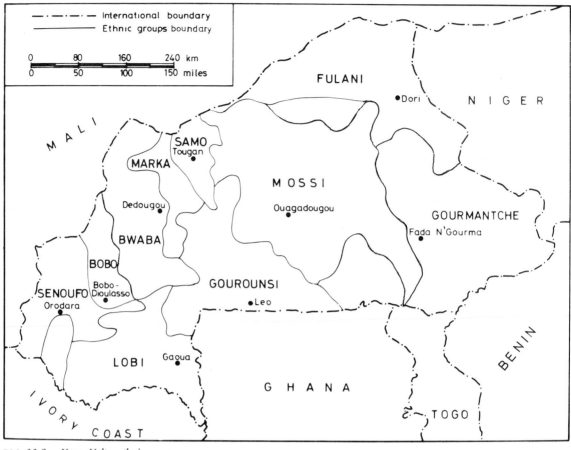

FIG. 32.8—Upper Volta: ethnic groups

May to take part in planting the crop for that year.

The growing concentration of manufacturing industries in Ouagadougou and Bobo Dioulasso has given rise to another dimension in the migration process. In addition to the long-distance migration to Ghana and Ivory Coast, an increasing number of young people now migrate into the three main cities of Ouagadougou, Bobo Dioulasso and Koudougou. These two types of migration have been largely responsible for the present limited success of the Upper Volta government's rural development policy which is designed to prepare young villagers for the task of agricultural modernization.

Apart from the Mossi, who number about 2.6 million, the other important ethnic groups include the Fulanis (565,400), the Libi (380,000) the Mandingo (375,150), the Bobo (364,000), the Senoufo (299,400), the Gourounsi (288,000) and the Biss (255,500). Europeans and other foreigners number about 5,000 and there is also a considerable number of Hausa traders. (See Fig. 32.8.)

URBANIZATION

The rapid rate of urban growth in Upper Volta since about 1955 is due largely to migration from the rural areas. In 1960 for example the urban population of the country was about 5 per cent of the total population, but ten years later, the figure had increased to over 7 per cent. The increasing concentration of people in the cities is not surprising in view of the greater increase in employment opportunities associated with industries located in the three main urban centres of Ouagadougou, Bobo Dioulasso and Koudougou. However, the vast majority of the people still live in rural settlements, most of which are small and dispersed.

Ouagadougou (110,000 in 1970) is the capital of Upper Volta. It is one of the old traditional towns of West Africa and was founded several centuries before the period of French colonization. Its main functions as a pre-industrial city were administrative and commercial. As the capital of the Mossi kingdom, Ouagadougou was also an important cultural and

Table 48—Trade balance of Upper Volta (million francs CFA)

	1964	1965	1966	1967	1968	1969	1970	1971	1972
Imports	9,794	9,169	9,293	8,970	10,122	12,861	12,963	14,054	15,312
Exports	3,005	3,680	3,985	4,429	5,288	5,329	5,055	4,408	5,141
Balance	−6,789	−5,308	−5,308	−4,541	−4,834	−7,532	−7,908	−9,646	−10,171

Note: 668 francs CFA = £1 = ₦2.00.

educational centre. Its importance as an administrative centre increased when it was selected as the capital of Upper Volta while the railway link with Abidjan contributed greatly to the growth of trade and modern industry in the city. It is linked by air to Paris and the capitals of other French-speaking West African countries.

Bobo Dioulasso (78,500 in 1970) is the second largest town in Upper Volta. Located in the heart of a rich agricultural district, Bobo Dioulasso has become a major collecting centre for cotton, groundnut and shea-butter, and was until 1954, the terminus of the Abidjan—Niger railway. Today Bobo Dioulasso has become a growing industrial town.

FOREIGN TRADE

Upper Volta is a poor country with a highly unfavourable balance of trade (Table 48). Before independence the trade deficit was relatively stable at about 3,500 million francs CFA per annum, but since 1960, the deficit has averaged about 5,000 million francs CFA. The annual trade deficit is partly offset by external aid as well as by the 5,000 million francs CFA paid every year as pensions to about 2,000 Voltaic veterans of the Second World War. Temporary migrants to Ghana and Ivory Coast also remit an estimated sum of 2,500 million francs CFA every year to the country.

Cattle remains the main export commodity and is sent mainly to Ghana and Ivory Coast. Other agricultural exports go to France, which is also the chief supplier of imported goods, including agricultural and industrial machinery, vehicles, food products and petroleum products.

Acknowledgements

The author and publisher would like to thank the following for permission to reproduce photographs in this book:

Philippe Billère for pp. 128 and 281; J. Allan Cash for pp. 24, 35, 66, 79, 140 and 185; Henri de Chatillon for p. 209; Documentation Française for p. 33; Jorbjorn Eriksson for p. 193; Peter Fraenkel for pp. 33, 106, 197, 206, 217 and 240; Ghana Information Services for pp. 49, 69, 74, 87, 104 and 146; Professor R. J. Harrison Church for pp. 10, 17, 24, 26, 35, 46, 52, 69, 73, 78, 83, 84, 98, 134, 138, 144, 161, 165, 188, 215, 220, 224, 250, 258, 261, 273, 276 and 284; Alan Hutchison Library for p. 37; IFAN photograph G. Labitte for p. 131; Margaret Murray for pp. 9, 25, 69, 71, 91, 94, 107 and 160; Margaret Murray/Christian Aid for p. 54; New African Development for pp. 96 and 170; Nigeria High Commission, London for pp. 2, 6, 8, 20, 21, 32, 36, 45, 56, 58, 59, 60, 66, 67, 71, 85, 95, 105, 110, 177, 238 and 243; *Nigeria* Magazine for p. 100.

Reading List

Allan, W., *The African Husbandman*, Oliver & Boyd, London, 1965.

Bauer, P. T., *West African Trade*, London, 1954.

Boateng, E. A., *A Geography of Ghana*, Cambridge University Press, 1965.

Bohannan, P., *Tiv Farm and Settlement*, London, 1954.

Bohannan, L. and Bohannan, P., *The Tiv of Central Nigeria*, International African Institute, London, 1962.

Bohannan, P. and Dalton, G., *Markets in Africa*, Evanston, 1962.

Boserup, Ester, *The Conditions of Agricultural Growth: the Economics of Agrarian Change Under Population Pressure*, Allen & Unwin, 1965.

Buchanan, K. M. and Pugh, J. C., *Land and People in Nigeria*, London, 1958.

Caldwell, J. C. and Okonjo, C. (eds.), *Population of Tropical Africa*, Longman, London, 1968.

Chubb, L. T., *Ibo Land Tenure*, Ibadan, 1961.

Clarke, J. I. (ed.), *Sierra Leone in Maps*, University of London Press, 1966.

Crowder, M., *The Story of Nigeria*, London, 1962.

Dike, K. O., *Trade and Politics in the Niger Delta 1830–1885*, Oxford, 1956.

Fage, J. D., *An Introduction to the History of West Africa*, Cambridge, 1962.

Gleave, M. B. and White, H. P., *An Economic Geography of West Africa*, Bell, London, 1971.

Gnielinski, S. V., *Liberia in Maps*, University of London Press, 1972.

Gusten, R., *Studies in the Staple Food Economy of Western Nigeria*, Munchen, 1968.

Hallet, R., *Peoples and Progress in West Africa*, Oxford, 1966.

Hance, W. A., *Population, Migration and Urbanisation in Africa*, Praeger, London, 1970.

Hance, W. A., *The Geography of Modern Africa*, New York, 1964.

Harrison Church, R. J., *West Africa – A Study of the Environment and Man's Use of It*, Longman, 1974.

Hill, P., *Studies in Rural Capitalism in West Africa*, Cambridge University Press, 1970.

Higson, F. G., *A Certificate Geography of West Africa*, Longman.

Hodder, B. W. and Ukwu, U. I., *Markets in West Africa*, Ibadan, 1969.

Hopkins, B., *Forest and Savanna*, Heinemann, London, 1965.

Hoyle, B. S. and Hilling, D. (eds.), *Seaports and Development in Tropical Africa*, Macmillan, London, 1970.

Iloeje, N. P., *A New Geography of Nigeria*, Lagos, 1965.

Irvine, F. R., *West African Agriculture*, Oxford University Press, London, 1970.

Jarrett, H. R., *A Geography of West Africa*, London, 1973.

Jarrett, H. R., *A Geography of Sierra Leone and Gambia*, Longman, 1954.

Jennings, J. H. and Oduah, S., *A Geography of Eastern Nigeria*, London, 1966.

Johnson, B. F., *The Staple Food Economies of Western Tropical Africa*, Stanford, 1958.

Kimble, G. H. T., *Tropical Africa* (2 vols.), New York, 1961.

Kuper, H., *Urbanisation and Migration in West Africa*, University of California Press, 1965.

Mabogunje, A. L., *Regional Mobility and Resource Development in West Africa*, Montreal, 1972.

Mabogunje, A. L., *Urbanisation in Nigeria*, University of London Press, 1968.

Mortimore, M. J. and Wilson, J., *Land and People in the Kano Close-Settled Zone*, Kaduna, 1965.

Oboli, H. O. N. and Harrison Church, R. J., *An Outline Geography of West Africa*, Harrap, 1971.

Ominde, S. and Ejiogwu, C. H. (eds.), *Population Growth and Economic Development in Africa*, Heinemann, 1972.

Post, K. W., *The New States of West Africa*, Penguin Books, 1964.

Prothero, R. M., *Migrants and Malaria*, Longman, London, 1965.

Roper, J. I., *Labour Problems in West Africa*, Penguin Books, 1958.

Stamp, L. D., *Africa: A Study in Tropical Development*, London, 1966.

Varley, W. J. and White, H. P., *The Geography of Ghana*, Longman, London, 1958.

Watson, G. D., *A Human Geography of Nigeria*, London, 1960.

Udo, R. K., *Geographical Regions of Nigeria*, Heinemann, 1970.

Udo, R. K., *Migrant Tenant Farmers of Nigeria*, Lagos, 1975.

Articles in Journals and Periodicals (for university students)

Cohen, A., 'Politics of the Kola Trade,' *Africa*, 36, 1966, p. 19.

Darksh, M., 'The Distribution of Manufacturing in Ghana', *Scottish Geographical Magazine*, 87, 1971, pp. 38—57.

Gleave, M. B. and White, H. P., 'The West African Middle Belt: Environmental Fact or Geographers' Fiction?' *Geographical Review*, 59, 1969, pp. 123—39.

Goddard, S., 'Town-Farm Relationships in Yorubaland,' *Africa*, 35, 1965, pp. 21—29.

Harrison Church, R. J., 'Problems and Development of the Dry Zone of West Africa, *Geographical Journal*, 127, 1961, pp. 187—204.

——'The Islamic Republic of Mauritania,' *Focus*, 12, 1961.

——'Senegal,' *Focus*, 15, 1964.

——'Niger Republic,' *Focus*, 16, 1965.

——'Guinea', *Focus*, 17, 1967.

Hilling, D., 'The Volta River Project', *Geographical Magazine*, 37, 1965 pp. 830—41.

Hilton, T. E., 'Ivory Coast', *Focus*, 16, 1965.

——'Mali', *Focus*, 18, 1967.

——'Ghana', *Focus*, 21, 1970.

Hodder, B. W., 'Tin Mining on the Jos Plateau of Nigeria', *Economic Geography*, 35, 1959, pp. 109—22.

Howe, R. W., 'The Ivory Coast and Ghana Compare Balance Sheets', *Africa Today*, 19, 1970, p. 44.

Hunter, J. M., 'River Blindness in Nangodi, Northern Ghana', *Geographical Review*, 56, 1966, pp. 398—416.

——'The Social Roots of Dispersed Settlement in Northern Ghana', *Annals of the Association of American Geographers*, 57, 1967, pp. 339—49.

Jarrett, A. R., 'Population and Settlement in the Gambia', *Geographical Review*, 38, 1948, pp. 633—36.

——'The Strange Farmers of the Gambia', *Geographical Review*, 39, 1949, pp. 649—57.

Khuri, F. I., 'Kinship, Emigration and Trade Partnership Among the Lebanese of West Africa', *Africa*, 35, 1965, pp. 385—95.

Laan, van der, H. L., 'Lebanese enterprise in Sierra Leone', *Sierra Leone Geographical Journal*, 13, 1969, pp. 45—50.

Ledger, D. C., 'Recent Hydrological Changes in the Rima Basin, Northern Nigeria', *Geographical Journal*, 127, 1961, pp. 477—87.

Mabogunje, A. L., 'Industrialisation Within an Existing System of Cities in Nigeria', *Nigerian Geographical Journal*, 12, 1969, pp. 3—16.

Morgan, W. B., 'Food Imports of West Africa', *Economic Geography*, 39, 1963, pp. 351—62.

Ofomata, G., 'Landforms of the Nsukka Plateau of Eastern Nigeria', *Nigerian Geographical Journal*, 10, 1967, pp. 3—10.

Ojo, G. J. A., 'Some Observations on the Journey to Agricultural Work in Yorubaland', *South-western Nigeria Economic Geography* 46, 1970, pp. 459—71.

Stanley, W. R., 'Transport Expansion in Liberia', *Geographical Review*, 60, 1970, pp. 529—47.

Swindell, K., 'Industrialisation in Guinea', *Geography*, 54, 1969, pp. 456—8.

Taaffe, E. J., Morril, R. L. and Gould, P. R., 'Transport Expansion in Underdeveloped Countries: a Comparative Analysis', *Geographical Review*, 53, 1963, pp. 503—29.

Thomas, B., 'Railways and Ports in French West Africa', *Economic Geography*, 33, 1957, pp. 1—15.

Udo, R. K., 'Disintegration of Nucleated Settlement in Eastern Nigeria', *Geographical Review*, 55, 1965, pp. 53—67.

——, 'Food Deficit Areas of Nigeria', *Geographical Review*, 61, 1971, pp. 415—30.

——, 'Sixty Years of Plantation Agriculture in Southern Nigeria (1902—62)', *Economic Geography*, 41, 1965, pp. 356—68.

Index

INDEX

Sample Examination Questions

Part I
A Systematic Study of West Africa

1. Write a short account of the River Niger, and explain its importance to the people of Mali and Nigeria.

2. (a) With reference to specific examples, discuss the uses that are made of the principal rivers of West Africa.
   (b) What factors limit the extent to which they can be used?

3. (a) Show with the help of a sketch map of West Africa the position and extent of:
   (i) the Futa Jallon Highlands
   (ii) the Niger Delta
   (iii) the Jos Plateau
   (iv) the Adrar des Iforas.
   (b) Describe briefly the characteristic features of the surface of any TWO of these regions.

4. Account for the differences between the total annual rainfall and its seasonal distribution on the coastlands as compared with the interior of West Africa.

5. Compare and contrast the climate of the Accra Plains with that of the Niger Delta.

6. Give an account of the climate of West Africa showing clearly the part played by relief, distance from the sea (continentality) and the wind system.

7. Write brief notes on THREE of the following:
   (i) the harmattan
   (ii) the Accra dry belt
   (iii) the short dry season of south-western Nigeria
   (iv) the length of the rainy season in West Africa

8. It is the relative humidity, more than any other factor, which has given the climates of West Africa a bad name. Comment.

9. Explain carefully how climate influences the calendar of agricultural activities in your home district.

10. Account for the distribution of the vegetation types of West Africa, illustrating your answer with a suitable sketch map.

11. Write an essay on the types and distribution of the soils of West Africa.

12. (a) Show on a map of West Africa any FOUR areas which experience serious cases of soil erosion.
    (b) Discuss the factors which have encouraged soil erosion in any ONE of these areas.
    (c) Comment on the efforts being made to check erosion in the area you have selected.

13. The rain forest does not increase the quantity of humus in soils, but maintains it. Discuss with special reference to any forested area in West Africa.

14. Laterite is utterly infertile and hostile to agriculture owing to its sterility and compactness. Comment with respect to the situation in West Africa.

15. Write brief notes on TWO of the following:
    (a) The distribution of lateritic soils in West Africa.
    (b) The effect of bush burning on soil fertility.
    (c) The causes of soil erosion in either the Jos Plateau or the Guinea Highlands.

16. (a) Show on a sketch map of West Africa THREE major areas of commercial extraction of timber and ONE port of export of timber for each area.
    (b) Describe the methods adopted to ensure the continued supply of timber.
    (c) Discuss the development of wood-based industries in any ONE country of West Africa.

17. (a) Draw a sketch map of West Africa and on it mark and name the approximate areas occu-

pied by the following peoples: the Mossi, the Kanuris, the Ewes, and the Ibos.
(b) Select TWO of these peoples and show how their lives are adapted to the geographical conditions in which they live.

18. Write an essay on the main occupations of Hausa migrants in south-western Nigeria.

19. Trace the origin and discuss the characteristic features of 'Sabon garis' (strangers' wards) in West African cities.

20. Describe the traditional systems of land tenure in your home district and account for the changes (if any) which have occurred during the last fifty years.

21. 'In general, the availability of land determines the type of tenure, and it is where the pressure is greatest that the few remaining areas of common land are most rapidly decreasing' (L. T. Chubb). Comment.

22. Describe and account for the distribution of the population in West Africa.

23. (a) Locate and name on a sketch map of West Africa ONE area of very dense population in the forest belt and ONE OTHER in the grassland area.
(b) Account for the concentration of population in any ONE area and explain how the people have adjusted to the situation.

24. (a) Show on a sketch map the chief sources and destinations of migrant labour in West Africa.
(b) Write a brief explanation of the direction of movements of these migrants.

25. One major problem of agricultural labour in West Africa is that in most areas of commercial cropping for export there is a shortage. Comment.

26. Describe briefly THREE of the following:
(a) Floodland cultivation in EITHER Mali OR northern Nigeria.
(b) Rice production along the coast of West Africa.
(c) Cattle-rearing in Niger Republic.
(d) Groundnut farming in the Kano district of Nigeria.

27. (a) Draw a large sketch map of West Africa to show the chief areas of floodland cultivation.
(b) Write briefly on the need for and the difficulties of developing modern irrigation schemes.

28. (a) Locate and name on a map of West Africa the areas of major irrigation schemes.
(b) Write a brief account of EITHER the inland Niger Delta irrigation project OR irrigation in the Chad Basin.

29. Compare farming in the Kano close-settled zone with farming in the cocoa belt of Ghana.

30. Discuss the prospects of developing the Middle Belt as a major food-surplus region in West Africa.

31. Select ONE of the following areas:
(a) the Jos Plateau.
(b) the inland Niger Delta.
(c) the Terre de Barre region of Benin.
(d) the Mossi district of Upper Volta.
Write a geographical account of the foodcrop economy of the area selected under the headings:
(i) Physical factors
(ii) Staple crop
(iii) Farming methods
(iv) Marketing of food crops.

32. Discuss the development of plantation agriculture in EITHER Nigeria OR Ivory Coast and assess its contribution to the production of industrial crops in the country that you have chosen.

33. Describe the main features of farming in EITHER the Ghanaian cocoa belt OR the Senegal groundnut belt.

34. Choose TWO of the following manufacturing industries: cotton textiles, beer brewing, cement.
For EACH of the two (a) locate ONE area in Nigeria or Ivory Coast where the industry is carried on, (b) describe and account for the importance of the industry in the area.

35. Write an account of the cotton textile industry in West Africa.

36. (a) Show on a map of West Africa FOUR areas of large-scale development of hydro-electric power.
(b) Explain in what ways the rivers of West Africa are (i) suitable and (ii) unsuitable for the development of hydro-electric power.

37. Account for the concentration of manufacturing industries in the coastal areas of West Africa.

38. (a) Draw a sketch map of West Africa and show on it THREE areas of intensive manu-

facturing industry and ONE important town for each industrial area.

(b) Explain the factors that have promoted the development of manufacturing in ONE of the areas shown on your map.

39. Discuss the main problem of industrialization in West Africa.

40. Discuss the relative importance of the market as a factor in the location of industries in West Africa.

41. Explain why road transport is now the most important means of transporting goods and passengers in West Africa.

42. Discuss the factors inhibiting the development of trans-continental railways in West Africa.

43. Consider the factors responsible for the concentration of development of port facilities to a few ports since about 1950.

44. Describe the structure and pattern of inter-regional trade in West Africa.

45. Discuss the case for and the prospects of a West African Economic Community.

PART II – THE COUNTRIES OF WEST AFRICA

1. With the aid of a sketch map, write a geographical account of EITHER Senegal OR Guinea Bissau OR Benin (Dahomey) under the headings:
   (a) Physical regions
   (b) Distribution and movements of population
   (c) Agricultural development.

2. Account for the rapid growth of the city of Cotonou as compared with the capital city of Porto Novo.

3. Discuss the view that the economic situation in Benin is the main cause and not the result of political instability in the country.

4. Write an essay on the role of migrant labour in the development of EITHER Fernando Po OR Ivory Coast.

5. (a) Write a short geographical account of the cultivation of groundnuts in EITHER Gambia OR Senegal.
   (b) Explain the importance of groundnuts in your chosen country's economy.
   (c) Point out three problems associated with the cultivation of the crop, and suggest solutions to them.

6. Using the headings (a) physical features, (b) climate, (c) occupations of the people, write a geographical account of EITHER Fernando Po OR any ONE of the following countries: Gambia, Togo, Upper Volta, Mali, Liberia.

7. Write a concise geographical account of mining and railway development in Ghana.

8. Discuss the factors that have favoured the development of industries in EITHER the Accra–Tema district OR the Lagos Metropolitan Area.

9. Discuss the importance of the Volta River Project to the economy of Ghana.

10. Under the headings climate, soils, drainage and economic production, write a geographical description of EITHER the Accra Plains OR the Chad Basin.

11. Explain where in Ghana, and under what geographical conditions, cocoa is cultivated.

12. Describe and explain the pattern of distribution of population in EITHER Ghana OR Nigeria OR Senegal.

13. Show how the rainfall regimes have affected agricultural development in any ONE of the following countries: Ghana, Mali, Sierra Leone.

14. Write briefly on THREE of the following:
   (a) The climate of Guinea
   (b) Soil erosion in Guinea
   (c) The Fulanis in Guinea
   (d) The importance of Conakry.

15. Discuss the relative importance of minerals and tree crops in the export trade of Guinea.

16. (1) Name and locate the area of production of THREE export crops in EITHER Guinea OR Sierra Leone.
   (2) For any ONE of these crops describe the physical conditions under which it is grown and the method of cultivation.

17. (a) Draw a map of Guinea and on it locate and name THREE areas where bauxite deposits occur and TWO areas where iron-ore occurs.
   (b) Describe the methods of mining of these minerals and name TWO countries to which each mineral is exported.

18. (a) Name THREE of the major food crops of Guinea and ONE area in which each is important.

(b) Select ONE crop and describe the conditions suitable for its cultivation and the method of cultivation.

19. Discuss the influence of physical conditions on the localization of agricultural production in Guinea Bissau.

20. Describe the relief, climate and resources of EITHER Ivory Coast OR Guinea Bissau.

21. Account for the fact that the Ivory Coast is the most prosperous country in French-speaking West Africa.

22. Write briefly on:
    (a) Tree-crop production in Ivory Coast
    (b) The food imports of Ivory Coast
    (c) Migrant labour into Ivory Coast.

23. Although Ivory Coast is a labour-deficient country, it has a large and increasing number of urban unemployed. Discuss.

24. Compare and contrast the development of the agricultural and mining sectors in Ivory Coast and Ghana.

25. Show on a sketch map the major food crop zones of Ivory Coast and discuss the attempts made by the government to remedy the food-deficit situation in the country.

26. Account for the location and growth of manufacturing industries in the Ivory Coast since independence in 1960.

27. (a) Name FOUR of the main agricultural products of Liberia and locate on a map an area in which each is cultivated.
    (b) Explain the location and describe the methods of cultivation of ONE of these crops.

28. Write an account of TWO of the following:
    (a) Iron ore production in Liberia
    (b) The Firestone rubber plantations
    (c) Labour shortage in Liberia.

29. Account for the comparatively slow development of the Liberian economy in spite of the fact that Liberia has been independent for more than 100 years.

30. Describe with the aid of a sketch map the distribution of population in EITHER Liberia OR Mali OR Niger. Point out any striking features and account for them.

31. With the aid of a sketch map describe and account for the development of irrigated farming in Mali.

32. Describe the main occupations of Mali and show how they are related to geographical conditions.

33. Write briefly on:
    (a) The inland delta irrigation scheme for Mali
    (b) Livestock and the Malian economy
    (c) The industries and functions of Bamako
    (d) The external trade of Mali.

34. Assess the significance of the upper Niger Basin to the economy of Mali.

35. Suggest reasons for the fact that no less than four of the famous ancient empires of West Africa were located in Mali.

36. Account for the concentration of the population of Mauritania in the Senegal Valley and the Hodh region.

37. Write an essay on the importance of iron ore mining to the economy of EITHER Sierra Leone OR Mauritania OR Liberia.

38. Compare the ways of life of the Moors in northern Mauritania with those of the Sarakoles of the south.

39. Write short notes on:
    (a) The growth and importance of Nouakchott
    (b) Oasis agriculture in Mauritania
    (c) The importance of livestock in the economy of Mauritania.

40. Explain the following:
    (i) the negative balance of trade of Niger Republic
    (ii) the large-scale migration of Hausas and Djerma-Songhai peoples from Niger into Nigeria, Benin and Ghana.
    (iii) the concentration of the population of Niger in the region of the Niger—Nigeria boundary.

41. Write an account of industrial development in Niger Republic noting particularly the types of industries and the problems of industralization.

42. Discuss the importance of irrigation to the economy of Niger and examine the present state of irrigation in that country.

43. Compare and contrast the areas north and south of the Middle Belt of Nigeria under the following headings: (a) relief and drainage, (b) climate, (c) vegetation, (d) products.

44. Describe the industries of the Kano Industrial Area and account for the geographical circum-

stances which have made their development possible.

45. (a) Draw a large map of EITHER Nigeria OR Ghana showing the distribution of the main types of vegetation.
(b) Discuss the factors controlling their distribution.

46. Write briefly on THREE of the following:
(a) Cattle-rearing in northern Nigeria
(b) The petroleum industry in the economy of Nigeria
(c) Fishing in Lake Chad
(d) Plantation agriculture in southern Nigeria
(e) Kola nut production in south-western Nigeria.

47. (a) In which of the states of Nigeria are groundnuts produced on a large scale? Describe the conditions which render the state particularly suitable for the production of this crop.
(b) Describe the routes through which groundnuts are exported from the state.

48. Explain why the road has become more important than the railway as a means of transporting goods and passengers in Nigeria.

49. Write a geographical account of fishing in any West African country under the headings: (a) fishing grounds (b) fishing methods (c) marketing of fish.

50. Write briefly on:
(a) the strange farmers of Senegal
(b) the Richard Toll Irrigation Scheme
(c) the manufacturing industries of Dakar
(d) rice production in Senegal.

51. Locate with the aid of a sketch map an area in which cocoa, coffee, swamp rice and ginger is produced in Sierra Leone. Comment on the location and methods of cultivation of EITHER swamp rice OR cocoa.

52. Write briefly on the following:
(a) the origin and economic importance of the *bolilands*
(b) the climate of Sierra Leone
(c) iron ore mining in Sierra Leone
(d) the closure of the Sierra Leone railways.

53. In Sierra Leone, there is very little industrial activity outside Freetown. Comment.

54. Examine the bases for industrial development in EITHER Sierra Leone OR Guinea OR Ivory Coast.

55. Write an explanatory account of the export trade of EITHER Sierra Leone OR Liberia OR Benin.

56. Describe the major features of food-crop production in EITHER Togo OR Liberia.

57. Explain why new villages were established by government in parts of Togo during the colonial period.

58. (a) On a map of Togo mark and name the main relief regions, two rivers and four towns.
(b) Write a brief account of farming amongst EITHER the Ewes OR the Cabrais, paying particular attention to farming methods, the farming calendar and the crops cultivated.

59. Write a comprehensive account of the development of transportation in EITHER Togo OR Liberia OR Senegal.

60. Account for the following characteristics of Togo:
(a) the concentration of cocoa cultivation in Palime district
(b) the sparse population of the Mango district
(c) the southward migrations of the Cabrais.

61. Write brief notes on:
(a) the effect of relief on the rainfall of Togo
(b) the deforestation of the Togo–Atakora Highlands
(c) the growth and functions of Lome.

62. Account for the fact that more than 800,000 Upper Voltaians migrate temporarily or permanently to work in Ghana and Ivory Coast.

63. Describe and explain the pattern of distribution of population in Upper Volta.

64. Explain why Upper Volta is a poor country with a highly unfavourable balance of trade.

65. Write briefly on THREE of the following:
(a) development of modern manufacturing in Upper Volta
(b) importance of cattle to the economy of Upper Volta
(c) the Kou Valley Rice Scheme
(d) farming activities in Mossi territory.

66. Discuss the need for large-scale irrigation projects for developing the agricultural economy of EITHER Upper Volta OR Niger.